Ada in Distributed Real-Time Systems

Ada in Distributed Real-Time Systems

Kjell Nielsen, PhD
Senior Scientist
Hughes Aircraft Company

Intertext Publications
McGraw-Hill Book Company

New York St. Louis San Francisco Auckland Bogotá
Hamburg London Madrid Mexico Milan Montreal
New Delhi Panama Paris São Paolo
Singapore Sydney Tokyo Toronto

Library of Congress Catalog Number 89-81477

10 9 8 7 6 5 4 3 2 1

ISBN 0-07-046544-4

Intertext Publications/Multiscience Press, Inc.
One Lincoln Plaza
New York, NY 10023

McGraw-Hill Book Company
1221 Avenue of the Americas
New York, NY 10020

Composed in Ventura Publisher by Context, Inc., San Diego, CA

To Vicki

Contents

Acknowledgements

The author is grateful for the contributions of several individuals during the preparation of this book. Don Batchelor, Harald Carlsson, Gary Pellecchia, and Ken Shumate reviewed a portion of the manuscript. Sandy Swimmer reviewed the complete document, and was brave enough to use an early draft during one of her Ada courses.

I especially wish to thank Corinne Finney, who diligently prepared most of the graphics on her Macintosh.

I thank TeleSoft AB (formerly TeleLogic AB) for letting me use some of their AdaLAN material in Chapter 13, including the code for the Echo Server. The original author of the RPC/XDR example is Harald Carlsson of TeleSoft AB.

Preface

The objective of this book is to present a balanced treatment of distributed system concepts and how to use Ada in a distributed real-time system.

This book is intended for the programmer or software engineer who is familiar with the design and programming discipline used for single-processor systems, or homogeneous multi-processor systems where the mapping of processing functions to one or more processors is completely transparent. A design methodology is specified here where the designer is aware of the concept of distributed nodes, where mappings of processing functions to nodes have to be made, and the communication between nodes is deterministic.

The emphasis of this book is on presenting design paradigms and heuristics for the practicing software engineer, but since many issues and principles of how to construct a distributed system that supports these paradigms are included, the book is also important as background material for the builder of operating systems and run-time support environments for distributed systems.

This book is about distributed systems, process abstraction and Ada for distributed real-time systems, design paradigms for distributed systems, inter-processor communication, virtual and physical nodes, and fault tolerance. Ada has been specified by the U.S. Department of Defense as the required programming language for mission critical embedded systems. These embedded systems have much in common with industrial real-time systems, and Ada is used today in a wide variety of applications, not only for U.S. DoD projects, but all over the world for military and commercial systems, research and development projects, and as a teaching tool in the academic community.

Ada has excellent software engineering features for designing large real-time systems including encapsulation for building abstract data types, generics for promoting reusability, exception handling to support fault tolerance, and a tasking model for implementing process abstraction. Many of these features support the concepts of object-oriented design, even though Ada is not considered an object-oriented language in the sense of Smalltalk-80 or Simula. Ada is the first programming language suitable for real-time systems that has been specified in an international standard. ANSI/MIL-STD 1815A was published in February 1983, and the corresponding international ISO standard in March 1987.

Distributed systems have evolved in concert with the evolution of increasingly powerful processors and range from wide-area networks with file servers to compact multi-board computers connected via buses. Architectures are described for both supercomputers using massively parallel structures, and the smaller real-time systems using multi-microprocessors. Some real-time systems use supercomputers for special processing requirements such as digital signal processing and graphics display.

Application areas of distributed systems using multi-microprocessors include data acquisition, avionics control, image processing, robotics, and industrial automation. The benefits of a distributed system with multi-microprocessors are (1) that the processing can be positioned close to the hardware it is controlling (e.g., a robot); (2) a system can easily be extended by adding software modules and microprocessors; (3) fewer processes are competing for the use of a single processor, resulting in less run-time overhead; (4) systems can be made more reliable by incorporating various models of load sharing and fault tolerance; and (5) as the price per unit of computing power of microprocessors comes down, it becomes more and more cost effective to create distributed systems rather than monolithic systems. For these systems to be efficient, the additional overhead of inter-processor communication must be overcome by the increased computing power and parallelism of the multiple processors.

Real-time systems have traditionally been designed for apparent concurrency on a machine with a single processor or homogeneous multi-processors, where the designer determined the process abstraction, and the operating system determined the processor selection for those processes. In a uniprocessor system, the processes had to compete for available processor time, with an associated run-time overhead of scheduling and context switching. The next step in the evolution of design methodologies is to give the designer the power to determine the allocation of processes to processors, to make process communication deterministic, and to prescribe a reasonable set of design constraints (e.g., shared memory only allowed between processes that reside on the same processor) to simplify the design decisions that have to be made (and the underlying run-time support).

Ada and distributed systems promote the design paradigm of *software-first* for real-time systems. The processes are determined first by employing a suitable process abstraction methodology, and a set of distributed processors is chosen to match the required functionality of the processes. This book extends the real-time design methodology of *apparent* concurrency to include *real* concurrency on multiple processors. The designer using this paradigm is very much aware of the multi-processor environment and does not leave the processor selection solely to the operating system or run-time support environment.

While this book was being written, vast improvements were occurring in microprocessor design, and the improvements are expected to continue at the same rate. Distributed architectures are easily configured today using existing buses and LANs as interfaces between the processors. The problem, however, is that the software support required to take advantage of the distributed architectures is not yet ready. This book is written with the appreciation that the implementation of a distributed application today represents a definite risk. This risk is directly related to the amount of software support available for the distribution of a given application program, and for the run-time support for a given set of processors and their interfaces.

Part 1 contains background material on distributed real-time system concepts and architectures. Real-time systems are described in terms of their operating characteristics, the requirements for interfacing with hardware devices, and the inherent concurrency in these systems. A taxonomy of parallel architectures used by modern supercomputers is presented, along with the advantages and applications of multi-microprocessor systems. Networks and buses are described as the primary mechanisms for inter-processor communication. This part concludes with a chapter on fault tolerance.

Part 2 describes the software required to support the distributed real-time systems described in Part 1. Process synchronization models and the Ada tasking implementation are discussed, along with some of the common real-time executives and programming languages that deal with concurrency. Database issues for distributed systems are included with regard to operations, how data is distributed, and protection against data corruption for shared data. This part concludes with a consideration of the software support environment required for implementing and executing distributed real-time systems.

Part 3 contains an analysis of how Ada can be used in distributed systems. The built-in parallel features of Ada are discussed in terms of asynchronous task behavior, the requirements for task communication and synchronization, non-determinism of task scheduling and selection of open task entries, and how Ada tasks relate to logical nodes. Run-time issues are discussed for task scheduling, task communication, handling of priorities and interrupts, shared memory, exception handling, and timing (real-time clock) issues.

Part 4 contains a software-first design methodology for real-time systems in a distributed environment. The primary focus is on a process abstraction paradigm for determining the set of cooperating sequential processes, the collection of Ada components into virtual nodes, the selection of processors in a heterogeneous processor environment, and the functional allocation among the chosen processors. A layered virtual machine approach is included for the decomposition of large Ada tasks. The design of fault tolerance for Ada programs is described in terms of failure detection and correction, failure semantics, and data consistency. This part concludes with a collection of design guidelines that represents a summary of the design paradigms presented in earlier chapters.

The appendices present two case studies that illustrate the use of the proposed methodology and design paradigms. Exercises are included for additional practical experience during a course of study. Further exercises can easily be created by changing the requirement specifications and by using different design paradigms.

An extensive bibliography on Ada and distributed systems is included in the Reference section.

This book can be used effectively as a reference text by software engineers responsible for developing distributed applications and by systems programmers responsible for developing support tools for distributed systems. It can also be used as an upper level or graduate text in a semester-long Computer Science curriculum. This course would typically follow courses on concurrency and real-time issues and operating system principles. The minimum prerequisites for such a course would include programming experience with a language that has a built-in tasking model, preferably Ada, or a combination of a programming language and a real-time operating system, e.g., C and a real-time version of Unix. The exercises provided at the end of the case studies can be used for individual student assignments or group assignments as part of a semester project.

Managers of large software development projects can skip directly to Chapter 17. Here they should get an appreciation for some of the problem areas associated with the design and implementation of large distributed real-time applications in Ada. The material in this chapter can be used as a basis for planning and risk assessment regarding the availability of tools and run-time support for the distribution of Ada programs.

Kjell Nielsen
San Diego, California

1

Distributed System Concepts

Scientists in government and private-sector research laboratories, in universities, and in industry have an ever-increasing need for more computing power to solve complex, computation intensive applications in fields such as weather forecasting, three-dimensional modelling, strategic air defense systems, molecular biology, and neural network modelling. Designers of real-time systems such as robotics, process automation, image processing, and radar signal processing use microprocessor architectures to solve their complex problems. The common solution for the architectures required by both the scientists and the real-time systems designers is the use of parallel processing and a distribution of the application domain among the available processors. The scientists rely primarily on powerful mini or mainframe computers with from one to thousands of processors. The systems designers typically create their real-time systems using a set of microprocessors and associated communication media and memory. A higher throughput of a given computer architecture can be obtained by replacing the existing processors by more powerful processors, but the cost may be prohibitively high, or the necessary technology for producing these new processors may not be available. The addition of processors that can operate in parallel, and a proper distribution of the problem domain over these processors have proven to be a viable solution to the ever-increasing demand for more computing power.

This part introduces distributed system concepts as they apply to the powerful computers used by the many different groups of scientists, as well as to the microprocessing architectures used by real-time systems designers. After a general discussion of the complexity of real-time systems and the general support required for distributed systems, we describe distributed architectures used in the large, modern parallel processing computers ("supercomputers"), as well as multi-microprocessor architectures used in real-time systems. The choice of architecture is usually dictated by the application. We don't need a supercomputer to rotate one of the axis of a robot; a microprocessor will be sufficient for the job. A supercomputer will probably be required, however, to solve large sets of linear equations.

An all-encompassing definition for real-time systems is difficult to specify. Instead we describe the general characteristics of real-time systems in terms of the software control of concurrently operating hardware devices and typical modes of operation. The process abstraction used to model the inherent concurrency of real-time systems is described in terms of processes and the various inter-process communication mechanisms: message passing, data sharing, and signaling.

Data and instructions are passed between the various processors and other hardware elements. The interconnections between these elements are described in terms of networks and buses.

A characteristic of real-time systems is that they must be highly reliable and able to sustain operation for long periods of time. This part concludes with an overview of fault tolerance, including error detection and correction, recovery procedures, and load balancing.

1

Introduction

In this chapter we describe the additional complexity facing the designer of a distributed system in comparison with systems that contain only a single processor or computer. We assume the designer is capable of designing real-time concurrent systems that do not use distributed processors, and describe the additional knowledge the designer must acquire for successfully creating a distributed real-time system. (A complete design approach for non-distributed real-time systems using Ada is described in [NIE88].) The organization of the book is also presented in this chapter.

1.1 Complexity of Distributed Systems

In designing software for real-time systems that do not employ distributed architectures, the primary concern is that the operating system be able to support such real-time features as interrupt handling, efficient process priority assignment and scheduling, accurate timing intervals for the expiration of periodic processes, and primitives for synchronous and asynchronous process communication. Concurrency in non-distributed real-time systems is only *apparent*, where several processes compete for the use of a single processor. The other processes are suspended while the executing process performs its processing functions.

The terms "process" and "task" are sometimes used interchangeably in the literature to describe concurrent elements. In this book, however, we refer to a *process* as an abstract concurrent element, and *task* as a software module that is implemented in a given programming language, e.g., an Ada task.

The overall design approach to non-distributed real-time systems is "hardware-first," where the design is made to support the processing functions for a given computer where the hardware architecture has been chosen during the systems analysis phase, or during the proposal phase for large, competitive procurements. The designer is phased with the primary task of creating the proper *correspondence* of process abstraction (for a concurrent solution) from the problem statement using a set of process selection rules [NIE88]. The resulting set of processes represents the solution of the concurrent elements of the system. These concurrent elements are translated to the software processes that will execute under the run-time support of the real-time target system. The translation of the abstract processes to software processes is dependent upon the available programming language and the executive or run-time support. If Ada is the implementation language, a separate executive is not required, since the run-time support for the real-time features is provided with the language. (Some Ada projects are not using the Ada tasking model and have replaced the rendezvous with tasking primitives provided by an executive.) If a language such as C is chosen for the implementation, the process structure and process communication have to be designed for the chosen executive, e.g., a real-time version of Unix.

The design issues facing the designer of distributed real-time systems are significantly more complex than for non-distributed systems. The overall design approach described later in this book supports the concept of "software-first." The process abstraction of the concurrent elements is first determined as in a non-distributed real-time system, and the processes are identified for the given programming language, i.e., the software is designed for the best possible correspondence to the problem solution without regard for a hardware architecture. The distributed hardware is then chosen to provide the most cost effective support for the software solution. The process abstraction has thus been moved from *apparent* concurrency, with processes competing for a single processor, to *true* concurrency, with the processes mapped to multiple processors. Some apparent concurrency may still be present in distributed systems, since it is not always cost efficient to map every process to a single processor. A group of processes may be assigned to a given processor. These processes will then execute under apparent concurrency. A group of processes comprise a *virtual node* that is mapped to a *physical node*, i.e., the processor, associated memory, buses, etc., that support the execution of the virtual node.

To be able to select a set of physical nodes that will properly support the virtual nodes of the problem solution, the designer must posses a broader knowledge than for non-distributed systems. We are broadening the term "designer" here from the traditional meaning of a software designer to a "systems designer." This may include more than one person, e.g., software engineers and hardware engineers that form a design team. The additional knowledge areas required for distributed systems include:

1. *Processor characteristics.* The characteristics of a suitable set of processors (e.g., 32-bit microprocessors) must be studied and understood.

2. *Support for a multiple processor environment.* The existence and features of a development system and run-time support for multiple processors must be analyzed and evaluated.

3. *Processor connectivity.* The various ways of connecting the processors (e.g., by networks or buses) must be analyzed and evaluated.

4. *Inter-processor communication.* The method of communication between the distributed processors (e.g., explicit use of remote procedure calls vs. a transparent, remote Ada rendezvous) may have a significant influence on the design of the virtual nodes (this may lead to an iterative software-first/hardware-first design approach).

5. *Bus protocols.* When the physical nodes are created using microprocessors, it is important to understand the protocols of the buses that will link the processors and their associated memories. It is especially important to be aware of existing protocol standards and to use the standards whenever possible.

6. *Performance evaluation.* The choice of processors for a distributed real-time system is dependent upon their performance for the given software solution. The only way to assess the performance features of a system that has not yet been built (the performance requirements are known) is to perform modeling

and simulation of the concurrent elements. The designer must be aware of existing modeling and simulation programs or create suitable models for the given design. This may require a significant effort of prototyping and benchmarking before the final design is chosen.

7. *Expanded design evaluation guidelines.* The evaluation guidelines used for non-distributed real-time systems (e.g., [NIE88, Chapter 26]) must be expanded to include the selection of virtual nodes, the mapping of virtual nodes to physical nodes, the connectivity between the processors, etc.

8. *Fault tolerance.* Many distributed real-time systems have the requirement that fault tolerance be built into the design. The designer must understand such concepts as fault detection and correction, reconfiguration of parallel processing resources, and load balancing.

The material in this book first provides the necessary background information for the designer of real-time distributed systems to understand the added complexity described above. A complete software-first design approach is then presented for these systems.

1.2   Organization of the Book

The remaining chapters in Part 1 contain background material on distributed real-time systems concepts. Review material about real-time systems is provided in Chapter 2. Chapter 3 presents an overview and taxonomy of distributed systems and describes why we are primarily concerned with multi-microprocessor systems. Chapter 4 comprises the various ways that distributed processors can be logically and physically connected. Part 1 concludes with a discussion of fault tolerance in Chapter 5.

The chapters in Part 2 describe the software aspects of supporting distributed real-time systems. Chapter 6 contains a description of some common process synchronization models and how they are implemented in Ada. Some real-time operating systems that can be adapted to distributed systems are discussed here, as well as some of the programming languages that deal with concurrency and functional distributions among processors.

The database functions required in distributed systems are described in Chapter 7.

The support environment required in distributed systems is discussed in Chapter 8 in terms of real-time executives, a software development system, linking and loading facilities, run-time support, and inter-processor communication.

The material in Part 3 is concerned with how the Ada language and associated run-time support can be used in real-time distributed systems. Chapter 9 provides a review of the tasking features available in Ada, with regard to asynchronous tasks, task communication and synchronization, and the mapping of tasks to nodes. Chapter 10 contains a discussion of Ada language features relative to their use in distributed real-time systems, and run-time issues in terms of how well Ada supports the run-time requirements of distributed real-time systems.

Part 4 contains a design approach for distributed real-time systems. Chapter 11 describes the traditional *hardware-first* methodology, where the designer creates the software modules that will reside in the processor(s) that have been determined a priori. This is contrasted with the proposed *software-first* approach, where the designer first designs the concurrent system with the best possible correspondence to the problem statement, and then determines the most suitable hardware to support the software functions. Chapter 12 contains heuristics and guidelines for creating the proper process abstraction as the model of the concurrent solution to the problem. This includes the specification of virtual nodes and their interfaces. Various mechanisms for communication between nodes are discussed in Chapter 13. Guidelines for selecting the proper processors for the set of concurrent modules are provided in Chapter 14, accompanied by a discussion of how the functions should be mapped to the chosen processors. A methodology for decomposing large Ada tasks is contained in Chapter 15. This includes a taxonomy for Ada packages, the use of layered virtual machines (based on structured design concepts) for functional abstraction, and object-oriented design for data abstraction. Chapter 16 contains a description of how failure semantics can be implemented to support fault tolerance in Ada real-time systems. This part concludes with a set of design guidelines in Chapter 17. This chapter represents a summary of the design features presented in earlier chapters.

Part 5 contains case studies that illustrate the use of the proposed design approach for distributed real-time systems implemented in Ada. The book concludes with a set of references and an index.

2

Distributed Real-Time Systems

The distributed systems we are primarily concerned with are systems that operate under critical time constraints, sometimes referred to as "hard" real-time systems. Distributed system solutions are not reserved for only the hard real-time applications, however; elegant distributed solutions can also be applied to "soft" real-time systems.

This chapter introduces the concepts of a real-time system. It is not adequate to give a simple definition of such a system, and the first section describes the major characteristics of real-time systems. These systems usually include hardware devices that need to be controlled by the software we are designing, and Section 2 describes typical hardware interfaces and the kind of design considerations we need to be concerned with. Most real-time systems include two or more hardware devices that operate asynchronously at widely differing speeds, leading to the concept of *concurrent operations* for these devices. Concurrent operations are also used in decomposing a large real-time system into a set of parallel processes. Section 3 describes the concept of concurrency and how we create a process abstraction by modeling various forms of asynchronous behavior in terms of processes and process communication.

2.1   Characteristics of Real-Time Systems

A real-time system can be defined as a controlled (by software or firmware) system that performs all of its process functions within specified time constraints. Although this is a brief and concise definition, it is inadequate in fully describing the primary features of real-time systems. We can supply such a description by discussing the characteristics of real-time systems.

A real-time system usually includes a set of independent hardware devices that operate at widely differing speeds, e.g., a magnetic disk and a line printer. These devices must be controlled such that the system as a whole is not dependent upon the speed of the slowest device, i.e., the faster devices must not be forced to wait and operate in synchronization with the slower devices. This would be a waste of resources, and stringent performance requirements may not be satisfied. Our aim is to design real-time systems that optimize the capabilities of the hardware devices involved, while satisfying the stated performance requirements. Examples of the real-time systems we need to control include process automation, air traffic control, digital signal processing, and robotics.

The context diagram shown in Figure 2-1 depicts a remote data acquisition system for a Remote Temperature Sensor (RTS) system [YOU82, NIE88]. The hardware devices consist of the input and output channels of the host computer and the digital thermometer. The host computer sends control data to the RTS (this is the system we are required to design and implement), including the furnace number whose temperature must be read by the digital thermometer and the interval between the temperature readings. Our control system (RTS) determines when the furnace number should be sent to the digital thermometer, receives a corresponding temperature value from the digital thermometer, and prepares data messages that are sent to the host computer via the output channel. In designing the RTS we will have to consider the required interfaces to the hardware devices and their speed of operation, which leads us to an important aspect of real-time design: the construction of device drivers and interrupt handlers. We must also decompose the functionality of the RTS into a set of communicating sequential processes that can be implemented as software modules on a specific hardware architecture.

A different way of characterizing a real-time system is to realize that it is much more difficult to design and implement than a non–real-time system. Some of these difficulties include:

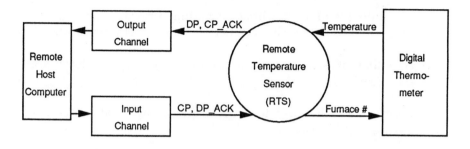

CP -- Control Packet (Host -> RTS)
DP -- Data Packet (RTS -> Host)
_ACK -- ACK or NAK

Figure 2-1.   RTS Context Diagram

1. Control of hardware devices such as communication lines, terminals, and computer resources.

2. Processing of messages that arrive at irregular intervals, with fluctuating input rates, and with different priorities.

3. Detection and control of fault conditions with facilities for various degrees of recovery.

4. Handling of queues and buffers for storage of messages and data items.

5. Modeling of concurrent conditions into a proper set of concurrent processes.

6. Allocation and control of concurrent processes to processors (if more than one processor is available).

7. Handling of communication and synchronization between concurrent processes for intra- as well as inter-processor communication.

8. Protection of data shared between concurrent processes.

9. Scheduling and dispatching (including priority handling) of concurrent processes that compete for the use of a resource.

10. Handling of stringent time requirements and performance specifications.

11. Interfacing with real-time clocks and avoiding (or at least minimizing) "drift" problems.

12. Testing and debugging of concurrent processes that reside on one or more processors.

13. Designing (software) simulators for the hardware devices that are not available for the test phase.

14. Reducing complexity by transforming the requirements into manageable units that can be designed and implemented by teams of designers and programmers.

15. Selecting the proper hardware architecture that can adequately support the software design.

We can also characterize real-time systems by the way they typically operate. A real-time system is expected to run continuously in an automated fashion with extremely high reliability. This is important from both a performance and a cost point of view. A processing plant with frequent shutdowns is not very cost effective, and an air traffic control system with a high failure rate would not make the skies very safe for flying. The requirement for high reliability is implemented with extensive error detection and recovery features. Some systems are designed with duplicate (stand-by) hardware components, and a switch-over is performed to the stand-by component when an error condition is detected. Other systems are designed with a *fail-soft* capability where the control program performs a *graceful degradation* by first saving as much of the current program states and data as possible, and then attempting to stage a recovery.

Another aspect of the operation of real-time systems is the rapid processing required to satisfy some of their performance requirements. Consider, for example, the on-board calculations of the trajectory of a heat-seeking missile. The hit/miss performance is directly related to how fast the processor can calculate required changes in the trajectory based on the data supplied by the missile's sensors.

Our primary design goals for real-time systems are to build them with a high degree of correspondence [ALL81] and to strive for simplicity. Correspondence in this context means how closely the software solution matches the problem specification. Examples of correspondence include the degree to which a system is inherently concurrent and the corresponding concurrency modeled in the solution, the data structures created and their corresponding operations, and the degree of non-determinism present in the problem and its corresponding solution (e.g., traditional cyclic scheduling specified with major and minor time frames versus the non-deterministic scheduling mechanism in Ada). A high degree of correspondence ensures that the problem solution closely matches the stated requirements and aids the designers and reviewers in determining program correctness. A simple design contributes to making the solution easy to understand and maintain and enhances reliability. Some of the tools we utilize to satisfy these design goals include guidelines for dealing with hardware interfaces and how to model the system into a set of concurrent processes. This is discussed in the remainder of this chapter.

2.2   Hardware Interfaces

In the context diagram shown in Figure 2-1 we noted three separate hardware devices that our system (RTS) needed to interface with: the input and output channels of the host computer, and the digital thermometer. As part of the design process we must create the necessary software components that accept inputs from these interrupt driven or polling devices and that transmit messages and signals to the devices. Control data arriving from the host computer must be accepted by RTS and checked for valid formats. At the appropriate time, RTS sends a furnace number to the digital thermometer and waits to receive the corresponding temperature value. RTS creates a data message containing the furnace number and its temperature value and transmits the message to the host computer via the output channel. The design elements that are used to control the interfaces to hardware devices are loosely classified as device drivers and interrupt handlers. These elements are described in the following paragraphs.

2.2.1   Device Drivers

Device drivers are required for both input and output devices, and the design considerations depend upon whether we have an input or an output device:

1. *Input Devices*. Design considerations for input device drivers include:

   a. Scheduled or irregular arrival of messages.
   b. Continuous or burst transmission.
   c. Message formats.
   d. Transmission protocol.
   e. Polling mode (by the device driver) or interrupt mode (by the transmitter).
   f. Rate of incoming messages versus processing required and whether or not they must be handed off to a buffer process for intermediate storage.
   g. Error detection and handling of invalid messages and transmission protocol.
   h. Handling of incoming messages when the message buffer is full (e.g., incoming messages can be ignored, or oldest message can be overwritten).
   i. Failure of the input device.

2. *Output Devices*. The design considerations for output device drivers are considerably less complex than for input devices (because we control the timing of the outgoing messages) and include:

   a. Transmission protocol (e.g., the whole message can be transmitted as a unit, or character by character with the output device sending an interrupt after each character which means "I'm ready to receive the next character").
   b. Error detection and handling of improper protocol by the output device, e.g., not receiving an expected ack/nak within a given time interval.
   c. Failure of the output device.

2.2.2 Interrupt Handlers

The traditional concept of an interrupt handler is that it is a part of a real-time executive or a supervisor program and written in assembly language or a suitable High Order Language (HOL). Ada, on the other hand, has neither an executive nor a supervisor program; real-time facilities such as task scheduling and dispatching are part of the run-time support, and interrupt handling is available with Ada language constructs. Interrupt handling in Ada is usually written as part of a device driver, and not as a separate unit, and the traditional concept of an "interrupt handler" may not be appropriate.

An example of interrupt handling within a device driver is shown in Figure 2-2. The task specification for the device driver Tx_Host_Msg contains the entry declaration for Output_Channel, which is associated with the interrupt location Output_Channel_Address, and the entry declaration Transmit_Data_Packet. The task body contains a local declaration Output_Buffer which is associated with the buffer location of the output channel. The executable statements of the task body accept a request to transmit a message to the host (via the output channel). The transmission is performed inside the for-loop one character at a time. After a character has been placed in the output buffer, the task waits for an interrupt from the output channel signaling that it is ready for the next character. The interrupt is handled with the single statement *accept Output_Channel*, and a separate interrupt handler is not required.

```
task Tx_Host_Msg is
    entry Output_Channel;
    for Output_Channel use at Output_Channel_Address;
    entry Transmit_Data_Packet (D : in DP_Format);
end Tx_Host_Msg;

task body Tx_Host_Msg is
    Output_Buffer : Character;
    for Output_Buffer use at Output_Buffer_Address;
begin
    loop
        accept Transmit_Data_Packet (D : in DP_Format) do
            for I in D'Range loop
                Output_Buffer := D(I);
                accept Output_Channel;    -- interrupt from output
                                          -- channel
            end loop;
        end Transmit_Data_Packet;
    end loop;
end Tx_Host_Msg;
```

Figure 2-2.   Interrupt Handling in a Device Driver

As we design the device drivers to control the hardware interfaces, we are also concerned with how these drivers must interface with the rest of the system. The general approach is to design the device drivers as part of a set of concurrent processes. These processes need to communicate and sometimes share data. This leads us to the concepts of *cooperating sequential processes* [DIJ68] and *communicating sequential processes* [HOA78]. To fully appreciate the design principles described in the later chapters, we need to understand the general concepts of process abstraction and process communication. This is discussed in the next section.

2.3   Concurrency

In this section we review the concepts used in describing concurrent programs. Even though we assume the reader has some previous knowledge of these concepts, we present a set of definitions that are used consistently throughout the remainder of the book. We start the chapter by distinguishing between primitive and non-primitive processes, and by defining *true* and *apparent* concurrency. We next establish the need for concurrent processes to communicate and describe the interactions between communicating processes.

2.3.1   Processes

We think of processes as functional or logical elements in a decomposition of a real-time system. They are independent virtual machines [DIJ71, NIE88] that can operate simultaneously on separate processors or that can share a single processor. A process can be further decomposed into sub-processes. If a process can be decomposed into one or more sub-processes, we refer to it as *non-primitive*. *Primitive* processes cannot be further decomposed into sub-processes. An example of a process (at the logical level) is shown in Figure 2-3. The process we have called Robot Axis accepts *Stop* and *Resume* signals to determine whether or not to continue to process motion data for axis positioning of a robot controller. For each set of motion data that this process receives and manipulates, an acknowledgement is sent to another process (not shown in this figure), and the axis data is updated appropriately. We make no assumptions about the processing speed of Robot Axis; we only know that it has to operate independently of and simultaneously with other processes.

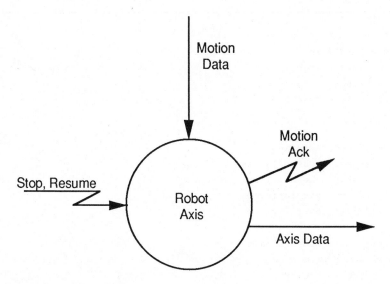

Figure 2-3.   Process Robot Axis

So far we have only considered a process at a logical level. We will now translate logical processes into their equivalent physical software components using Ada constructs. An example of a non-primitive process is illustrated in Figure 2-4 as an Ada package. The package specification of Axis contains the three *entrance procedures* Stop, Resume, and Take_Block. (These entrance procedures are used to control access to the task entries.) The specification does not tell us whether the process is primitive or not, but in the package body we see the declaration of the two Ada tasks Axis_Controller and Axis_Manager. Axis is thus a non-primitive process since it contains other processes (Ada tasks) within it. The details of the two task bodies have been deferred using the *separate* clause, and we cannot determine at this level whether or not the two tasks represent primitive processes. A task body can have task declarations within it, which will make that task a non-primitive process. An example of a primitive process is shown in Figure 2-5 for the subunit Axis_Manager. The declarative part only contains local objects, there are no task declarations. The executable part is implemented within a *select* statement and represents a *single thread of control*. Packages and subprograms can be declared within an Ada task and would not invalidate the single thread of control of a primitive process.

```
with Definitions;   use Definitions;
package Axis is
   procedure Stop;
   procedure Resume;
   procedure Take_Block (B : in Motion_Block);
end Axis;

package body Axis is
   task Axis_Controller is
      entry Take_Block (B : in Axis_Block);
      entry Axis_Interrupt;
   end Axis_Controller;

   task Axis_Manager is
      entry Stop;
      entry Resume;
      entry Take_Block (B : in Motion_Block);
   end Axis_Manager;

   task body Axis_Controller is separate;
   task body Axis_Manager    is separate;

   procedure Stop is
   begin
      Axis_Manager.Stop;
   end Stop;

   procedure Resume is
   begin
      Axis_Manager.Resume;
   end Resume;

   procedure Take_Block (B : in Motion_Block) is
   begin
      Axis_Manager.Take_Block (B);
   end Take_Block;

end Axis;
```

Figure 2-4.   Non-Primitive Process (package Axis)

```
with Motion;
separate (Axis)

task body Axis_Manager is
   Stop_Flag    : Boolean := False;
   Axis_Motion : Motion_Block;
   Axis_Output : Axis_Block;
begin
   loop
      select
         accept Stop;
            Stop_Flag := True;
      or
         accept Take_Block (B : in Motion_Block) do
            Axis_Motion := B;
         end Take_Block;

         Prepare_Axis_Block (Axis_Motion, Axis_Output);

         if Stop_Flag then
            accept Resume;
         end if;

         Axis_Controller.Take_Block (Axis_Output);
         -- Task waits here for block completion
            Motion.Take_Motion_Ack;
      or
         terminate;
      end select;
   end loop;
end Axis_Manager;
```

Figure 2-5.   Primitive Process (task body Axis_Manager)

The concept of two or more processes operating simultaneously leads us to the notion of *concurrency*. Processes can operate with *true* concurrency if their executions overlap in time on separate processors. If the processes share a processor, they operate with *apparent* concurrency. Our objective is to design a real-time system as a set of concurrent processes that can execute on one or more processors. In the sharing of a processor, the execution of the processes is somehow interleaved in a non-deterministic manner that we (the software engineers) do not control directly. The mechanism for the interleaving is provided for us by an executive or a run-time support package. In some implementations we may be able to assign process priorities or invoke specific conditions, such as the expiration of a time delay, to reduce the amount of non-determinism. The processes in a concurrent program may operate entirely independently of each other in an asynchronous manner, or they may be coupled through the use of shared data or message passing between them. The requirement for a coupling between concurrent processes necessitates the provision for a communication mechanism between them.

2.3.2 Communication

We can describe communicating processes as a set of concurrent processes that access common variables or that respond to signals or parameters received from other processes. An example of two processes communicating via message passing is shown in Figure 2-6a, where the Producer creates data and sends it to a Consumer. The requirements for this type of interaction are that the data items cannot be received faster than they are sent and that the consumption of the data items must be completed within a finite (but unspecified) time period. On a uniprocessor, the passing of data elements can be accomplished with a synchronized rendezvous or message passing via mailboxes. In a distributed system, an inter-processor communication (IPC) mechanism is required for exchanging data elements between processes that reside on different processors. This mechanism may be transparent to the application, or specific primitives may have to be invoked. This is discussed in greater detail in later chapters.

If two or more concurrent processes access shared data, as shown in Figure 2-6b, the data must be protected with a monitor or a critical section, i.e., we must guarantee *mutual exclusion*. If this is not guaranteed, we have the potential for an *erroneous* program where timing problems may occur but cannot necessarily be reproduced. The requirement of mutual exclusion for shared data (or resources) is considered [BEN82, page 19] to be one of the most important problems in concurrent programming because it represents an abstraction of the interactions between two or more communicating processes that operate in parallel. In a distributed system that includes heterogeneous processors, data translations may be required for the

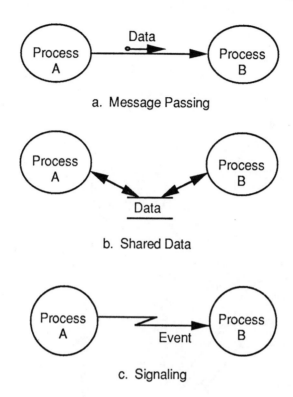

a. Message Passing

b. Shared Data

c. Signaling

Figure 2-6.   Communicating Processes

data elements since the internal data representations will be different for the various processors.

Figure 2-6c illustrates an example of a communication between two processes where a signal is sent by one process and received by another. Data elements are not consumed or manipulated in this type of communication. A distributed system will require an IPC mechanism for sending a remote signal, but there is no actual data passed.

A complete design for a large real-time system will consist of a set of communicating sequential processes as shown in Figure 2-7. We are here illustrating a typical combination of process communication with shared data, message passing, and signaling. (The symbols used in this chart will be explained in detail in Chapter 12.)

The timing of communicating processes must be carefully controlled and synchronized. We should never make any assumptions about the absolute or relative processing speeds of the communicat-

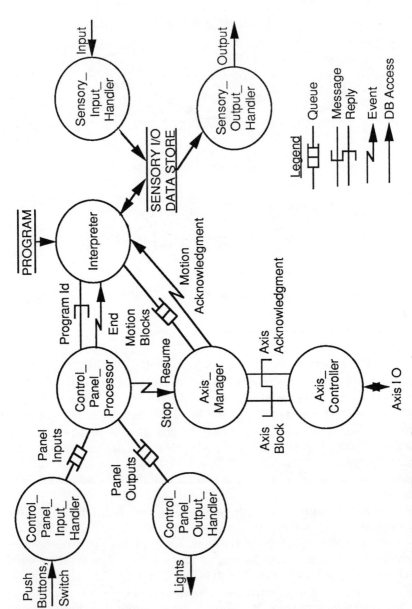

Figure 2-7.   Process Structure Chart

ing processes, and synchronization points must be provided for an orderly progression in the information transfer. The mechanisms used to provide the required synchronization are considered as part of the software support and are discussed in Chapter 6.

Real-time systems can be implemented with a single processor or in a typical distributed architecture with multi-microprocessors. In a uniprocessor system, all the functions of the application are executed in the same processor, and the concurrent elements are competing for the use of that processor. In a distributed real-time system, various portions of the application are dispersed among two or more processors. There may be one processor for the control of each external device and at least one processor for the analysis and manipulation of the internal data elements. The processors may share common memory, have their own local memory areas, or have both local and shared memory. There is usually a requirement for an efficient interprocessor communication mechanism if the processors do not share memory. If this is not available, too much time is spent during the communication between the processors, and this can drastically reduce the benefits of the parallel execution of the distributed system.

2.4 Summary

Real-time systems typically consist of a set of hardware devices that operate at widely differing speeds and are managed by a control program. The systems operate in a continuous mode, with stringent performance requirements, and with facilities for error detection and recovery. Our primary design goal is to build real-time systems with a high degree of correspondence and simplicity.

It is relatively simpler to design an output device driver than an input device driver. In general, device drivers should be made as simple as possible. Interrupt handlers in Ada may be incorporated in device drivers, rather than designed as separate tasks.

If a process can be further decomposed into one or more sub-processes, it is non-primitive. Primitive processes cannot be further decomposed and represent a single thread of control through the concurrent program.

Processes operate with true concurrency if their executions overlap in time on separate processors. If the processes share a processor, they operate with apparent concurrency, and their execution is interleaved in a non-deterministic manner.

Concurrent processes need to communicate. This can be implemented with message passing, signaling, or shared data. Access to shared data (or shared resources) must be protected with mutual exclusion to prevent erroneous programs. A large real-time system will consist of a set of concurrent processes that will communicate via a combination of message passing, signaling, and shared data.

We should make no assumptions about the absolute or relative execution speeds of concurrent processes, and they must be carefully controlled with a synchronization mechanism to allow proper communication between them.

Real-time systems may be implemented with a single processor or with a distributed architecture in a multi-microprocessor configuration. If these processors do not share memory, an efficient inter-processor communication mechanism is required.

3

Distributed Systems

When a particular computer configuration is no longer capable of performing the required expanded or new applications — beyond those applications for which it was originally intended — the system designers have two basic choices: (1) get a more powerful computer; or (2) add processors to the existing configuration.

As more and more complex problems are specified for solutions on computers, an increasing number of supercomputers and distributed systems have emerged. The supercomputers consist of from a few up to hundreds and thousands of processors that share the computational load for a given solution domain. The distributed systems consist of individual computers or processors that communicate via a network. The basic concept behind all modern computer hardware configurations for large, complex systems is *parallel processing*. The complex problem is divided into a number of smaller tasks which are distributed among the various processors. The use of parallel processing architectures will result in a greatly increased effective computing speed, provided that the communication mechanism between the processors is efficient. In some applications (e.g., robotics and factory automation), it is necessary to dedicate a processor to each external device. Distributed microprocessors provide a cost effective solution for these applications.

After the parallel processing software elements have been determined, the problem that remains is how to distribute these elements among the processors. The distribution can be left entirely to the operating system controlling the computational flow, or the programmer/designer can specify the distribution using primitives or directives.

Some supercomputer manufacturers such as Cray Research rely on a few very fast processors and pipelined operations to obtain higher performance. These machines are quite expensive, and incremental performance improvements are difficult to achieve without a complete redesign of the architecture or a replacement with new, expensive processors.

The most flexible and least expensive way of achieving supercomputer performance is by connecting a large number of processors in a distributed architecture. Incremental improvements in performance are then relatively easy to achieve by expanding the architecture with additional processors, using newer, state-of-the-art processors, or by improving the efficiency of the communication links between the processors.

In this chapter we first describe the (sometimes confusing and redundant) terminology used for parallel processing architectures. This is followed by a taxonomy of distributed architectures and a description of various multiprocessor architectures used in modern parallel processing supercomputers. The chapter concludes with a description of multi-microprocessor systems that are used in real-time systems.

3.1 Terminology

There are a myriad of terms used to describe the dispersion of processors in distributed systems. Some of these terms are used interchangeably to describe the same concept. Others may differ only in the use of a hyphen, or a slightly different word, and have a different meaning, e.g., multiple processors, multi-processor, or multiprocessor. To avoid the confusion of these terms, we will define the most commonly used phrases and their meaning, and throughout the remainder of the book we will only present a single, consistent term for a given concept. The following terms are commonly used in the literature to describe the dispersion of processors in a distributed system:

1. *Multiprocessor computer.* A parallel processing computer consisting of a set of homogeneous processors for the execution of major applications. Other heterogeneous processors may be included for special processing such as I/O and interfacing with

peripherals. The processors may have local memory, shared memory, or a combination of both. The distribution of processing functions is usually not visible to the designer/programmer, except for certain programming language constructs for structuring complex algorithms for concurrent execution. The computer is most likely a mini or a mainframe, and the number of parallel processors varies from a few up to thousands. A multiprocessor with a large number of parallel processors is referred to as a *massively parallel* system.

2. *Multi-processor computer.* Same as multiprocessor computer.

3. *Multicomputer system.* A distributed system consisting of a set of parallel processors connected by an inter-processor communication system. Each processor has its own local memory and may share global memory with some of the other processors. The processors are typically of heterogeneous architectures.

4. *Multiple-processor system.* Sometimes used for multicomputer system, other times for multiprocessor. We will not use this term in this book.

5. *Microprocessor.* The CPU of a computer reduced in size to make it fit on a single chip.

6. *Microcomputer.* The physical collection of a microprocessor, memory, and peripheral control circuits.

7. *Multi-microprocessor system.* System that uses more than one microprocessor to perform a given application. This ranges from a simple personal computer to complex distributed real-time systems. The latter is the class of applications for which we are developing our design methodology. This includes multicomputer systems where the physical nodes may consist not only of microprocessors, but also their associated memories and the necessary communications interfaces.

8. *Multiple microprocessor system.* Same as multi-microprocessor system. We will use the hyphenated term throughout this book.

9. *CISC.* Complex instruction set computer — a general purpose microcomputer.

10. *RISC.* Reduced instruction set computer — a microcomputer with a specialized, reduced instruction set and certain architectural innovations that greatly increase the processing speed.

11. *Single-chip microcomputer.* Microcomputer (including CPU, memory, and I/O lines) that fits on a single chip.

12. *Physical node.* Closely coupled processing elements (one or more CPU and local memory pairs, and possibly shared memory) connected via a bus or network. The design methodology described in later chapters will be concerned with physical nodes constructed from one or more microprocessors or microcomputers.

13. *Virtual node.* Concurrent software elements (i.e., one or more processes and associated support software) that are mapped to a physical node in a distributed system.

14. *Granularity.* The grain size of a parallel computer architecture is based on a combination of how many processors the machine contains, and how much memory is associated with each processor. A *fine-grained* architecture consists of up to several thousand processors with only Kbytes of memory associated with each processing element (PE). A *coarse-grained* parallel architecture employs few processors, no more than a few hundred, but each PE is associated with Mbytes of local memory.

3.2   Taxonomy of Multicomputer Architectures

We describe distributed multicomputer systems based on their memory and processor organization as follows:

1. *Decentralized System.* The computers are geographically distributed to provide local processing functions as required for geographically separate organizational elements within a company. Limited communication capabilities are provided between the computers, since each computer performs an independent function for the individual organizational element. The only communication required may be to provide statistical data to the corporate office. The advantage of this approach is that the computing functions are tailored to the exact requirements of the local organizational element. The disadvantage is the po-

tential for duplication of effort of developing computing functions and loss of control by the corporate office.

2. *Distributed Network*. The computers are distributed geographically and communicate over a wide area network (WAN). Computer resources with this architecture can be shared between the various sites, but each computer provides the functional capabilities required for the local site, just as for the decentralized system. Operational control can be under a central, corporate organization to reduce the management and technical problems, or left to the individual local organizations.

3. *Local Area Network (LAN)*. The computers are physically close, i.e., in the same room or building. They share computing resources and communicate over a network, e.g., Ethernet, but each computer supports a separate functional area. Computers, peripherals, and communication equipment are, typically, under control of a single organization and are easier to manage than the architectures described above. The computers communicating over the LAN may be mainframes, minis, workstations, personal computers, and microcomputers. In some cases the computers may support a single, large application, and will then fall in the category described next.

4. *Locally Distributed Multicomputer System*. Multicomputer *nodes* are distributed locally to support a single function. The distribution may be within the same building, room, or computer chassis. A node consists of closely coupled processing elements (one or more CPU and local memory pairs, and possibly shared memory) typically connected via a bus, although they may also communicate via a LAN. Various forms of nodes are depicted in Figure 3-1. The important distinction between this architecture and those described above is that the distributed computing elements for the latter architectures support functional requirements for different problems. *Locally distributed multi-computer systems support the requirements of a single problem*. The processors (microprocessors for our real-time applications) within each node may be homogeneous or heterogeneous, where the processors are chosen to support the (distributed) function they are best suited for. Examples of real-time systems using locally distributed multicomputers (multi-microprocessors) include message switching, air traffic control, radar tracking, and robotics.

(a) Single Processing Element

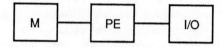

(b) Processing Element with Memory
and I/O Modules

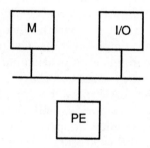

(c) Bus Connection

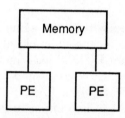

(d) Multiprocessors with Shared Memory

Figure 3-1.   Examples of Individual Network Nodes

5. *Geographically Distributed Multicomputer System.* This architecture is similar to the locally distributed multicomputer system, except that the nodes are geographically separated. This
system also supports the functional requirements of a single
problem. This is different from a distributed network, where
each computer supports a different function. Examples of real-

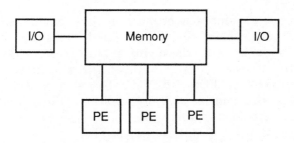

Figure 3-2.   Multiprocessor Architecture

time systems using this architecture include missile tracking, weapon systems control, and remote sensor monitoring. The communication between the various nodes can be a combination of LANs and WANs.

3.3 Taxonomy of Multiprocessor Architectures

A multiprocessor computer consists of a set of processors that are distributed within a single computing entity to perform one or more functions. The processors may share global memory, or they may each have their own local memory, or a combination of both. The type of function to be performed determines the distribution selected by the operating system. The user/programmer of a multiprocessor with a parallel architecture has little control over the distribution aspects, although certain coding techniques may be used to take advantage of the parallel features of the machine [KAR88]. An example of a multiprocessor is shown in Figure 3-2, where the PEs share memory and special processors are used for I/O functions. Examples of multiprocessors are those used for weather forecasting, three-dimensional graphics modeling, solutions to fluid dynamics equations, neural network modeling, image processing, and speeding up the processing of the solutions to large sets of linear equations, e.g., for matrix manipulations.

The general concern with using multiprocessors in scientific applications is how to code the solution of a given (not necessarily real-time) problem to take advantage of the parallel processing features of the machine. Our specific concern is with the distribution of processing elements in the solution of a real-time problem. Even though our design methodology is intended for multi-microprocessor systems, it is important to understand the most common architectures for multiprocessors, since one or more of these may be part of a distributed real-time system (e.g., digital signal processing). We will describe two basic ways of classifying multiprocessors. The first is based on the degree of parallelism of the instruction and data streams described by Flynn [FLY72]. The second classification is based on processor and memory organization. Other efforts to classify hardware architectures have been made [SKI88] but are not as well known as the classifications described here.

3.3.1   Classification by Instruction and Data Streams

The following classes were originally proposed by Flynn [FLY72] and have become a standard for describing parallel processing architectures:

1. *Single Instruction Single Data (SISD)*. Only one instruction is decoded per instruction cycle, and the memory affected is only used for that instruction. This concept has been expanded to include *pipelining*, where several instructions can be processed simultaneously, but in various stages of completion during each cycle. The instruction and data flows of an SISD architecture are shown in Figure 3-3(a). Most uniprocessor computers use this architecture, and it represents the basic von Neumann structure [GOL72].

2. *Single Instruction Multiple Data (SIMD)*. Identical processors with their own memory execute the same instruction under control of a master controller or host processor. The host broadcasts the instruction to be executed to the parallel processors simultaneously. The relations of the instruction and data streams for this architecture are shown in Figure 3-3(b). Array processors (described in the next section) consisting of n homogeneous processing elements (PEs) are typical multiprocessors using the SIMD architectures.

3. *Multiple Instructions Single Data (MISD)*. A number of processors execute a different instruction stream, but sharing common data. The same set of data is operated on simultaneously by different instruction streams in the various processors. The PEs operate in lockstep such that sequential data items are operated on in adjacent PEs during the same instruction cycle. Figure 3-3(c) shows the relations between the instruction and data streams for MISD architectures. This is not a widely used architecture for modern parallel processing machines.

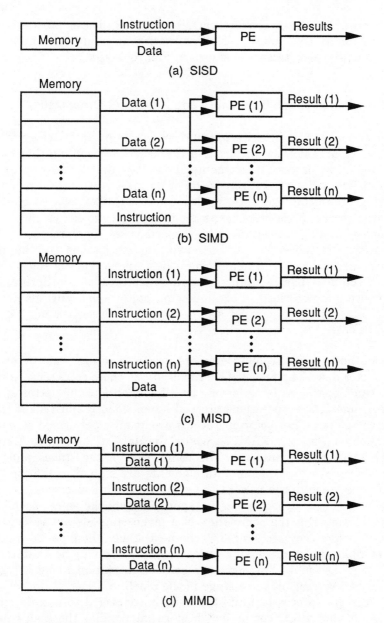

Figure 3-3.   Multiprocessor Architecture

4. *Multiple Instructions Multiple Data (MIMD).* Each of a number of processors has its own instruction and data stream. Many of today's multiprocessors are classified as MIMD machines. These include data flow computers, systolic array processors,

and various massively parallel systems. These are described later in this chapter. The instruction and data streams for an MIMD architecture is shown in Figure 3-3(d).

3.3.2   Classification by Memory and Processor Organization

A common way to classify multiprocessors is by their memory and processor organization in terms of the degree of coupling that exists between the processing elements. Loosely coupled multiprocessors are distributed systems (consisting of processors with local memory) that communicate over a network for access to their shared memory address space or via message passing. Tightly coupled systems share memory or communicate over high speed buses. The processor organization is closely linked to the networking mechanism and the maximum distance between connecting nodes. An overview of some of the most common parallel processing architectures of multiprocessing computers is described in the following paragraphs. Further details of these and other parallel architectures are described in [DES87] and [HWA84].

Vector Processors   Vector processors are used to perform operations on vector data. The primary characteristic of these processors is that the same operation is performed on all elements of the vector at the same time. These operations proceed independently until all of them are completed. The vector operations are usually performed as parallel pipelined stages [RAM77], where the data items operated on in each stage do not interact. The completion of the stages must be synchronized, since all the data elements are shifted in the pipeline from one stage to the next at the same time. This also requires that the time taken in each stage be approximately the same, such that data elements at the completion of a given stage do not suffer long delays before they are shifted to the next stage. The pipeline concept is similar to the processing that takes place on items that travel along an assembly line conveyor belt. Each station along the conveyor belt corresponds to a stage in the pipeline.

The vector processor units are usually connected to a scalar mini or mainframe SISD computer ("host") that handles the scalar functions of the computations and processing control. A typical architecture of a vector processing computer is shown in Figure 3-4. The tightly coupled vector processing elements (PEs) of the vector unit share memory, where the memory is organized in banks to facilitate interleaving of operations. The vector unit receives control signals

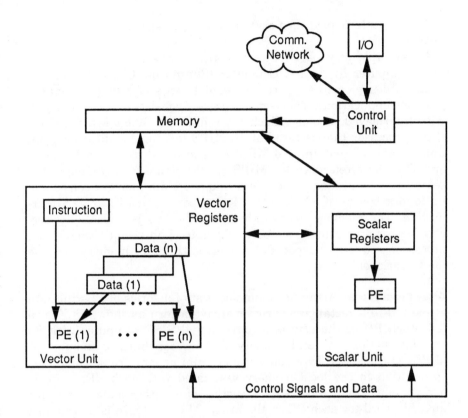

Figure 3-4.   **Vector Processor Architecture**

and data from the scalar unit. The scalar unit in a vector machine does not have to be a separate processor, the scalar functions can be integrated with the vector processor. The computational efficiency of vector machines increases with the size of the vector to be processed and is quite inefficient for small vectors due to the overhead involved in preparing the vector operations. A vector machine with n PEs can efficiently process a vector with n or more elements. For vectors larger than n, the elements are partitioned to fit in the n processors, and the parts are processed serially across the PEs in the vector unit. For vectors smaller than n, some of the PEs are turned off and are not used for the current processing cycle.

A vector processor is a SIMD machine since all the PEs perform the same operation on the different parts of the vector. The special purpose PEs are tightly coupled via the synchronized data exchanges (using the interleaved memory) between the host, the PEs, and the memory.

An example of a parallel vector processor is the Titan Graphics Supercomputer by Ardent Computer (Sunnyvale, CA) [DIE88]. The Titan is designed to support the requirements of high-performance graphics applications. The vector processor consists of up to four PEs with interleaved memory. Each PE contains a 32-bit MIPS R-2000 RISC processor that is rated at 10 MIPS (average), a floating point unit capable of sustaining 6 MFLOPS and 32 Kbytes of cache memory. (The first reference to "MIPS" is the name of a company, the second the usual measure of performance.) Main memory consists of up to four boards of 8, 16, or 32 Mbytes per board with 8-way interleaving. The memory bandwidth across the bus is 256 Mbytes/second. Vector processing is supported by 256 32-bit vector registers per processor and four independent pipelines: three for memory and one for operations.

Array Processors   Array processors consist of a series of PEs that are connected in a rectangular grid or array pattern as shown in Figure 3-5. Each PE in the grid is a conventional SISD computer with its own instruction set, local memory, and I/O capabilities, and the set of PEs is controlled by a conventional mini or mainframe computer. In addition to the local memory associated with each PE, there is array memory that reflects the structure of the processing array with an n-bit word for each PE in the array. The word size is determined by the type of PE, which can vary from a very simple 1-bit processor to a sophisticated 32-bit supermicro (i.e., n can range from 1 to 32). The array memory is arranged in horizontal and vertical planes to provide for the simultaneous transfer of a complete row or column to the next set of PEs in the array.

A separate host computer is used to provide programming support for the user. An individual PE can communicate with its adjacent neighbors in the grid using serial or parallel point-to-point links. The local memory of each PE is used to store local programs and data, results of intermediate calculations, and communication data involving neighboring PEs. The I/O subsystem is usually used for the connections with the controlling computer, and the connections with the neighboring PEs.

The control unit is (usually) a conventional SISD computer whose functions include providing access to the PEs from the host computer program, collecting results from certain array operations, and specifying the transfer of data between the PEs.

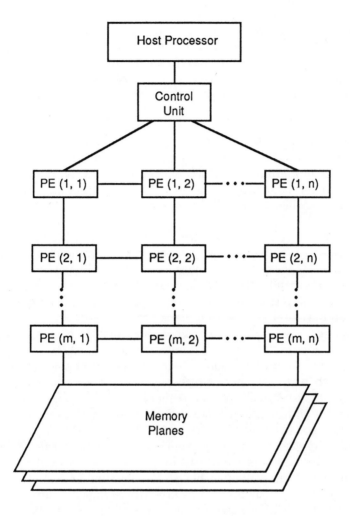

Figure 3-5.   Array Processor Architecture

The function of the host computer is to provide the software development environment (including debugging facilities) and the run-time support.

The PEs are special purpose processors that are tightly coupled through synchronized data exchanges. Array processors are SIMD machines since the instructions received from the control unit are operated on simultaneously by all the PEs in the grid.

Array processor architectures provide for simple, regular structures that are readily scalable for the solution of large problems. The individual node processors need to communicate with at most four neighboring nodes and the control processor. The ratio of computation to the additional communication overhead (as the array size increases) can thus be kept reasonably well balanced for large problems.

Array structures have been used in combination with pipelining processing in the formation of systolic array machines to support the solution of numerous scientific applications, such as image processing, character recognition, and dynamic programming. Systolic arrays are described later in this chapter.

Hypercubes Parallel architectures referred to as *cubes* (also referred to as boolean n cubes or binary cubes) contain a set of n processors, where n is a power of two, with the processors positioned at the corners of a virtual cube, and the connections between the processors form edges of the cube. The *dimension* of a cube is expressed as $\log_2 n$, and architectures with dimensions greater than 3 (i.e., greater than 8 nodes) are called *hypercubes*. An example of a hypercube is shown in Figure 3-6 with a dimension of 4 (i.e., 16 nodes). Two cubes, each with a dimension of 3 are connected at the corner nodes, where each node is a microprocessor. The corner nodes may share memory, or have their own local memory. The processors are connected with point-to-point links and use message passing for communication. Cube architectures are constructed as SIMD or MIMD, depending on their intended application. In general, a MIMD hypercube architecture will result in less redesign of existing sequential programs than a comparable SIMD machine for certain scientific applications. The node processors in a MIMD machine are more complex than in a SIMD, however, since they must fetch their own instructions, as opposed to receiving instructions from a broadcast in a SIMD machine.

Applications that use computers with a cube structure include weather forecasting, real-time image processing, solutions to fluid flow hyperbolic equations, finite element analysis, and numerous other scientific applications that are generally computation intensive. The great advantage of the hypercube architecture is scalability. Since there is no central resource for inter-processor communications, processors can be added with almost linear performance improvements. One of the primary reasons why the hypercube is a popular architecture for massively parallel systems is that the maximum distance between communicating processors is less than in

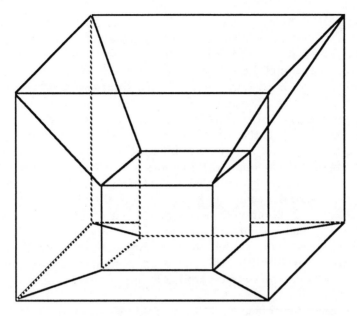

Figure 3-6.   Hypercube Architecture (n = 4)

most other architectures and is fixed by the dimension of the cube. This maximum distance is proportional to the edge of the cube, and the average distance is one half of the cube edge. Another reason for the popularity of the hypercube is that other topologies can be considered subsets of the hypercube. This means that programs that have been written for other parallel topologies can be transferred to hypercubes with relative ease.

The architecture of the hypercube is completely symmetrical and can be decomposed into hypercubes of smaller dimensions for applications that do not require the complete architecture of a given machine. For any given application there is an optimal hypercube dimension that should be used. If the dimension is too large, the communication time (message passing) between the host and the various nodes becomes proportionately too long. If the dimension is too small, the processing time of the individual nodes increases beyond the optimal point in a well balanced system. Most commercial hypercube machines are configured with local memory and I/O channels for each node and a parallel bus for communication within the node.

One example of a commercial computer that employs a cube architecture is the Intel iPSC/2 (Intel, Beaverton, OR). This is a coarse-grained MIMD hypercube with configurations up to 128 nodes (dimension 7). The nodes are 32-bit 80386 processors with local memory. Messages are passed between nodes over 7 full-duplex serial channels at a rate of 2.8 Mbytes/second for each channel. An eighth channel is used as the link to the 80386 front-end processor. Peak performance of the 128-node hypercube is reported to be more than 500 MIPS and 1.2 GFLOPS [CUR89].

Another example is the NCube hypercube (NCube, Beaverton, OR). The system can be configured for different dimensions; one of these systems is the NCube/ten which includes a host and 1,024 processors (dimension 10) and is rated at 500 MFLOPS [HAY86]. This is a medium-grained MIMD computer where each of the nodes consists of a custom-designed 32-bit processor (680X0) with 512 Kbytes of local memory. The nodes communicate via 10 full duplex serial I/O lines at a rate of 1 Mbytes/second in each direction. Up to 8 front-end processors (with 80x86 boards) are used to manage I/O operations, where these processors are controlled by a multiuser Unix operating system.

The Connection Machine (Thinking Machines, Cambridge, MA) employs a massively parallel hypercube architecture with up to 64K processors [TUC88]. The CM-2 computer consists of 64K processors composed of four hypercubes, each with a dimension of 14 (16K processors). This is a fine-grained SIMD parallel architecture where each node consists of an 8-bit processor with 64 Kbits of bit-addressable local memory. The instructions to be processed are broadcast from a front-end processor or a sequencer associated with each of the four hypercubes. The performance for 32-bit integer arithmetic has been measured at 2,500 MIPS, and floating point arithmetic at 20 GFLOPS [TUC88]. The application domain for this machine includes geophysics, particle simulation, fluid flow modeling, and neural net simulation.

Data Flow Computers In computers employing the traditional von Neumann model, there is single (sequential) control of the data flow. The instructions are stored in memory and executed sequentially. An instruction counter points to the next instruction to be executed, the data needed for the execution is fetched from memory based on the instruction sequence, and intermediate or final results are stored in memory after each execution cycle. The programming languages developed for von Neumann machines can be described as *control flow* languages. It is the instruction sequence that determines the execution of the program in these machines. A *data flow* computer, on the other hand, is based on the concept that the *availability of data* con-

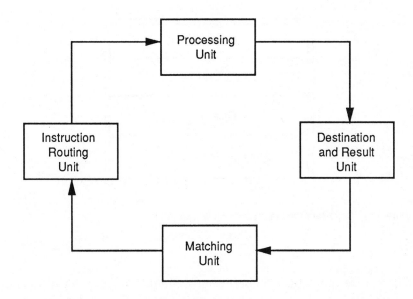

Figure 3-7.   Data Flow Computer Architecture

trols the execution flow, and not the sequence of instructions. Operations on operands take place when the operands are ready, rather than when they are required by the instruction sequence. This implies that program statements prepared for a data flow machine are not necessarily executed in their textual order in the program. If data is available for more than one instruction, these instructions are executed in parallel. The software developed for this architecture is based on data flow programming, rather than control flow programming.

An example of an architecture for a data flow computer is shown in Figure 3-7, and sometimes referred to as a circular pipeline [DES87]. Data is routed circularly from one unit to the next, and operations are performed in parallel by the various units. The processing that takes place within each of the units shown in Figure 3-7 can be described by a logical *cell* (or packet), which contains the parts shown in Figure 3-8. The processing unit consists of a number of homogeneous or heterogeneous PEs that process the operation of a given cell and produce the required (intermediate) result. The cell is reformatted by attaching the results to the destination information in the destination and result unit. In the matching unit the destination information portion of the cell identifies the other cells into which the results should be stored as operands and the operations

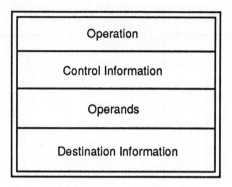

Figure 3-8.   Cell (Data Packet) in Data Flow Computer

that require the data. It is here that the data flow is determined for those operations that can proceed in parallel. The control information part of a cell specifies the conditions that must be satisfied before an operation can take place. When the required data is available for the next operation(s) (i.e., the required conditions are satisfied), the cell is sent to the instruction routing unit. This unit is similar to the destination and result unit, and special routing techniques are used to send cells to an idle or special-purpose PE.

Data flow architectures are considered loosely coupled MIMD machines, since different sets of operations are performed on different sets of operands.

A characteristic of data flow computers is that they offer a high degree of parallelism but are considerably more difficult to program than control flow computers. The data flow aspects must be specifically accounted for, and the parallelism is at the program statement level, rather than at the process abstraction level, as is the case, for example, in Ada.

One example of a data flow machine is the Manchester Prototype Dataflow Computer [GUR85]. The processing unit in this architecture consists of up to 20 PEs. Other examples include the data flow machines developed at UC Irvine [ARV78] and MIT [DEN79].

Systolic Arrays Systolic array processors combine the regular and simple architecture of a grid topology with a high degree of parallelism without a substantial increase in communication overhead. These architectures are composed of either special-purpose (i.e., simple) processors or general-purpose (i.e., complex) processors. In general, the use of systolic arrays requires a careful identification and mapping of a specific application to the appropriate array size.

Parallel architectures that employ systolic arrays can be characterized as an extension of the concept of pipelining. The word *systolic* refers to the mode of the processing that takes place and is borrowed from the medical field where it means "a rhythmically recurring contraction; a contraction of the heart by which the blood is forced onward, and the circulation kept up" (*Webster's New Collegiate Dictionary*, 1981). The extension to pipelining is twofold: (1) whereas pipelining usually has one-dimensional, unidirectional flows, systolic architectures can have multi-dimensional, multidirectional flows; and (2) whereas only partial results flow between processing stages in a pipelined system, both partial results and original data move between processing stages in systolic architectures. The *array* part of this architecture refers to a grid in which each node corresponds to a processor and the lines between the nodes represent the links between the processors. The characteristics of systolic architectures can be described as follows [KUN82]:

1. Every data item input to the system is operated on several times before it is returned to memory.

2. Several data items are operated on concurrently.

3. Operations performed at each processing stage are usually quite simple, and the PEs used are homogeneous with a simple, regular design.

4. Control and data flows within the systolic architecture are regular and consistent across the PEs.

Systolic architectures are typically created for algorithmically specialized systems with a given set of requirements. Applications for other algorithms may require a partitioning of the system, or a reconfiguration of the array structure. For each algorithm, the designer must specify the most efficient systolic architecture and provide a mapping of the solution domain to the architecture. Applications that are well suited to the use of systolic arrays include signal and image processing, matrix manipulation, and non-numeric applications such as graph algorithms, language recognition, and dynamic programming.

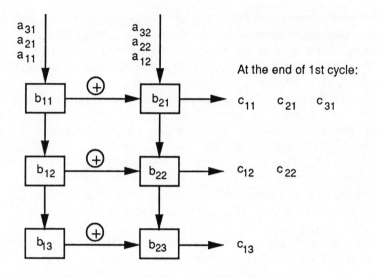

Figure 3-9. Matrix Multiplication in a Systolic Array Processor

An example of the computational flow for the matrix multiplication

```
A[3x2] x B[2x3] = C[3x3]
```

in a systolic processor is shown in Figure 3-9. The columns of the matrix B are distributed (horizontally) across the array elements, and the rows of matrix A are fed in parallel (vertically) to the PEs. The results of the products and additions of the individual matrix elements are processed in parallel (horizontally) across the PEs, with the elements of C appearing on the right as columns. Applications that are compute bound and with regular computations are candidates for systolic architectures. The architecture is classified as SIMD with the processors tightly coupled.

Parallel architectures with systolic arrays are extremely cost effective because of their extensive replication of a small number of simple, basic functions and their highly dense and regular array structures. This architecture is highly amenable to low-cost fault tolerance schemes that can be tailored directly to the application algorithm and to the array architecture [ABR87]. Some implementations of systolic array architectures are described in the paragraphs that follow.

The Systolic Linear Algebra Parallel Processor (SLAPP) has been developed to support the solutions of real-time signal processing applications [DRA87]. The solutions are formulated in terms of matrix algebra, and the systolic array operates in parallel on the matrix equations. SLAPP is implemented as a dual-processor machine, where one processor can be operating on one algorithm while data for a second algorithm is being received from an adjacent processor.

The Saxpy Matrix-1 is implemented as a general-purpose systolic computer [FOU87]. This is a programmable and reconfigurable systolic array processor for signal processing applications and matrix manipulation. Matrix-1 is a SIMD machine with up to 32 processing elements. The system controller (used for broadcasting the instructions of the application program) is a DEC VAX that runs the VMS operating system. The *matrix processor* is an array of 8, 16, or 32 vector processors and performs the systolic computations with performance up to 1 GFLOPS [FOU87]. Each PE has 4K 32-bit words of local memory, and the system can be configured with up to 128M words of global memory.

The Adaptive Antenna Processor Test Bed (AAPT) was developed in England to support the real-time application of the vector formation of the receive beam for an adaptive antenna array [MCC87]. The systolic array portion of the AAPT consists of 33 processing nodes which use the Texas Instrument TMS32010 chip as the PE. The system performance is rated as approximately 150 MIPS (TMS32010 instructions).

Transputers A transputer can be classified as a high-performance RISC micro-processor with on-chip memory and serial links, as shown in Figure 3-10. The links are normally used for inter-process communication between processing nodes.

A single *transputer* does not represent a distributed parallel architecture, but provides an attractive building block for constructing the parallel processing systems described above. The design characteristics of the transputer include simplicity, regularity, lack of bus interfaces between the processors, a high degree of scalability, high performance, and high connectivity.

An example of a simple transputer network is shown in Figure 3-11 in a grid architecture. The serial links can also be used for downloading of a program to an embedded transputer. The RISC instructions can be augmented with an application-specific extended set of instructions, resulting in a high-throughput processing element. The core instructions and extensions are implemented in microcode, rather than being hardwired as is common in most RISC machines. The use of microcode makes the transputer a very flexible processing element that can easily be tailored to a specific applica-

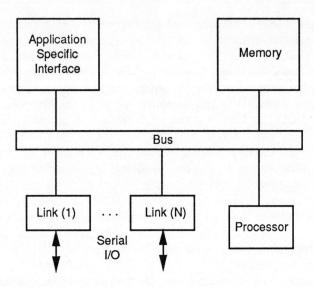

Figure 3-10.   Transputer Architecture

tion. Pipelining is not used in the transputer, in contrast to many of the common RISC machines. The lack of pipelining provides for a reasonably simple design, and avoids the high complexity of many modern parallel processing architectures.

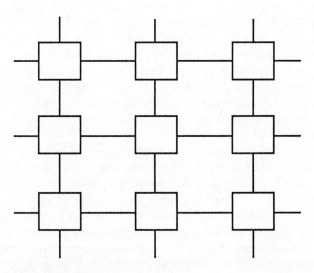

Figure 3-11.   Transputer Network

Transputer-based multiprocessing machines can be constructed from a standard bus mother board with sockets for plugging in a set of transputer modules. The mother boards have the necessary circuitry for connecting to a bus backplane such as VMEbus, Multibus II, or NuBus. This modular architecture provides for a straightforward implementation of rapid prototyping for a given application. Increased performance, as well as functional extensions, can be obtained by simply adding modules. When all the sockets on a motherboard have been used, another mother board and modules are added for the complete system implementation. Claims are made that near-linear gains in performance are achieved as transputer modules are added [AND88]. Transputer chips are commercially available from Inmos (Colorado Springs, CO). Both Inmos and other commercial vendors supply mother boards and various system boards that are tailored to interfacing with real-time systems that use certain processor/bus combinations, such as 680X0 and VMEbus, or 80X86 and Multibus II.

Each transputer in a parallel architecture contains its own program counter, and the instructions are executed from its own local memory. This classifies the architecture as an MIMD machine.

The internal structure of the transputer is optimized for programs written in the special high-level programming language occam, created by Inmos [INM84]. This language contains constructs for sequential processing, as well as for communication between concurrent processes. (The features of occam are described in a later chapter.)

Applications for the use of transputers include the gigaflops operations on supercomputers, and real-time systems that range from avionics and robotics to remote data acquisition. The flexibility of designing special purpose systems allows transputers to fully exploit the concurrency that is inherent in most real-time systems. Current supercomputer applications include fluid flow and finite elements analysis, image processing, molecular modeling, and artificial intelligence.

An example of a multiprocessor computer using transputers is the FPS T Series Parallel Processor (Floating Point Systems, Beaverton, OR). The system is configured as a hypercube with the number of nodes varying from 8 (dimension 3) to 16,384 (dimension 14) and is an example of a massively parallel architecture. It uses occam as the programming language for parallel applications.

A transputer chip that has been used in numerous parallel architectures is the T800 [INM87]. This includes a 32-bit processor rated at 10 MIPS, a 64-bit floating point unit rated at 1.5 MFLOPS, 32-bit wide memory interface with bandwidth of 26 Mbytes/second, 4 Kbytes high speed RAM, and four Inmos serial links with bandwidths of 5, 10, or 20 Mbits/second. The next generation of 32-bit Inmos transputers is the T801, rated with a 50% performance increase.

The serial links can be used as point-to-point connections between nodes in the various architectures described above. If, for example, a hypercube with a dimension higher than four is required, transputers can be combined into a node to satisfy the required higher number of links between nodes. A single transputer per node can support the construction of a 4-cube, two transputers per node can support a 6-cube, and so forth.

3.4   Multi-Microprocessor Systems

In the paragraphs above we described various parallel architectures for multiprocessing systems. These systems are primarily used for "number crunching" in scientific applications. They can also be used in real-time systems as host computers or special purpose engines, such as for digital signal processing or graphics processing. In the following paragraphs we focus on the microprocessor systems that *control* real-time systems, as opposed to the more powerful machines that manipulate the data obtained during the execution of real-time systems.

As microprocessors have become increasingly cost effective in terms of computing power and versatility, they have been employed in the control of more and more complex real-time applications. The paragraphs that follow describe the advantages of using multi-microprocessors for distributed systems (as an alternative to larger uniprocessor or multiprocessor computers) and some of the applications that lend themselves to their use.

3.4.1   Advantages of Multi-Microprocessor Systems

With the recent advances in microprocessor manufacturing technology that are producing ever more powerful processors on smaller and smaller chips at decreasing costs per unit of performance, it has become increasingly cost effective to employ microprocessors in real-time systems. The systems we are concerned with usually employ a set of heterogeneous, special-purpose processors that are connected via one or more buses or LANs. These processors can be a mixture of

8-, 16-, and 32-bit architectures that are tailored to a specific application. In general, these real-time systems support the *software-first* paradigm, where the process abstraction is determined first in terms of a set of concurrent processes [NIE88, SHU88]. The hardware configuration is then designed using multi-microprocessors to implement the concurrent system solution.

The advantages (aside from the cost issue) of using microprocessors for distributed real-time systems include:

1. *Concurrency modeling.* It is reasonably straightforward to create a true concurrency model that corresponds accurately to the asynchronous processing that is inherent in most real-time systems.

2. *Modular design.* Functional areas of a given application can readily be identified and associated with physical microprocessor nodes. A properly partitioned system makes the design easier to complete; functional allocations can be made for optimum performance; and easier maintenance provides for an increased life cycle.

3. *Extendibility.* If a given system needs to be extended, additional microprocessors can be added for the new functions without a major redesign of the whole system. This also provides for an increased life cycle.

4. *Fault tolerance.* Redundant microprocessors can be built into the solution to implement dynamic system reconfiguration and load balancing in the event of a fault during execution. It is much more cost effective to replicate a microprocessor or a circuit board than a complete system such as a minicomputer.

5. *Maintainability.* It is relatively easy to isolate hardware faults to a given physical node and to the board or chip level, and thus reduce the mean time to repair (MTTR). This reduction complements the fault tolerance property. Fault isolation is simplified by the functional partitioning and distribution to specific processors.

6. *Rapid prototyping.* Rapid prototyping can be facilitated by first creating a "breadboard" system that will be evaluated to validate the design concept. The breadboard will typically consist of a portion of the overall design complete enough to evaluate

the approach. Less powerful processors, less memory, and reduced functionality of the software than that required for the full-scale system can be used in the breadboard design. This design is benchmarked, and an evaluation is performed to determine the feasibility of the approach for a complete design. If the design is determined to be suitable for the full-scale application, the system is designed with the more powerful processors and sufficient memory. Otherwise, the system is redesigned, and further benchmarking is performed to validate the new design. With a highly modular design approach, both the scaling-up and a potential redesign is easy to accomplish at a reasonable cost.

Some of the disadvantages of using multi-microprocessors as compared to multiprocessor systems include (1) higher complexity of hardware interfacing; (2) a requirement for inter-processor communication primitives; and (3) more sophisticated support for software development and run-time execution. The advantages far outweigh the disadvantages, however, and make multi-microprocessors ideal for implementing numerous real-time distributed applications. Some examples of these applications are described below.

3.4.2 Multi-Microprocessor Applications

The most effective use of multi-microprocessors is for applications where functional areas can be identified for concurrent processing, and where only minimal communication is required between these functional areas. The functional areas will be transformed to virtual nodes and mapped to physical nodes (discussed in detail later in the book). Some of the general application areas include the following:

1. *Data acquisition systems.* The example shown in Figure 3-12 is for a remote temperature sensor system used to control a set of furnaces. The sensors are driven by a set of microprocessors that send the data they receive to the control unit (remote temperature controller). The latter microprocessor accepts commands from the host computer and returns sensor data in the form of data packets. The host computer can be a mini, mainframe, or microprocessor depending upon how much processing has to be done on the data received. Multi-microprocessor systems offer low cost and programming flexibility for a variety of data acquisition systems.

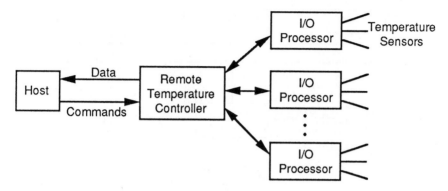

Figure 3-12.   Remote Temperature Control System

2. *Automated process control systems.* The system shown in Figure 3-13 is for the control of an assembly line in a bottling plant. Data from each control station is obtained by an associated microprocessor (PE) and sent to the host for analysis. The PEs are located near their associated control stations, whereas the host is located in another room. The PEs are polled periodically for data by the host, and current status for the complete assembly line is displayed on the synoptic panel. Besides the low cost and programming flexibility, a multi-microprocessor system offers a relatively easy implementation of fault tolerance with redundant PEs for the various stations along the assembly line.

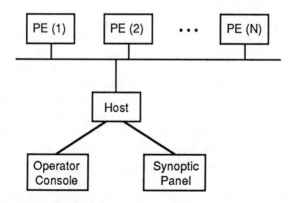

Figure 3-13.   Bottling Plant Control System

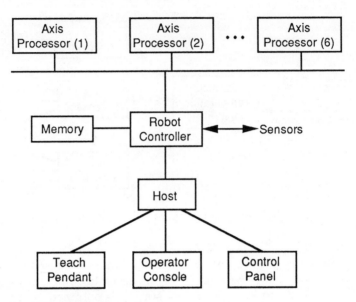

Figure 3-14.   Robot Control System

3. *Robotics*. Microprocessors are used extensively in the control of robots. The processors for the robot control system shown in Figure 3-14 includes a host, a central robot controller, and six axis controllers. The teach pendant is a peripheral device that enables an operator to teach a robot to perform a given task in a step-by-step manner. The operator console is used to create computer programs (sequence of instructions that translate to axis motions) for automated operations of the robot. A given program is selected for execution by setting switches on the control panel. This panel also contains commands for stopping and resuming a program, and it shows the execution state of the current program. The host processor interacts with the peripherals and sends commands to the robot controller processor. The controller accepts and interprets the commands from the host and controls the execution of a given program. The sensors are part of a feedback loop to control the motion of the robot. The axis processors execute the motion commands received from the robot controller for each of the axes (we have assumed six axes for this example).

4. *Extensive I/O processing*. A single processor can easily become overloaded if it is to perform polling functions as well as ac-

cepting interrupts from several devices. Multi-microprocessor systems lend themselves nicely to this type of real-time system. A microprocessor can be assigned to handle the interrupts or polling function for each device. Appropriate signals are then sent by the microprocessors to a central host for further processing by its control program.

5. *Highly reliable systems.* Multi-microprocessor systems offer an excellent opportunity for selective redundancy to provide fault tolerant systems. The cost of adding redundant microprocessors is significantly less than adding minis or mainframes. The programming flexibility of a multi-microprocessor also adds to the ease of implementing fault tolerance requirements.

3.5 Summary

In this chapter we have described general features and terminology of distributed systems and parallel processor architectures. The sections on multiprocessor architectures are included only to provide an overview of the main characteristics of some of the more prominent classes (a detailed treatment can be found in [DES87]). Multiprocessors may play a role in some real-time distributed systems that have computation intensive functions but are not the architectures we focus on in the remainder of the book. We have not discussed how to program multiprocessors. The topic of parallel programming is out of the scope of this book and can be found in texts such as [ALM89] and [PER87].

Multi-microprocessors are ideal building blocks for the construction of the type of real-time systems we are concerned with. Their relatively low cost and wide variety of performance characteristics will allow us to find a set of suitable microprocessors that can support the distributed functions of most real-time systems. The problems of how to interface the microprocessors and the programming support required for distributing the software modules are described in later chapters.

4

Inter-processor Connections

As we described the concepts of concurrency and process abstraction in a previous chapter, we realized the requirement for processes to communicate, but we did not specify *how* they communicate in a distributed system. In this chapter we first describe general processor interconnection networks for various processor/memory configurations and the most common network topologies. Networks are classified according to the physical distance separating the communicating processors, and a distinction is made between wide area networks and local networks. One of the most common mechanisms for interconnecting microprocessors in real-time systems is the use of a bus, and this chapter concludes with a discussion of the common bus architectures we expect to be using in our real-time designs.

4.1   Interconnection Networks

A network can be loosely defined as the set of communication features provided for interconnecting a variety of communicating devices within a specified geographical area. The communication features include the physical data links (e.g., cables and connectors), the protocols, and the software and hardware required for the proper data interchanges between the communicating devices. These devices include computers (mainframes, minis, and microprocessors), terminals (e.g., keyboards and monitors), peripherals (e.g., printers and

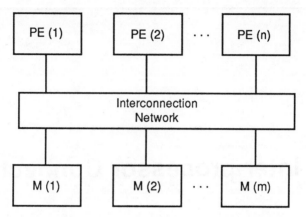

Figure 4-1.   Distributed System of Processing Elements (PE) and Shared
Memories (M)

disks), sensors (e.g., for radar signals and pressure readings), and miscellaneous devices such as facsimile machines and telephones. The specified geographical area can include wide area communication via satellites or cables, local area communication within a group of buildings (e.g, industrial park or college campus), single building or office via cables or microwave, or within a single computer via dedicated point-to-point links or buses.

During the earlier discussion of parallel architectures for multiprocessors and multi-microprocessors, we were primarily concerned with the distribution and coupling of processors and memories. An example of a network is shown in Figure 4-1 for a set of processing elements (PEs) and associated shared memories. All of the PEs in this figure can communicate using the interconnection network, and they have access to all of the memory modules. This arrangement could be used in a distributed multicomputer system where the PEs represent the computers, and the memories could be general, shared resources such as a file server. It could also represent the parallel architecture of a multiprocessor where the individual PEs have access to the various memory modules. The example shown in Figure 4-2 depicts a network of PEs with local memories that do not share any resources. This could represent a wide area or local network multicomputer system, or a set of microprocessors connected via a bus. Figure 4-3 shows a network of PEs with local memories that also have shared memory. This represents a combination of the two previous configurations, and the number of variations of these configurations is limitless by creating hierarchies of subnetworks.

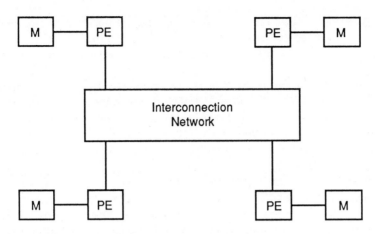

Figure 4-2. Distributed System of Processing Elements with Local Memories

4.2 Network Topologies

One of the most important design decisions to be made in selecting a suitable network architecture is its topology, i.e., the particular configuration of nodes in the network and how they communicate. For the parallel processing that takes place within multiprocessors (supercomputers), we have no control over the architecture or the

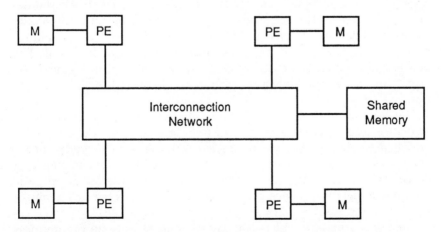

Figure 4-3. Distributed System of Processing Elements with Local Memories and Shared Memory

configuration of the processors. The topology is not part of the design decisions we need to make. For real-time distributed multi-micropro- cessor systems, however, it is imperative that we, as software engi- neers, understand the various topologies that can be used for alter- nate designs. Complete taxonomies of topologies have been proposed and analyzed [FEN81, STA84], but for our purposes we will only discuss a small subset that pertains directly to our design efforts. In a later section we will focus on what is probably the most important topology for implementing our process abstractions of concurrent real-time systems: the bus structure.

Network topologies are depicted as graphs where each rectangle represents a node (a PE, or computer) and the edges the communica- tion links between the nodes. Topologies are generally described as one-, two-, or three-dimensional, and examples of each of these are shown in Figure 4-4. The *linear array* depicted in Figure 4-4a is a one-dimensional topology used in pipelining architectures. The nodes are connected linearly with point-to-point dedicated links.

The *bus* structure shown in Figure 4-4b is a two-dimensional topol- ogy used for connecting computers in local networks (e.g., Ethernet) and multi-microprocessors in real-time systems. A bus structure is usually not fast enough to accommodate the parallel processing speeds of supercomputers. The bus is a multi-point access broadcast medium, where each device is given an address on the bus and con- tends for the use of the bus. The originator sends a data packet, which contains the source, destination, and data, to the destination address. The destination device recognizes that the packet is ad- dressed to it and copies the contents of the data packet. All the de- vices connected to the bus share a common medium, and only one of them can transmit at any one time. All the devices listen simulta- neously and a specific device copies data packets addressed to it. The bus is the only multi-point structure shown in Figure 4-4, and the contention problems associated with it are discussed in the next sec- tion.

The *star* topology shown in Figure 4-4c is another two-dimensional structure and includes a central switching controller and the nodes attached to it. The PEs are connected to the controller via point-to- point links and send requests to the controller for a connection to a destination node. When the controller establishes the circuit, data is exchanged between nodes as if they were connected by a single point-to-point link.

The *ring* structure depicted in Figure 4-4d represents communica- tion between nodes in a closed loop. Each node is attached to a re- peater, and each repeater is connected to its two immediate neigh- bors in the ring via point-to-point links. Each station waits for its

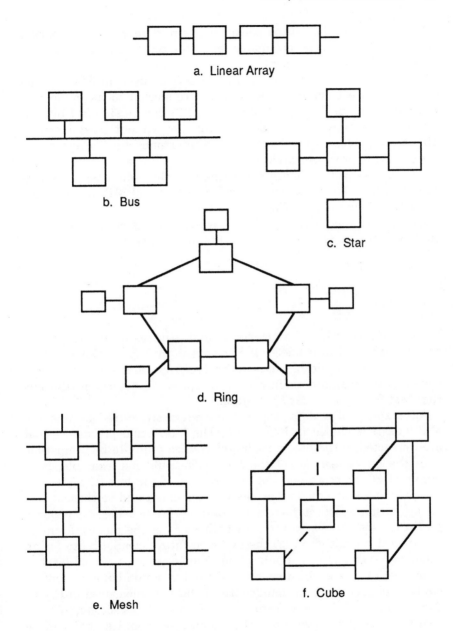

a. Linear Array

b. Bus

c. Star

d. Ring

e. Mesh

f. Cube

Figure 4-4.   Network Topologies

turn and then sends a data packet into the ring environment. The packet circulates around the ring in one direction and is passed from repeater to repeater. The destination station copies the data addressed to it and passes the packet to the next repeater. The packet eventually reaches the originator, and this constitutes an acknowledgement for the data it sent.

The *mesh* topology shown in Figure 4-4e is used in SIMD array processors (see Chapter 3). Each PE is connected to its immediate neighbors with point-to-point links. The PEs can be simple 1-bit machines or complex 32-bit machines with or without local memory. This topology forms the basis for the interconnections used in the various array processor architectures.

The *cube* shown in Figure 4-4f is the only three-dimensional structure included. This topology is used in SIMD and MIMD massively parallel systems (e.g., NCube and Intel's iPSC). Each node is connected to the neighbors that form the edges of the cube, a 3-cube in our example (i.e., the *dimension* of the cube is three).

4.3 Buses

We now consider the characteristics and features of bus structures as they are used in connecting elements in microprocessor systems. There is a multitude of buses to choose from, and the system designer must evaluate their relative features to determine the one that best fits a particular application.

An example of a data acquisition system structured around the Multibus II is shown in Figure 4-5. The interfacing processors that are connected to the bus must be selected carefully to be compatible with the characteristics of the bus. This could, for example, be a family of 80x86 processors and controllers. If the bus is, instead, a VMEbus, a family of 680x0 processing elements could be chosen.

The most important factors to consider in choosing a bus for a particular system design are (1) whether or not the bus conforms to a standard specification; (2) the expected future compatibility for an expanded system, e.g., a migration from a 16-bit to a 32-bit bus structure; (3) the arbitration method used in minimizing contention for the bus; (4) the total bandwidth of the bus, measured either as data transfers in Mbytes/second or I/O operations/second; (5) the board size, which determines the number of modules that can be connected to the bus; and (6) the connector type(s) that the board is using, e.g., some boards use a combination of two different connectors for full 32-bit data paths and addressing.

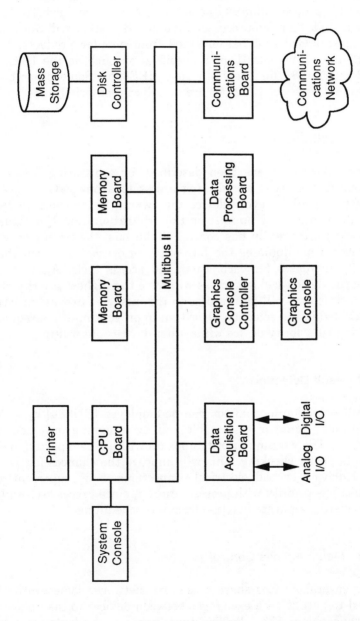

Figure 4-5.   Data Acquisition and Processing System Using Multibus II

The initial focus of the following paragraphs is how to cope with the problems of multi-media access and bus contention. This is followed by a description of the most common standard 32-bit buses used in today's microprocessor systems. By "standard" we mean either a standard that has emerged from popular products, such as VMEbus or Multibus II, or a specification such as the IEEE Standard 896.1-1988 for the Futurebus [IEE88b]. Some other common buses (not necessarily 32-bit) are also discussed briefly.

4.3.1   Arbitration

A general scheme has been described for arbitrating between the various devices that are seeking access to a bus [GUS84, TAU84]. With this method, every device that wants to transmit on the bus puts its own priority number on the arbitration unit. If a higher priority device currently has control of the bus, the processor seeking bus access manipulates the bits of its priority value such that the priority increases for each attempted access cycle. After a certain delay the device seeking access will have the highest priority of waiting devices and will gain access to the bus. A "fairness" mechanism is included in the selection algorithm to prevent multiple requests by the highest priority device while other devices are waiting.

4.3.2   Fault Detection

A fault detection mechanism can be employed [GUS84] by widening the priority number by one bit and by assigning only odd parity numbers. The winning priority appears with its own parity, and thus permits parity checking. This will improve the chances for detecting failed drivers or bad electrical connections. It is important not to confuse bus priority with process priority, since process scheduling is a completely separate function from bus scheduling.

4.3.3   Media Access Control

Since several devices share a common network, some control is required to permit data exchanges between devices to take place in an orderly fashion. The following three common methods are used for that purpose:

1. *Time Division Multiplex (TDM).* The mechanism of multiplexing [LIE85] is controlled by a special processor that contains the network interface control algorithms. TDM is typically used with vendor-supplied (off-the-shelf) buses for systems with homogeneous processors that the vendor is supplying. Specific time slots are allocated to the various devices in a round robin fashion, and there is no problem with contention. A higher proportion of time slots can be assigned to critical devices to effect a "priority" scheme. To be able to connect other processors and devices in addition to those supplied by the vendor usually requires special bus interface units that can transfer data between the bus and the foreign devices.

2. *CSMA/CD.* The Carrier Sense Multiple Access with Collision Detection method is used to minimize collisions when two devices are attempting to use the bus simultaneously. Nodes contending for the bus listen before they attempt to transmit to sense if another carrier is already using the bus. If the bus is busy, the node waits until it is free. An alternate method is where the node listens while it is transmitting to detect a collision. If a collision is detected, the node backs off a certain amount of time and tries again. The delay time should be random (within reasonable constraints) to prevent the same collisions to appear repeatedly. It should be adaptive to account for variations in the system load on the bus.

3. *Token-Passing.* Instead of contending for the bus, a token may be passed from node to node using a special message. When the node receives the token, it transmits its packet (if any) and passes the token to the next node. All of the nodes need not be part of the token-passing scheme [LIE85]; only those nodes that can initiate a transmission must be included in the token-passing order. These primary nodes may call upon the secondary nodes to initiate their transmissions. An example of primary and secondary nodes is a set of computers (primary nodes) that poll their terminals (secondary nodes) for messages.

Efforts have been ongoing for some time both in the United States and overseas to standardize the various buses used for connecting computing elements. The standardization efforts have sometimes occurred after commercial vendors create buses that become popular with several different computer architectures. This may result in a standard where a specification is written from the technical data provided by the vendor, perhaps with some recommendations for improvements. Other efforts are initiated with a committee specifying the requirements for a certain bus interface, and the vendors create the buses based on these specifications. One of the most influential organizations for specifying bus standards in the United States is The Institute of Electrical and Electronics Engineers (IEEE). Several different committees within the framework of IEEE have created numerous bus standards that are in common use today, both in the United States and overseas.

In the following paragraphs we focus on some of the most important standard buses used for interfacing microprocessor elements.

4.3.4 VMEbus

The VMEbus is the oldest of the 32-bit buses and was introduced by Motorola (Phoenix, AZ) in 1980. It supports 8-, 16-, 24-, and 32-bit data widths over a non-multiplexed 32-bit data and address highway and provides arbitration and interrupt capabilities for multiprocessor systems. This bus was initially developed to support microprocessor architectures that use the Motorola 68000 family of chips.

The VMEbus uses a Eurocard format for its board [DAL84] and two connectors for full 32-bit data paths and addressing. One connector (P1) handles 16-bit data transfers and 24-bit addresses. The other (P2) accommodates 16-bit data and 8-bit addresses. The combination of the P1 and P2 connectors provides the full 32-bit paths for both data and addressing.

The basic communication mechanism used is asynchronous (via interrupts), and data and addressing is non-multiplexed. The asynchronous feature allows processors to transfer data at their natural speed; they do not have to synchronize with the (possibly slower) bus controller. A centralized arbitration scheme uses a global arbiter that handles bus access requests over dedicated bus-request and bus-grant lines. Processors (boards) sharing the same request lines are given a priority based on their slot position, e.g., by their proximity to the arbiter. The basic mechanisms are called Release On Request (ROR) and Release When Done (RWD) [BOR85].

The ANSI/IEEE standard that emerged since the introduction of the VMEbus was specified as ANSI/IEEE 1014-1987 [ANS87]. The latest specification is IEEE 1014-1988. The VMEbus International Trade Association (VITA) has been formed to address software issues that relate to the development of portable device drivers and the development of an open strategy for taking advantage of the coming RISC processors.

Various expansion buses are available to provide greater flexibility in board designs. These secondary paths allow the primary processors access to more memory and I/O modules without tying up the system bus. Expansion buses for VMEbus designs include VMX by Motorola (Phoenix, AZ) and On-Board Module Expansion (OME) by Siemens (Munich, West Germany). These two expansion buses support both memory and I/O functions.

4.3.5 Multibus II

Multibus II was introduced around 1984 by Intel (Portland, OR) to support its 80x86 family of chips. It provides for 8-, 16-, 24-, and 32-bit data paths, and up to 32-bit addressing.

Multibus II uses a synchronous communication mechanism for the bus contenders and multiplexing of addressing and data on the same lines. This allows the packing of both 32-bit data and address lines on a single connector.

The processors on the bus must synchronize with the system clock (10 MHz) to transfer data. A distributed arbitration mechanism is used where the bus masters arbitrate among themselves for access to the bus. Up to 20 boards can have access to the bus without the restriction of dedicated lines, and they have an equal opportunity for gaining access. One disadvantage of the data transfer mechanism is that block transfers can be quite long, and this will delay the other boards in using the bus, unless a special coprocessor is used for the message passing function.

The standard for Multibus II is specified in IEEE 1296-1988 |IEE88a|.

Multibus II expansion buses include the Single-Board Expansion Bus (iSBX) and Local Bus Expansion (iLBX) by Intel. The iSBX provides for 16-bit data paths and addressing, and supports parallel, serial, and other I/O functions. The iLBX is used only for memory expansion capabilities. It supports 8- and 16-bit data transfers and 24-bit addressing.

4.3.6 Futurebus

The features and characteristics of the Futurebus have been specified by the IEEE P896 Working Group. This standardization effort preceded any development of a commercial 32-bit bus. The committee work to specify this bus started in 1984 and influenced the design of the current VMEbus and Multibus II and NuBus (discussed in the next section). Several of the features and concepts specified for the Futurebus are incorporated in these three buses. The Futurebus is proposed as a general purpose bus for high-performance microcomputer systems, with a strong emphasis on speed and reliability. Some of the features that are unique to the Futurebus include support for fault tolerance with certain mechanisms to maintain data consistency among caches residing in different processors [BOR85]. The bus is also designed to support interconnections of heterogeneous processors and connections and disconnections of devices while the system is running, i.e., live insertion and withdrawal.

The Futurebus supports 8-, 16-, and 32-bit data widths, and up to 32-bit addressing. It is intended to support a general class of 32-bit microprocessor chips and was not specified with a particular processor family in mind.

Futurebus is specified with a single connector for 32-bit data paths and addressing.

This bus employs asynchronous communication with multiplexing and is intended to support future microprocessors regardless of their speed. Since these new processors do not have to synchronize with a fixed bus clock rate, the asynchronous protocol will allow future speed enhancements as processor technology advances.

The arbitration scheme is the same as that used for the Multibus II where the masters arbitrate among themselves for access to the bus. A fairness mechanism is proposed whereby the masters are divided into priority modules for those masters that have an urgent need for access to the bus and fairness modules for those with less urgent needs [TAU84].

The standard for Futurebus is specified as IEEE 896.1-1988 [IEE88b]. Future extensions may include 64-, 128-, and 256-bit data paths.

4.3.7   NuBus

The concepts and characteristics of the NuBus were initially conceived at MIT in 1979, and the first products supporting the bus were created by Texas Instruments (Dallas, TX) during 1986. It is a full 32-bit bus that also supports 8- and 16-bit data paths. The bus clock rate is 10 MHz. The NuBus is used as the primary bus in the 68020- and 68030-based Macintosh II computers. It is also used in the NeXT computer, but with a bus clock rate of 25 MHz, rather than the standard rate of 10 MHz. Other applications include systems using RISC-based boards such as Motorola's 88000 family of chips. A consortium of NuBus vendors have formed the trade association NuGroup for furthering the development and acceptance of the bus. The basic design goal for the NuBus was to provide a simple bus architecture that could be implemented at a lower cost than the comparable Multibus II.

NuBus uses a large card size and a single connector for 32-bit data widths and addressing.

NuBus employs a synchronized protocol, and multiplexing is used for data and addresses on the same line. Arbitration is provided by a fairness mechanism, with slots competing for bus ownership and gaining access in order. A priority scheme is not used.

The standard specification for NuBus is IEEE 1196-1988 [IEE88].

A summary of the 32-bit buses described above is provided in Table 4-1.

4.3.8 Other Buses

Numerous other buses in addition to the 32-bit buses described above are used for various parallel architectures and in real-time applications. Some of these buses are described briefly in the following paragraphs.

IBM AT Bus   The IBM AT bus was developed by IBM and is used in its PC AT systems. It supports 16-bit data paths and 24-bit addressing and was a precursor to the IBM 32-bit Micro Channel. The AT bus is used in several IBM AT clone computers and has a well-established base of general support for these 16-bit systems.

EISA   The Extended Industry Standard Architecture (EISA) bus is an extension of the AT bus, with the specific charter of not making the AT bus obsolete, and is thus a direct competitor to the Micro Channel (see below). It is aimed at a network of PCs with the EISA computer as a shared resource. The maximum transfer rate across the bus is specified as 33 Mbytes/s.

Micro Channel   This bus was developed by IBM for its PS/2 systems with 80386 chips. The bus design is patented by IBM, and the use of this bus by other vendors requires a licensing agreement with IBM. Micro Channel supports only 32-bit data paths and addressing and is not compatible with the AT bus.

Table 4-1.   Comparison of 32-Bit Buses

Feature	VMEbus	Multibus II	Futurebus	NuBus
Bus type	Asynch, 32-bit, non-multiplexed	Synch, 32-bit, multiplexed	Asynch, 32-bit, multiplexed	Synch, 32-bit, multiplexed
Standard	ANSI/IEEE 1014-1987	IEEE 1296	IEEE 896	IEEE 1196
Data Widths	8, 16, 24, 32 bits	8, 16, 24, 32 bits	8, 16, 24, 32 bits	8, 16, 32 bits
Addressing	16, 24, 32	32	32	32
Clock Rate	Variable	10 MHZ	Variable	10/25 MHZ
Bus Bandwidth (Mbytes/s)	20-57	40	100-280	40
Expansion Buses	VMX, OME	iSBX, iLBX, OME	No	No
Fault Tolerance	No	No	Yes	No
Origin	Motorola	Intel	IEEE P896 WG	MIT, TI
Message Passing Mode	No	Yes	TBD	No
Arbitration	RWD, ROR	Fair, priority	Fair, priority	Fair

The card size of this bus is small, and the number of devices that can be attached is limited.

Multiprocessor use of the bus is supported, but the PS/2 processor uses Micro Channel cycles when it communicates with program memory. Similarly, boards using the bus for board-to-board communications steal cycles from the main processor.

Cache Bus The C (cache) bus is based on the AT bus and is intended for high-speed multiprocessing with a maximum transfer rate of 64 Mbytes/s. It uses a cache coherency scheme for data consistency among multiprocessors. The architecture is similar to the EISA bus with a segmentation of memory and I/O buses. In both systems the I/O bus is the AT bus.

MIL-STD-1553 Bus   This bus is intended for use in systems requiring high reliability and immunity to noise and is designed for military aeronautical applications [DEL88]. The standard specifies only three types of devices that can be interfaced to the bus: a bus controller, a bus monitor, and remote terminals. These devices are connected by serial data lines and run at a clock rate of 1 MHz.

Up to four redundant buses can be used for maximum reliability, but the most common configuration makes use of dual redundancy. Only one bus is active at any one time; the others function as backup modules. The bus controller decides which bus should carry the data to be transferred.

The bus uses a master/slave arrangement with the master as the bus controller. One bus controller and up to 32 remote terminals can contend for the bus at the same time.

The MIL-STD-1553 bus is not designed for the transfer of large amounts of data. It is intended for distributed systems where each of the remote terminals functions as an intelligent subsystem that is managed by the bus controller. A message in this system contains up to 32 words, with each word on the bus consisting of 16 data bits and 4 overhead bits, including one for (odd) parity. Three modes of message transfers are defined: controller to terminal, terminal to controller, and terminal to terminal.

VXIbus   The VMEbus Extensions for Instrumentation (VXI) bus has been specified for use in systems requiring the interface of various instruments [NOV88], generally referred to as "instruments-on-a-card." As the name of the bus implies, it is based on the VMEbus and provides an extension that allows test and measurement instruments to be added to VMEbus architectures.

The VXIbus uses a word-serial protocol modeled after the IEEE-488 bus-communication protocol, and includes a specification for shared memory, switchless configuration, and guidelines for error handling. The shared memory provision provides all the devices with access to the same memory block. This will speed up signal processing of analog or digital waveforms as compared to IEEE-488 interfaces. The dynamic, switchless configuration is a way to assign logical addresses to VXI devices, where a device's address is based only on its slot position. There are no switches to be set for the module, in contrast to IEEE-488 devices.

The VXIbus can be used in heterogeneous architectures that, for example, use both 680x0 and 80x86 processors. Special hardware can be added to account for the byte-swapping problem associated with the simultaneous use of these two processors.

4.4 Summary

The processors in a distributed system are connected via a network in a one-, two-, or three-dimensional topology. Some of the most important network topologies include linear arrays, buses, stars, rings, meshes (or grids), and cubes.

Proper design decisions of a particular hardware architecture for a distributed system cannot be made without considering how the processors should be connected. Buses represent the most important mechanism for interconnecting microprocessors in a distributed real-time system. We need to understand the control mechanisms and characteristics of these buses to be able to choose the one that will be most suitable for a given application. Some of the control mechanisms are listed with merely a cursory description. The detailed mechanisms of bus arbitration, fault detection, and media access control are beyond the scope of this text. Details can be found in |GUS84 and TAU84|.

The performance and design characteristics are described.for some of the most popular buses, such as VMEbus, Multibus II, Futurebus, and NuBus. The hardware design of a given distributed real-time system must be made with these characteristics in mind.

5

Fault Tolerance

During our earlier discussion of real-time systems, we noted that their mode of operation is characterized as an automated system that is expected to run continuously with an extremely high reliability. The continuous operation implies that these systems are available and reliable over long periods of time with acceptable performance characteristics. *Availability* can be defined as the probability that a real-time system will be operating at a given point in time, and *reliability* as the probability that the system will operate correctly over a specified time period [LIE85].

The performance of a real-time system is dependent upon a high degree of correspondence between the correct software design and the specification of the application, and the proper hardware architecture to support the design. Hardware components degrade with time and represent the most important factor in ensuring reliability of real-time systems. It is virtually impossible to prove the correctness of large, complex real-time systems, even after the normal extensive testing and debugging phase of the software. Software does not degrade with time as hardware does, but additional program errors ("bugs") may surface after the system has been put into operation. These bugs are, typically, the result of timing problems between the concurrent processes and are difficult to reproduce in a system with many processes that operate under varying load conditions.

It is expected that hardware will eventually break down and that software bugs may appear during the normal life of a real-time system. To satisfy the performance characteristics of these systems, it is necessary to include a certain degree of *fault tolerance* into their design from the start of the first design phase. Fault tolerance is the ability of a system to continue to operate during the presence of hardware faults and software errors and still satisfy at least a portion of the requirements. A fault tolerant system includes a mechanism for the detection of hardware faults and program errors, and the correction of the problem to allow the system to continue to operate under full or reduced capability. The correction includes a set of recovery procedures, e.g., switching of a faulty hardware component to a standby unit, eliminating a hardware component and reconfiguring the system architecture, or reloading software modules if a program error is detected.

The performance of a real-time system is also dependent on the current load on the system, and a certain amount of load balancing may be required for a continuous, acceptable performance.

The primary mechanism for achieving the required degree of reliability in real-time systems is the use of *redundancy*. In a monolithic system, this means having a complete spare computer that is switched in when a failure is detected. A distributed system is easier to design for fault tolerance and is usually more cost effective than a monolithic system. Redundant hardware elements in a distributed system can be limited to replacing only a fraction of the total number of processors and certain of the other elements, but not the complete system. Software redundancy is also part of the overall design strategy to achieve fault tolerance. The two primary methods of software redundancy include *N-version programming* and *recovery blocks* [OZA88].

The degree of fault tolerance built into a system can range from an almost 100 percent reliability with standby auto-switchable spares, to a state of "graceful degradation" where as much backup and recovery as possible is performed before the system is brought down for repair or bug fixes. Some of the most important factors to be considered when designing fault tolerant systems are described in the following sections.

5.1   Error Detection and Correction

Fault tolerance can only be effective if failures are detected quickly. Hardware repairs or the installation of replacement circuit boards must be performed within specified time limits that are unique for each application. Software errors must be isolated quickly and corrected by restoring the damaged modules or corrupted data areas. If the software must be repaired by a "patch" or recompilation/relinking/reloading, the application will most likely have to be halted, and the system is no longer fault tolerant, unless a portion of the application can operate while the software is being corrected.

The kinds of hardware faults expected include damaged circuitry or connections in processors, memory modules, I/O devices, and communications links. Software errors will manifest themselves as inconsistent data in the databases; process deadlock, starvation, and premature termination; and run-time failures due to out-of-range values, attempts to divide by zero, and lack of storage for dynamically allocated objects.

The detection of faults and bugs can be classified in the following categories [LIE85]:

1. *Self-Diagnosis.* Memory can be protected with parity, and if the processor detects a parity error, it can generate an interrupt or employ error-correcting codes. Memory can also be protected by read-only circuitry, and attempts to write to the protected addresses will cause an interrupt. Processor faults will also create interrupts that are vectored to the appropriate handlers. Peripherals can be checked with each data transfer using checksums and error-correcting codes.

2. *Error Checks by Other Processors.* Messages received from another processor can be checked for errors upon reception. If the same error occurs after a certain number of retries, a failure is recorded. It is necessary to determine whether the communication link or the processor is at fault. This can be done by selecting alternate communications routes and using a process of elimination or a voting scheme [LIE85].

3. *Software Checks.* Failures can be detected by using checksums, e.g., a cyclic redundancy check (CRC). Exception handling can be used with a combination of predefined system exceptions and user defined fault exceptions designed into the application software. The predefined exceptions are raised by the run-time system, e.g., as a result of an attempt to divide by zero, and the user defined exceptions are detected within the application software, e.g., the expiration of a timeout in a process that is waiting for a reply from a device.

4. *Operator Observation.* An operator may detect erroneous system conditions and has the ability to selectively disable certain functions. The system will then continue with a reduced capability until the errors have been corrected.

5.2 Recovery Procedures

Regardless of the method used to detect a failure, sufficient information must be generated at the point of detection to allow the proper recovery procedures to take place. This information should include such things as processor identification, process name, data reference or memory location, error type, and time of detection.

The specific recovery procedure employed depends upon the real-time application. For data acquisitions in remote areas, for example, the recovery should be highly automated since there is no local operator to make decisions and repairs. In industrial automation, on the other hand, some of the recovery procedures may be left to an operator. In either case, sufficient data must be generated to facilitate the recovery process. As a general rule, as much information as possible should be gathered at the point of detection before an alert or error message is propagated to another software module or processor. The further we get from the point of the failure, the more difficult it becomes to predict the cause of that failure.

The recovery process usually consists of two primary steps: (1) a physical reconfiguration of the hardware architecture with the failed element replaced or eliminated, and (2) a logical reconfiguration that may include a redistribution of processes to the available processors. If a processor that failed cannot be replaced immediately, a reduction in functionality may occur, and the system will operate with a reduced capacity.

Numerous recovery mechanisms are used to facilitate fault tolerance in distributed real-time systems. Only an overview of the concepts has been presented here. A detailed account of these mechanisms can be found in [LIE85].

5.3 Load Balancing

Failure conditions may be caused by overloading in one or more of the processors in the distributed system. This could be due to a sudden increase in message traffic and the inability of a processor to perform within the required time constraints. Load balancing may be accomplished by shifting functions from the overloaded processors to idle or less busy processors. This requires a logical reconfiguration of the functional elements and a redistribution of the software components.

Load balancing is inherent in parallel multiprocessor (supercomputer) architectures since the processing elements are assigned tasks on an as-needed basis and processing functions are assigned continuously throughout the calculations for a given application. For real-time systems employing multicomputer and multi-microprocessor systems, however, the load on each processor depends on the dynamic nature of the overall system with varying load conditions depending on the message traffic. If the processing functions are dedicated to specific processors, dynamic load balancing cannot be accomplished. Effective load balancing must be built into the design and may have the effect of a considerable overhead on the system. The added overhead must be included in a performance analysis to make sure the real-time requirements will be satisfied in a fault tolerant configuration.

A distributed system with dedicated functions for each of the processors is relatively easy to design and inexpensive to implement. To account for expected peak loads, however, additional processors may have to be included in the design and may be idle a large portion of the time the system is running. Load balancing for this architecture is strictly static, and any fluctuations in the message traffic outside the expected peak loads cannot be accommodated, unless the system is halted and the functions redistributed.

In a traffic sharing system, the message stream is distributed among the processors, rather than the functions. This means that the functions must be duplicated in the processors, but load balancing can be accommodated without too much overhead. A traffic coordinator (usually a separate processor) keeps track of the relative load among the various processors, and assigns the message traffic accordingly. An example of a dynamic traffic sharing system is shown in Figure 5-1 for three functional processors. The traffic coordinator processor receives the total message traffic and distributes the messages to PE(1), PE(2), or PE(3) depending upon the PEs current load. An account of the current load is maintained internal to the traffic coordinator and is updated each time a new set of messages is assigned. A disadvantage of this approach is that the traffic coordinator may become a bottleneck and degrade the overall performance of the system.

A hybrid architecture combining the features of dedicated functions and traffic sharing is shown in Figure 5-2. The message traffic

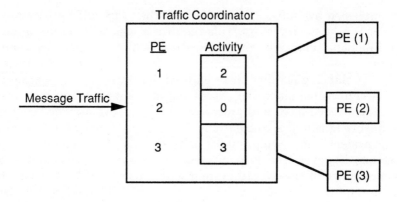

Figure 5-1.   Dynamic Traffic Sharing System

is shared between the n processing elements, and the other functions are distributed to the algorithmic, graphics, and database processors. All of the functions required for the message processing are duplicated in the PEs, whereas only the functions dedicated to a specialized processor need reside in that processor. This architecture has excellent load balancing potential since only the message traffic changes dynamically. The requirements for the dedicated functions can be estimated fairly accurately and do not depend heavily upon the fluctuations in the message traffic.

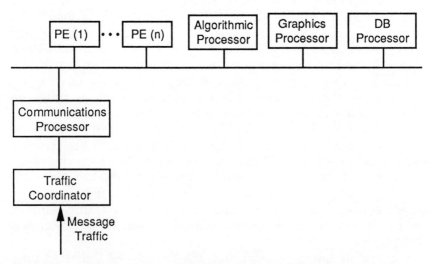

Figure 5-2.   Hybrid Architecture with Traffic Sharing and Dedicated Functions

5.4 Summary

Distributed systems offer great potential for the design of fault tolerant real-time systems. The use of multi-microprocessors avoids the single point of failure of minis and mainframes, and provides a lower-cost alternative to the processor replication that would be required for minis and mainframes if they were used in fault tolerant systems. The software modules that are lost when one of the microprocessors fails can be reconfigured and dispersed among the remaining processors in the distributed system. Fault detection is simplified, and it is relatively straightforward to identify a processor that has failed or a processor that contains software modules with errors.

There are very few general guidelines for how to build fault tolerant real-time systems; adequate error detection mechanisms and recovery procedures must be determined for each unique application. The only general rule is that fault tolerance must be designed as an integral part of the real-time system and must be planned from the very beginning of the design phase.

In this part of the book the emphasis has been on the characteristics and hardware architectures of real-time distributed systems. In the next part we discuss the software required to support these systems.

2

Distributed System Software Support

No matter how powerful a distributed system is made available to us, in terms of the parallel architectures described in Part 1, there must be adequate software support to write the control programs, to develop and maintain these programs, and to execute the translated and linked instructions. Without adequate software support for developing parallel programs that take advantage of the increased execution speed and efficiency of the new machines, the advanced features of massively parallel supercomputers and cost-effective distributed multi-microprocessors are for the most part wasted. The requirements for such software support are described in this part.

The software support required for multiprocessing computers includes the same tools as for a traditional von Neumann machine. Some of these tools must be a bit more sophisticated, however. The operating system must control the parallel processing features of the given architecture, and the programming language should have features whereby the programmer can partition the problem domain to match the parallel architecture of the machine. Various Fortran dialects have been developed for specific parallel processing machines [KAR88], and the programming language VAL was developed for data flow architectures [PER87]. A general category of software development for parallel machines has been specified as parallel programming. *The parallel nature of the solution is either detected by the parallel architecture machine or specified using special constructs in the programming language.*

Software support for distributed multi-microprocessors include special tools in addition to those required for multiprocessor systems. Communicating processes need to be synchronized, and messages must be passed between them. The programming language must include features for specifying concurrent processes (or tasks), and a facility must exist for the mapping of concurrent processes to processors. Special software is required for downloading the executable image to the target machines, and the symbolic debugger must not only handle the multiple processes within a single processor, it must also provide access to the other processors in the distributed architecture.

The software development associated with distributed systems is classified as concurrent programming. *Concurrent programming is used to express process abstraction, i.e., the model of the concurrent elements of the real-time system. It is also used to express the interfaces between the processes and data passed between them. This differs considerably from parallel programming which is at a lower level, e.g., using language statements to express parallelism within a program loop. Concurrent programming is not used exclusively in distributed systems, it is also used to express concurrency on a uniprocessor. The processes will then compete for the use of the single processor, i.e., we have* apparent concurrency. *In a distributed system the processes operate with* true concurrency *in the various processors.*

Concurrent programming languages include Ada [DOD83], Concurrent C [GEH88], and occam [DOW88]. Of these languages, Concurrent C and occam explicitly address distributed systems, with a mapping of processes to processors. Ada has language constructs for concurrent processes, but not for how these processes should be distributed among available processors. The Ada Language Reference Manual (ARM) does not preclude Ada programs from being used in distributed systems, but provides no guidance or constructs for how these programs should be distributed [DOD83, page 9-1].

The chapters in this part focus on software support for distributed multicomputer and multi-microprocessor systems. Software support for multiprocessor systems (parallel programming) is not treated here, but can be found in [PER87, BAB88, and ALM89].

6

Process Specification and Communication Support

In this chapter we discuss the general characteristics of software support for distributed systems with regard to the requirements for process synchronization, run-time support for process scheduling, dispatching, and interrupt processing, and some of the programming languages that contain constructs for concurrent programming and program distribution.

6.1 Characteristics of Distributed System Software

A single program for a distributed system is partitioned into components that match a particular hardware configuration. The system may also be structured with multiple programs, where each program resides in a different processor. For either a single or multiple program structure, the various components residing on different processors have a need to communicate. Distributed system software must not only provide tools for mapping software components and programs to processors, it must also provide a means for efficient communication between processes. This requires a mechanism for message passing between processes that reside in different processors that do not share memory and for managing the message flows when the system is operational. Real-time distributed system software can be characterized by the support it provides for satisfying the following basic requirements:

1. The capability for specifying software modules and communication paths between them, i.e., the transformation of the process abstraction model into programming language constructs.

2. A mapping scheme of the software modules (virtual nodes) to processors (physical nodes).

3. A name space to support the communication between processes, e.g., a table of processes that reside on different processors.

4. Run-time support for inter- and intra-processor communication in the form of process prioritization, scheduling, and dispatching; message queueing management; interrupt handling; and access to real-time clocks.

The real-time systems we are dealing with are inherently concurrent, and our designs include a process abstraction with the highest possible correspondence to the requirements specification. The process abstraction encompasses a set of cooperating sequential processes and the interfaces between them. These processes represent the software modules that are distributed among the available processors, and operate concurrently as the real-time system is running. The concurrency is *real* since the processes are mapped to different processors. Some *apparent* concurrency may also occur if more than one process is mapped to a given processor.

The sections that follow describe the requirements and possible implementations of process synchronization, remote communication mechanisms for processes that reside on different processors, and some of the programming languages that deal with concurrency and distributed systems.

6.2 Process Synchronization Models

We described previously (Chapter 2) the inherent concurrency of real-time systems and how we must decompose each system into a set of communicating sequential processes. The mechanism used to satisfy the timing constraints of two communicating processes and the protection of access to shared data is called *synchronization*. Mutual exclusion is an abstraction of the synchronization problem: e.g., we cannot have two concurrent processes access the same data at the same time. If this was allowed, the interleaving of operations could corrupt one or more of the data items accessed, and the result would be an erroneous program, where the error symptoms would be very difficult to reproduce. Mutual exclusion will allow only one process to access the shared data within its *critical region*, i.e., the set of instructions to be treated as an indivisable operation.

The timing of communicating processes must also be carefully controlled and synchronized. When process A is ready to communicate with process B, but B is not yet ready, process A must be forced to wait until B is ready. We must thus provide *synchronization points* for communicating processes, since we can never make any assumptions about their relative or absolute processing speeds. For a processor where two or more processes are competing for the use of the CPU, this will involve executive services or run-time support for context switching, and for process prioritization, scheduling, and dispatching. Synchronization must also be provided for inter-processor communication. Context switching is not required if each processor contains only a single process, but a processor may be delayed as it waits for another processor to participate in the required communication.

The mechanisms used in solving concurrent programming problems have traditionally been based on a set of primitives including fork/join, parbegin/parend, and cobegin/coend instructions [BRI73, DIJ68a], semaphores [DIJ68a, BEN82], critical regions [BRI73], monitors [HOA74, BEN82], and coroutines [BEN82, FOR85, KNU69]. It is incumbent on the programmers to use these primitives correctly, e.g., to remember to reset a semaphore after a resource has been used.

In modern software engineering the emphasis is on the use of high level language constructs and on avoiding the use of complex primitives that are permeated throughout a program. Two important concurrency models describe high level programming primitives for use in implementing a set of communicating sequential processes. They are important to us because many of their concepts have been included in modern high-level programming languages that deal with concurrency and distributed systems. These concurrency models are Communicating Sequential Processes (CSP) and Distributed Processes (DP), and are described in the next two sections.

6.2.1 Communicating Sequential Processes (CSP)

CSP was developed by Hoare [HOA78] and specifies how a program can be described as a set of independent processes that communicate via synchronous message passing. This model was not developed specifically for distributed systems, and apparent concurrency is assumed within a single processor.

Inter-process communication is expressed by matching input and output commands in which each process names the other, i.e., the communication is symmetric. The syntax of the caller/called constructs is of the following form:

```
<destination_process_name> ! <expression>
<source_process_name> ? <destination_variable>
```

where the first statement would appear in the calling process and the second in the called process.

Values to be output are copied from the caller to the callee. No automatic buffering is provided. Data can only be passed in one direction from the caller to the callee. This is referred to as a *simple rendezvous*, as opposed to the *extended rendezvous* in Ada and Concurrent C that permits two-way message passing. The processes are delayed until copying of the values contained in the messages can take place. Processes are only allowed to communicate via the specified input and output commands — shared data is not permitted. Input commands in the called process may appear within a "guard" (with a boolean expression or input statement, but not an output statement), and will accept input from the caller only when the condition is satisfied. Several guards can be used with a set of alternative input statements, but only one alternative can be selected in an arbitrary (non-deterministic) fashion if more than one condition is satisfied. In the following example [HOA78]:

```
*[                                     -- loop command
      (i : 1, 10) continue (i)         -- guard
         consoles (i) ? c              -- input from console
                                       -- (i)
      x ! (i, c)                       -- output to x
      consoles (i) ! ack()             -- ack to console (i)
      continue (i) := (c =/ sign off)  -- check for sign off
 ]
```

inputs are repeatedly accepted from any one of 10 consoles, provided the corresponding element of the boolean array *continue* is true. The input character c is output to the process x along with the value of the console index i. An acknowledgement is output to the originating console. If a console signs off, no further input is accepted from that console. The loop terminates when all 10 elements of continue are false. A semaphore may be implemented as follows:

```
*[
    x ? V()                      -- release resource
    value := value + 1
or
    value > 0                    -- guard
        y ? P()                  -- reserve resource
        value := value - 1
]
```

For each iteration, either a V() signal from x is accepted with an increment of value, or a P() signal is accepted with a decrement of value. The second selection is only accepted when the guard (value > 0) evaluates to true. When the guard is true, and there is input pending from both x and y, the selection of one of the two is arbitrary, i.e., non-deterministic. The selection mechanism should be implemented such that "no executable and ready output command should be passed over unreasonably often" [HOA78].

A CSP program consists of a static collection of processes. It does not provide for separate compilation, real-time features, or exception handling. The suggested implementation of this model is for programs that will execute on a single processor, or a fixed network of processors that are connected by I/O channels such as for the transputer architecture (the occam programming language was created to provide programming support for the transputer, and is described below).

Some of the drawbacks of CSP include the cryptic notation for specifying the caller/called relations between processes, the one-way passing of data, and the symmetric naming of producer/consumer statements. The consumer must know the name of the producer, and this prevents the creation of general purpose reusable library processes that can be shared throughout a program. Since only one-way message passing is specified for the producer/consumer communication model, two rendezvous are required if an acknowledgement or reply message is to be returned to the caller. This may prove to be inefficient for the run-time support in hard real-time systems.

The specification of CSP is primarily concerned with the expression of programming constructs for concurrent operations. The issue of creating a modular design for large real-time systems is not addressed, and hence, no specifications are included for the declaration and instantiation of processes as program modules and objects. There are also no constructs for the distribution of software modules among a set of processors, since the implementation of CSP was intended for uniprocessors.

6.2.2   Distributed Processes (DP)

DP was created by Brinch Hansen [BRI78] and is a successor of Concurrent Pascal [BRI77]. In DP a program can be specified in terms of a fixed number of concurrent processes that are intended to be dispersed over a network of distributed processors. There are no shared data structures in DP, variables are private to the process that declares them, and they can only be accessed by that process.

Process communication is provided by allowing a process to call common procedures defined within other processes. Processes are synchronized by means of non-deterministic statements called *guarded regions*. Guarded commands are provided for the usual conditional and loop constructs, as well as with the effect of a delay statement. The caller/called relations between processes are not symmetric, and the called process does not know which process is calling it, unlike CSP. The syntax of a remote procedure call is of the form

```
call <process_name>.<procedure_name> (<parameters>)
```

i.e., both the process name and the procedure name of a given operation is known to the caller. The specification of a procedure within a process is similar to Pascal, except that input parameters are grouped together in the parameter list and precede the output parameters. The two groups are separated by a hash mark:

```
proc Get_Track_Data (Track_ID : int # Track_Data : track_type);
```

where we clearly see the asymmetry in the caller/called relation, since the procedure does not specify any callers.

Parameter passing between processes is implemented by designating the parameters as either input or output, and actual data transfers are restricted to "call by value."

When a process is waiting for a certain condition to become true (e.g., an external call to one of its procedures), the processor is idle. This is not to be considered as a wasted resource, but rather as a temporary condition of lack of useful work. When one or more of the guarded conditions evaluate to true, a non-deterministic selection is performed to determine which remote procedure call or delayed operation should be executed next.

The processes are used as program modules in a multiprocessor system with common or distributed memory. Each processor is dedicated to a single process, where a process and nested procedures for a buffer can be specified as

```
process buffer
    s : seq [n] char
    proc send (c : char)
        when not s.full
            s.put (c)          -- add charater to buffer
    end
    proc receive (#v : char)
        when not s.empty
            s.get (v)          -- retrieve charater from buffer
    end
    s := []                    -- initialize buffer
```

where the initial statement clears the buffer. (The "#" in the parameter list specifies a parameter that can be modified, i.e., of mode out.) Buffer operations can be called as follows:

```
call buffer.send (x)        call buffer.receive (y)
```

Non-determinism for the selection among a list of statements within a process can be controlled by *guarded regions*, which make it possible for a process to delay operations until certain events take place:

```
when
    condition1
        S1          -- set of statements
    condition2
        S2          -- set of statements
    condition3
        S3          -- set of statements
```

If several of the conditions are true within the guarded region, an arbitrary choice is made of which set of statements are executed next. Although this uncertainty reflects the non-deterministic nature of real-time systems, the run-time support may have to satisfy cer-

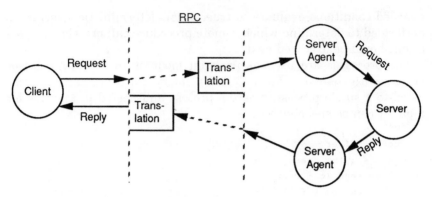

Figure 6-1.   Remote Procedure Call Model

tain design requirements. We may require, for example, that the selection algorithm is "fair," and that an operation is guaranteed to be
serviced within a certain number of iterations to avoid starvation.

DP processes are created statically, and the process topology must
be specified at compile time. There are no facilities for separate compilation or exception handling, but real-time features exist where a
process can be associated with a hardware device.

6.3   Remote Communication Mechanisms

One of the fundamental language independent mechanisms used to
provide support for inter-processor communication is the *remote procedure call* (RPC). A *client* process on one processor sends messages
to or receives messages from a *server* process on another processor,
as shown in Figure 6-1. The client process issues the RPC. An agent
process on the server processor receives the RPC and assigns it to
the server process for execution. The server process performs the
RPC and returns results, if any, to the client, possibly via one or
more intermediate agents.

RPCs can either be implemented with a synchronous or an asynchronous mechanism, or it can be restricted to synchronous message
passing. A synchronous implementation implies that the client process issues the RPC and waits for a response from the server process. An asynchronous RPC implies that the client process issues the
RPC and continues its execution without waiting for a response from
the server process. An asynchronous acknowledgement may be received later from the server process.

Layer	ISO	DoD	Layer	
7	Application	Process	4	◄━ RPC
6	Presentation			
5	Session	Host-to-Host	3	
4	Transport			
3	Network	Internet	2	
2	Data Link	Network Access	1	
1	Physical			

Figure 6-2.   RPC Relation to ISO and DoD Layers

The most general form for RPC services includes support for heterogeneity in both programming languages and processor architectures. To maximize the level of portability of the application programs designed, it is important that clean interfaces are provided for the use of RPC facilities. This is usually accomplished by implementing a layered design for the protocols [STA88]. As shown in Figure 6-2, the RPC services are available at the ISO Presentation Layer (Layer 6) or DoD Process Layer (Layer 4). The implementations of the various protocols are hidden from the application programs, and if a different protocol is chosen, it is transparent to the application provided the interfaces remain the same. An example of an implementation is the RPC used on Sun Microsystem computers [SUN86]. This employs the User Datagram Protocol (UDP) for transport, External Data Representation (XDR) for the data representation standard, and proprietary Sun protocols for naming conventions and control.

The construction of an application program and the use of the services of an RPC can be divided into three phases with five major components [BER87]:

1. *Compile time.* Clients and servers are created as if they would be linked to the same executable image on a uniprocessor. These clients and servers make calls to client and server agents that contain interfaces to services that manage client

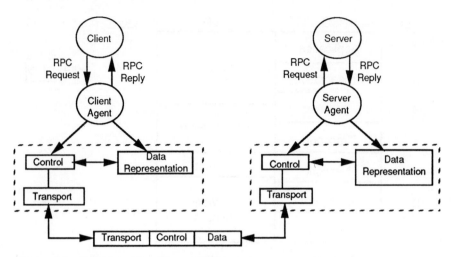

Figure 6-3.   Call Time Client/Server RPC in Heterogeneous Environment

and server names that reside on the various processors. The existence of agents may be hidden from the applications programmers; the degree of transparency depends on the level of preprogrammed services already available for the RPC.

2. *Bind time.* A client binds itself to a server by making import calls, and a server registers itself by export calls via the binding agents. The binding phase includes (1) *naming*, with translation of application specific client name to an internal name; (2) *activation*, with the creation of server processes (if they don't already exist); and (3) *port determination*, with the identification of the server on the associated processor, e.g., sockets or ports [SUN86].

3. *Call time.* The three components used during this phase include (1) *transport protocol*, where parameters and results are transported between clients and servers; (2) *control protocol*, with control information for the state of each call made to a transport service; and (3) *data representation*, which accounts for heterogeneities in languages and processors with regard to, for example, data constructs, representation of data values, and byte or word ordering and alignment.

An example of the structure of the client/server relations in a heterogeneous RPC environment is shown in Figure 6-3.

The degree of portability achieved for an application program depends upon how well the interfaces between the various RPC components have been implemented. All of the call time implementations should be hidden from the applications programmer, such that the most efficient protocols can be chosen for a given system without causing a rippling effect of changes throughout the application code.

The RPC model described assumes that the application programmer is aware of the distributed environment and that the specific distribution configuration is deterministic.

Another model for remote communication is *symmetric multiprocessing*, where the distribution is non-deterministic and the application programmer has no control over the distribution configuration. The application is designed with process abstraction just as it would be for a uniprocessor, and the mapping of processes to processors is handled entirely by the operating system and run-time support. This model is typically implemented for tightly coupled processors that share memory. The processors are most likely homogeneous, and (non-deterministic) load balancing can be implemented by queueing and scheduling processes for available processors.

The RPC mechanism is used for loosely coupled systems that do not share memory. The processors can be either homogeneous or heterogeneous, and load balancing has to be designed as part of the application program. Multiple programs, as well as a single program with distributed processes, can use the RPC model.

6.4   Concurrent Languages and Distributed Environments

Concurrent languages usually provide structures for expressing modules (processes) that can execute in parallel, either by competing for available resources on the same processor, or by being distributed among two or more processors. These languages typically include very specific inter-process communication mechanisms such as asynchronous message passing or synchronous rendezvous. Very few programming languages include constructs for inter-processor communication. This is usually implemented with specific protocols made available as communication services. Communication between processes that reside on different processors may be transparent to the application programmer if a global executive supports and controls the distribution of the processes. Otherwise, the programmer has to explicitly include the inter-processor mechanism for a given process distribution. This is typically done by calling services that are included in special communication packages (e.g., RPC) and makes the application program dependent on the communication mechanism used. The degree of this dependency is determined by how well the details of the implementations of the communication model are hidden from the application programmer. A layered approach will minimize this dependency.

In the sections that follow we describe the syntax and semantics of concurrent language features of Ada, Concurrent C, and occam, and discuss whether or not they have specific features that apply to distributed systems.

6.4.1 Ada

Many of the concepts included in CSP and DP have been incorporated in the general Ada tasking model and, specifically, in the synchronization mechanism used for the communication between Ada tasks. (The process abstraction of concurrent software modules are implemented as 'processes' in CSP and DP. In Ada the corresponding programming constructs are called 'tasks.') Processes in Ada are declared with a *task specification* that contains the visible interfaces to the task, and a *task body* that contains the implementation details:

```
task Buffer is
    entry Enqueue (C : in Character);
    entry Dequeue (C : out Character);
end Buffer;


task body Buffer is separate;
```

The entries Enqueue and Dequeue represent the operations that can be performed on a buffer declared within the task body and are similar to the procedures used as operations in processes defined in DP. The use of the *separate* statement provides us with a mechanism for deferring of detail; at this time we are not concerned with the implementation of the buffering algorithm. The caller of the buffer operations must specify both the task name and the entry name:

```
Buffer.Enqueue (Char);    Buffer.Dequeue (Char);
```

just as in DP, with syntax and semantics for the parameters very similar to procedure calls.

The task synchronization mechanism employed in Ada is called a *rendezvous*. An example of a rendezvous is shown in Figure 6-4, where the task Producer is calling the task entry Relay_Item in the second task Relay. The two tasks execute independently as separate threads of control until the rendezvous is attempted. Synchronization between these two tasks is established with a blocking scheme. When Producer has executed the statement Relay.Relay_Item (R), this task is blocked (at least) until the rendezvous is completed. The rendezvous (statements within the accept body) is executed when the task Relay reaches the accept statement. If Relay reaches the accept statement before any calls are made to this entry, the task is blocked and waits for arriving calls. If several calls are made to the same entry, they are placed in a queue for that entry and selected in a first-in-first-out order.

```
task Relay is
   entry Relay_Item (I : in Item);
end Relay;


task body Relay is
   X : Item;
begin
   loop
      accept Relay_Item (I : in Item) do   -- task waits
                                            -- here for
                                            -- rendezvous

         X := I;
      end Relay_Item;
      Consumer (X);
   end loop;
end Relay;


   . . .


task body Producer is
   R : Item;
begin
   . . .      -- produce item to be relayed
   Relay.Relay_Item (R);   -- rendezvous is established when
                           -- Relay task is ready to accept
                           -- this entry call

   . . .

end Producer;
```

Figure 6-4.   The Ada Rendezvous

Messages can be passed between tasks in Ada by using parameters exactly as for procedure calls. The three parameter modes *in, out,* and *in out* are supported, and messages can thus be passed with or without a reply. Signaling is implemented by parameterless entry calls:

```
Task_Name.Signal_Name;
```

The Ada rendezvous joins together, into a single synchronized thread of control, what had been two separate threads of control. Information may be transmitted while the tasks are executing as a single thread of control. Hence the rendezvous is the Ada mechanism both for task coordination and for sharing of information. It is sometimes referred to as an *extended* rendezvous [GEH88], since it provides for bidirectional passing of data in a single rendezvous. The CSP model provides message passing in one direction only, and two rendezvous are required for bidirectional data transfer.

For each entry declared in the task specification, there will be a corresponding accept statement in the task body:

```
task body Buffer is
   . . .  -- local declarations
begin
   loop
      select
         accept Enqueue (C : in Character) do
            . . .        -- statements
         end Enqueue;
      or
         accept Dequeue (C : out Character) do
            . . .        -- statements
         end Dequeue;
      end select;
   end loop;
end Buffer;
```

Multiple callers to Enqueue and Dequeue are placed on their respective FIFO queues and serviced in that order. The selection mechanism for choosing Enqueue or Dequeue is arbitrary and non-deterministic, just as for CSP and DP. Boolean guards can be employed to control multiple accepts, as shown in the complete Buffer implementation in Figure 6-5. Calls to Enqueue are only accepted when the buffer is not full (Count < Size), and to Dequeue when the buffer is not empty (Count > 0). If more than one guard evaluates to true, the same selection algorithm is used as when guards are not present.

```
separate (<parent name>)

task body Buffer is
    subtype Index_Type is Positive range 1 .. Size;
    subtype Count_Type is Natural  range 0 .. Size;

    Buf    : array (Index_Type) of Item;
    Insert : Index_Type := 1;
    Remove : Index_Type := 1;
    Count  : Count_Type := 0;
begin
    loop
        select
            when Count < Size =>
                accept Enqueue (I : in Item) do
                    Buf (Insert) := I;
                end Enqueue;
                Insert := (Insert mod Buf'Last) + 1;
                Count  := Count + 1;
        or
            when Count > 0 =>
                accept Dequeue (I : out Item) do
                    I := Buf (Remove);
                end Dequeue;
                Remove := (Remove mod Buf'Last) + 1;
                Count  := Count - 1;
        or
            terminate;
        end select;
    end loop;
end Buffer;
```

Figure 6-5.   Buffer Implementation

Processes in Ada can also be specified by using task types:

```
task type Semaphores is
    entry P;
```

```
    entry V;
end Semaphores;
task body Semaphores is separate;


Semaphore_1, Semaphore_2 : Semaphores;
```

Task types are declared just like data structures, and task objects are created by referring to the task type. Dynamic tasks can be created with pointers (access types) and the allocator *new*:

```
type Semaphore_Pointer is access Semaphores;
New_Semaphore : Semaphore_Pointer;
 .  .  .
New_Semaphore := new Semaphores;
```

The pointer New_Semaphore contains the address (probably points to the task control block) of the dynamically created task of type Semaphores.

The degree of symmetry inherent in a given communication model may have a direct influence on process design. If, for example, a called process must know the name of its caller (as in CSP), it is difficult to design a general purpose server process. The Ada rendezvous differs from CSP, and the following asymmetries should be noted:

1. The calling task must know the name of the called, or accepting task, as well as the specification of the entry point. The called task does not know the name of its caller, just as in DP. The task providing the entries and accepts is a server. It is essentially passive: it provides a service to any task that knows its name.

2. A task calling an entry point may be on only one queue at a time. It may choose between calls to alternate task entries, but is not allowed to wait for two or more entries in order to be served by the first one ready for a rendezvous. On the other hand, a task providing entries may have a number of tasks queued up waiting for service at a number of different entry points.

3. A calling task may issue an entry call in a procedure nested within the task. The called task may *not* similarly accept a call

in a nested procedure. This has implications for modularity as discussed in later chapters.

The asymmetry described here allows us to distinguish between active (caller) and passive (called or server) tasks. Passive tasks are those that provide services through entries and accepts. Such tasks are general in purpose (sometimes encapsulated in generic packages), able to cope with the non-determinism of when they are called, and able to administer the queues of tasks waiting for service. Active tasks use the services provided by issuing entry calls. We sometimes have hybrids of passive and active tasks, where tasks that contain accept bodies make calls to entries in other tasks. (A set of heuristics for creating active and passive tasks is included in Chapter 12.)

Shared data is allowed in Ada, but mutual exclusion is not guaranteed with any high order language construct. The rendezvous mechanism should be used in real-time designs to protect shared data as shown in Figure 6-6. The data (Shared) declared in the declarative part of the task body is protected by the two accept bodies for Enqueue and Dequeue. Mutually exclusive access to Shared is guaranteed by placing the two rendezvous within a select statement, since only one rendezvous can be executing at any one time, i.e., an accept body functions as a critical region.

```
task Protect is
    entry Read  (I : out Item);
    entry Write (I : in  Item);
end Protect;

task body Protect is
    Shared : Item := Initial_Value;
begin
    loop
        select
            accept Write (I : in Item) do
                Shared := I;
            end Write;
        or
            accept Read (I : out Item) do
                I := Shared;
            end Read;
        or
```

```
        terminate;
      end select;
    end loop;
end Protect;
```

Figure 6-6.   Protecting Shared Data in Ada

In using the Ada rendezvous we encounter non-determinism at two levels. There is an implicit non-determinism present in the blocking mechanism used to synchronize two or more communicating tasks. When one of the tasks that shares a processor loses control of that processor, we can make no predictions about when that task will regain control. We can also make no predictions about the order in which a set of tasks with equal priorities will execute on a single processor. There is an explicit non-determinism associated with the selective wait statement that we program within a task body. For example, in the task Buffer shown in Figure 6-5, we can make no predictions about the order in which the two accept bodies will be executed when there are multiple callers waiting on both queues and both guards are true. We will point out the significance of the non-determinism for design decisions at the appropriate places in later chapters.

We have only provided a brief description here of the Ada rendezvous and have said nothing about how tasks are created and terminated. Detailed accounts of these features can be found in [SHU88, BUR85, PYL85, and BAR89].

The semantics of the Ada rendezvous does not distinguish between local and remote processor communication. In the ideal case, we should expect to be able to use the Ada rendezvous on a single processor, as well as in a distributed system. For the near term, however, support for the distribution of a single Ada program among a number of heterogeneous, loosely coupled processors will not be available, and we will probably have to design our distributed systems with multiple Ada programs (for a single application) that will communicate via a remote communication mechanism such as RPC. For the far term, support should be available for the distribution of a single Ada program across a set of processors, and no difference should be made between local and remote rendezvous. (This is discussed further in later chapters.)

6.4.2   Concurrent C

The most commonly used specification of C [KER78 and KER88] does not contain any constructs for concurrent programming. With the increase in use of distributed real-time systems and the popularity of C as a programming language, it is not surprising that numerous applications for these systems are written in C. The expression of concurrency for real-time systems has been obtained either by using process primitives available with a real-time kernel or by calling routines that are part of special libraries. A different approach has been taken by AT&T Bell Laboratories by extending the C specification to include constructs for specifying concurrent processes and the communication between them. The following paragraphs contain a description of Concurrent C as specified in [GEH86 and CME89] and discussed in [GEH88].

The constructs for expressing concurrency and the process model in Concurrent C are tailored after Ada. The process communication model is the extended rendezvous (with bidirectional flow of parameters), and processes are specified using task types only, with separate declarations for a specification part and a body:

```
process spec buffer (int max)     /* buffer with size max */
{
    trans void put (char c);      /* put c into buffer */
    trans char get ();            /* get char from buffer */
};

process body (max)
{    . . .
    select {
       accept put (c)
          { . . . }
    or
       accept get ()
          { . . . }
    }
    . . .
}
```

Each transaction (visible entry) has a corresponding accept in the process body just as in Ada. It is not required to repeat the type specification of parameters in the process body declaration. Boolean guards can be used to determine "open" accepts, just as in Ada. In addition, the selection mechanism (specified as arbitrary, but fair) can be modified by a *suchthat* clause:

```
select {
   accept reserve_lock (id) suchthat (unlocked (id))
      {local_id := id}
   lock (local_id);
or
   accept release_lock (id)
      {local_id := id}
   unlock (local_id);
}
```

A call to reserve_lock will only be accepted if the (boolean) value of *unlocked* (*id*) is returned as true. The parameter *id* is used in the evaluation, unlike Ada where a boolean guard has to be evaluated independently of any parameters furnished in the entry call.

Multiple callers to a given entry in Ada are queued in FIFO order. This is also the case in Concurrent C, but the order can be modified with a by clause:

```
accept diskoperation (cyl, . . .) by (abs (cyl -
                            current_position))  { . . . }
```

where the value of cyl is used in the expression following the *by* clause. The order in which calls are accepted is in ascending order of the values calculated by the expression, i.e., the caller with the minimum value is accepted first. This can be used to implement priority scheduling by prefacing the priority value with a minus sign in the expression (assuming priorities with ascending values). The caller with the largest negative value (highest priority) will then be chosen first.

Processes in Concurrent C can be assigned different priorities, even though they are specified with process types. Tasks in Ada that are created from a given task type must have the same priority.

Processes must be created explicitly using a *creator* function and the process type:

```
create process_type_name (parameters)
   [priority (p)]  [processor (id)]  e.g.,
```

```
process spec consumer ()
    . . .
process consumer q;
q = create consumer ();
```

where q is a process variable that holds an identifier for a process of type consumer. The parameter *id* is an integer value that specifies a processor. If the processor clause is omitted, the implementation can place the newly created process on any processor of its choice, e.g., on an idle processor for load balancing. Note that the process variable q must be declared before the create function is invoked.

A set of C library functions has been created to provide information to the real-time application program about such features as the processor id of a given process, the least loaded processor, and an array of all the processors assigned to the given application [CME89].

Since the standard version of C only allows functions (no procedures) and nesting of functions is prohibited, the extensions for the specification of concurrency in Concurrent C include the same restrictions. Process definitions are made with similar syntax and semantics as for functions, and these definitions cannot be nested within functions or other process types.

Concurrent C should be considered an experimental language that is likely to undergo numerous changes in the near future. A standardized version of Concurrent C should not be expected soon.

6.4.3 Occam

Occam is a programming language |INM84, DOW88| designed to directly support the transputer architecture described in an earlier chapter. Where the transputer is used as a building block in a concurrent system, occam is used to specify the associated design formalism. Occam includes constructs for specifying processes that communicate with each other and with external devices through *channels*. A "hard" channel is implemented as a point-to-point link for inter-processor communication, and a "soft" channel as a single word in memory for intra-processor communication between processes. Occam uses the symmetric rendezvous model of CSP, and similar syntax for input and output statements, and includes an assignment statement for the three primitive statements (these statements are considered to be processes) [POU87]:

```
c ! e      -- output expression e to channel c
c ? v      -- assign input from channel c to variable v
v := e     -- assign the value of expression e to
           -- variable v
```

These primitives are combined into constructs:

```
SEQuential     -- components are executed sequentially
PARallel       -- components are executed in parallel
ALTernative    -- wait for input from channels, or until
               -- time expires
```

Conditional and looping constructs are also provided.

Concurrent programs in occam are expressed with channels, inputs, and outputs which are combined in parallel and alternative constructs. Each channel specifies a communication path between two concurrent processes, where communication is synchronized and can only take place when both processes are ready for the rendezvous. An alternative process can be considered a multi-channel server, and may be ready for input from any one of a number of channels. The input is accepted from the channel that is first used for output by another process. For inter-processor communication, the channel maps directly to one of the four point-to-point serial transputer links. The input and output message instructions use the channel address to determine whether the channel is hard or soft. This means that the processes can be designed and compiled without specifying how the channels are connected, i.e., local and remote rendezvous are transparent to the application programmer.

When a message is passed via a hard channel, the output process is descheduled, thereby allowing other processes within that transputer to execute while the message transfer is taking place. After the message transfer, the waiting process is rescheduled and continues its execution. The following example illustrates the specification of channels and parallel processes:

```
CHAN OF INT comm1, comm2:
PAR
    INT x:
    SEQ
        comm1 ! 50    -- send the value 50 to channel comm1
        comm2 ? x     -- accept an integer value and store in x
    INT y:
    SEQ
```

```
comm1 ? y      -- accept an integer value and store in y
comm2 ! 3*y    -- send the value 3*y to channel comm2
```

In this example, each process sends a value to the other, where y receives the value 50, and x the value 150. It is extremely important that the sequential input and output statements within occam processes are ordered properly. As illustrated in the following example, deadlock can easily occur:

```
CHAN OF INT comm1, comm2:
PAR
    INT x:
    SEQ
        comm2 ? x
        comm1 ! 50
    INT y :
    SEQ
        comm1 ? y
        comm2 ! 3*y
```

The first process is waiting for input from the second process which is waiting for input from the first, and the result is deadlock.

The ALT(ernative) construct can be used with boolean guards to create a set of alternate input statements within a process:

```
CHAN OF INT chan1, chan2, chan3:
INT x:
ALT
    (y < 0) & chan1 ? x
        . . .              -- 1st process
    (y = 0) & chan2 ? x
        . . .              -- 2nd process
    (y > 0) & chan3 ? x
        . . .              -- 3rd process
```

This is the equivalent of a deterministic selective wait statement in Ada, with the semantics that the first open channel input is accepted.

A message type or protocol for a given channel can be coded as follows:

```
PROTOCOL Message IS BYTE; INT; INT:
CHAN OF Message comm:
```

```
PAR
    SEQ
        . . .                  -- processes
        comm ! 25(BYTE); 425; 11
    BYTE x:
    INT y, z:
    SEQ
        comm ? x; y; z
        . . .                  -- other processes
```

which specifies a message format of a byte, followed by two integers. Type checking makes sure that this protocol is followed, or error messages will occur. Variable message formats can also be programmed using a variable array size or a *case* statement.

Some of the disadvantages of occam include the column-oriented format of the statements (e.g., level of indentation determines compound statements) and the limited facilities for modular software construction. Specification of procedures and functions is supported, but no encapsulation mechanisms like Ada's packages and private types are available. Support for multiprocessing, however, is quite powerful. In addition to the process structure and channel specification, features are included for the placement of processes on specific processors. Numerous real-time features are also part of the language specification, e.g., ports can be specified for memory mapped external devices, with input and output statements just like for channels.

A language standard is not available for occam, and Inmos is constantly improving the language constructs; the latest version is referred to as occam 2 [DOW88].

Multiple processes within a single transputer are supported by a microcoded scheduler. This obviates the need for a software kernel and provides an extremely efficient run-time environment.

6.5   Summary

The creation of distributed systems requires support for the expression of process abstraction and for communication mechanisms between the processes. A large real-time system will consist of a set of concurrent processes that will communicate via a combination of message passing, signaling, and shared data.

The programming languages Ada, Concurrent C, and occam all provide support for the expression of multiple communicating processes. Occam and Concurrent C both include programming constructs for the representation of distributed processes; Ada does not. The programming constructs in occam and Concurrent C are quite cryptic, and the languages are constantly undergoing changes. Ada is a standardized language with easily readable and consistent constructs. A choice between these three languages could depend heavily on the hardware architecture used in a given real-time application, the size of the system, and the expected longevity of the maintenance period.

The two most important models for process communication and synchronization are the classical Communicating Sequential Processes (CSP) and Distributed Processes (DP). Even though these two models have not been implemented as programming languages, many of their concepts are employed in Ada, occam, and Concurrent C.

One of the fundamental language independent mechanisms used to provide support for inter-processor communication is the *remote procedure call* (RPC). A *client* process on one processor sends messages to or receives messages from a *server* process on another processor. The RPC mechanism is used for loosely coupled systems that do not share memory. The processors can be either homogeneous or heterogeneous, and load balancing has to be designed as part of the application program. The RPC model can be used by multiple programs, i.e., a separate program on each processor, as well as by a single program with distributed processes. The design decision for one of these two choices will be based on the amount of software support available for the hardware chosen for the application. A support environment for distributed real-time system is described in Chapter 8.

Another model for remote communication is *symmetric multiprocessing*, where the distribution is non-deterministic and the application programmer has no control over the distribution configuration. The application is designed with process abstraction just as it would be for a uniprocessor, and the mapping of processes to processors is handled entirely by the operating system and run-time support. This model is typically implemented for tightly coupled processors that share memory. The processors are most likely homogeneous, and (non-deterministic) load balancing can be implemented by queueing and scheduling processes for available processors.

7

Distributed Database Systems

In addition to communicating via message passing (e.g., remote procedure calls), distributed elements can communicate by sharing data that is collected in a database. A database can be described loosely as a collection of data structures that supports certain applications and that is controlled by a database management system (DBMS).

Distributed systems may consist of (1) processors with their own local memory, (2) processors that have a common memory, or (3) a combination of these two: processors with local memory may also have access to common memory areas. The data required for the operation of a distributed system consists of files that are located in the local or shared memory associated with the processors. These files could be centralized in a single memory or distributed among several different memories with the data accessed via local and remote operations. The latter organization of the data is referred to as a distributed database (DDB) structure, and has the primary advantages that several operations can be performed concurrently on different parts of the database to increase throughput, data can be replicated to support fault tolerance, and it is less complex to manage small chunks of data than a huge, monolithic data structure. Disadvantages include the increased communication that is required for passing data remotely between memories and processors, the effort required to maintain consistent data values with multiple access, and the potential for deadlock by processors competing for the use of the same portions of a database.

In many distributed real-time applications the overhead incurred by the additional communication is more than offset by the efficiency of the parallel execution of concurrent database operations and the opportunity for increased reliability with data replication. In some applications, a separate database machine may be implemented as part of the distributed solution. This machine will typically consist of a processor to execute the queries made by the users, sufficient memory to contain the database structures, and the necessary software and firmware for efficient implementation of the required instructions and for the protection of the data during simultaneous queries.

In general, the availability of data is higher with a distributed database, but critical response times may be more difficult to satisfy. The paragraphs that follow describe the components of a DDB, the design factors to consider, some potential problem areas, a scheme for data replication with voting, and the structure of typical database machines.

7.1   Components of a Distributed Database

A general database consists of one or more data structures of related data elements that support certain applications, with access to the database controlled by a database management system (DBMS). Databases are used in transaction oriented applications such as off-track betting and banking systems, and in real-time applications that include avionics, robotics, and sensor tracking systems.

A formal database system has three basic components: (1) the *data*, used by the application algorithms; (2) a *schema* which describes the structure of the data; and (3) the *access interface*, i.e., the operations that control the data. The schema includes directories for the location of the data. When an access request is made with a key or logical name, the DBMS will analyze the request and map the key or logical name to physical memory locations. The result of an access request (or query) for a read operation is that data is retrieved from the appropriate physical memory location and passed to the requestor. A write query results in data being stored in certain memory locations.

Distributed real-time systems may be designed without the use of formal databases and a DBMS for control as described above; they are likely to employ customized, highly efficient database designs for a given application. A general DBMS is intended to support a variety of applications and is inherently inefficient. It may also not have the required interface mechanisms for the chosen implementation language. Some real-time systems may employ special database machines that are sufficiently efficient to satisfy the response requirements of a given application.

Many of the design considerations and problem areas discussed below apply to both formal and customized databases.

7.2   Design Considerations

The designer of a distributed database for real-time systems is faced with numerous design decisions that are not present in a centralized design. Some of these design decisions include the following:

1. *Distribution of Data.* One of the initial decisions to make is how the data should be distributed among the memory associated with the various processors. This can be determined by a functional analysis that will place data as closely as possible to the processor that needs it. Local communication is much more efficient than remote communication, and every effort should be made to minimize the amount of remote communication required. For the typical real-time system shown in Figure 7-1, this would mean to place sensor data with the data acquisition processor, and a track file with the processor that maintains the tracks (where a "track" would be the data associated with a specific aircraft, missile, ship, etc.). More than one copy of a database may be required to provide a level of fault tolerance. One approach is to collect all the data structures in one central file, and to replicate the data structures at the processor where they are used most frequently. An adequate updating mechanism will have to be available for maintaining data consistency between the multiple copies of the same data structures.

2. *Program Distribution.* The application programs that access the various portions of the total database are distributed across the memories associated with the processors. The decision of where to place these programs, relative to the data they access, should be based on a minimization of communication costs and response time. The most likely approach for real-time systems is to load the programs with the database they access for maximum use of local communication in the associated processor. Whenever these programs need to access data that is associ-

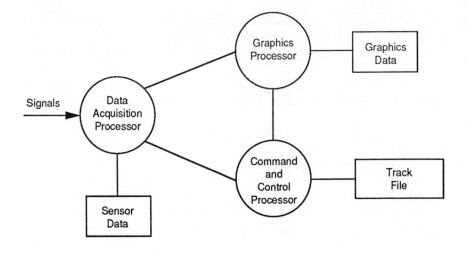

Figure 7-1.   Data Distribution

ated with another processor, a directory (implicit or explicit) must be available for the appropriate reference to the remote data.

3. *Communication*. The distributed database is closely interrelated with the communications capabilities of the system. In a typical real-time system, the processors are connected via buses and LANs. An analysis must be made of the data rates required to support the communication between the processors, and suitable communications channels with sufficient bandwidths must be selected. For the system shown in Figure 7-2 (a), the bandwidth of the VMEbus represents a design limitation for the bus traffic between processors and memories. Data associated with individual processors may instead be stored in local memories and accessed via the VME Subsystem bus (VSB) as shown in Figure 7-2 (b). This will offload the VMEbus and improve the overall throughput of the system. For a LAN, an appropriate data transfer mode, such as a virtual circuit or packet switching, must be chosen along with a suitable protocol. The protocol can be based on a standard, such as TCP/IP (Transmission Control Protocol/Internet Protocol) or UDP (User Datagram Protocol), or it can be tailored to the specific application for maximum efficiency.

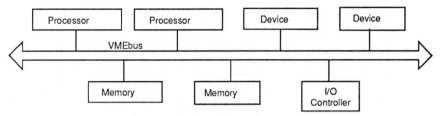

Figure 7-2(a).   VMEbus Bandwidth Limits Memory Access

4. *Fault Tolerance.* The distributed system should provide recovery for lost data and for continuous operation when one or more of the processors fail. Data recovery can be accomplished with redundant data files, and recovery procedures executed by the processor that detects the loss of data. Appropriate messages must be sent to the other processors to inform them of the location of the recovered data. A timeout delay could also be used as the error detection mechanism by a process waiting for remote data to arrive. Only the data that is crucial to continuous operation need to be replicated. Transient data that can be classified as "self-repairing," e.g., sensor data, does not have to be duplicated.

5. *Concurrency Control.* Portions of a distributed database are accessed by the concurrently executing processes for maximum efficiency. The concurrent access to resources may lead to deadlock (see problem areas below), and the concurrency must be controlled by cooperating processes executing at the various nodes. Some form of mutual exclusion must be provided for multiple access requests, and data updates must be performed to maintain data consistency across multiple, redundant copies of the data structures.

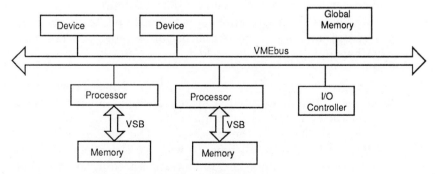

Figure 7-2(b).   Special Buses Used for Memory Access

6. *Dedicated Database Machine.* A dedicated database machine may be included in the distributed solution for maximum data access efficiency. The increased system cost of such a machine will have to be evaluated against the efficiency gained. Once the decision has been reached to use a database machine, other considerations include the use of a commercial product or custom building one for the given application, and whether the operations should be implemented in hardware or with software. Most commercially available database machines include a query language as the primary (and possibly only) interface for access to the data elements. It is important that this interface be compatible with the chosen programming language for the application and that it will support the construction of portable code.

7.3 Problem Areas

The use of a DDB creates numerous problems that are not present in a centralized database. Some of these problems include the following:

1. *Data Consistency.* Data consistency must be maintained dynamically throughout the operation of a real-time system. Inconsistencies may occur where multiple copies of the same data are dispersed throughout the system, and where multiple processes can update the same data elements simultaneously. The latter can be remedied by providing mutually exclusive access by queueing queries for update operations. The problem of how to update multiple copies and having consistent data values is not that easy to solve. One approach is to lock the other copies while one copy is being updated. This could cause substantial delays in the processing, however, unless the lock can be limited to a specific data element or data structure, rather than the whole file. Another approach is to limit updates to the local processes that access a particular database copy. The local copy will then only have to be locked out for the duration of the update.

2. *Response Time.* A distributed system includes an inherent latency associated with the communication that takes place over the channels between the processors. The process making a query on a database will have to wait for the query to be accepted, and for the messages to be transmitted across the com-

munication channels. Every effort should be made to design the database such that most of the communication between processes takes place locally rather than remotely between processors. A remote transaction may also require directory searches, which further increase the communication latency.

3. *Deadlock.* Deadlock may occur in a concurrent system if two processes are delayed indefinitely while waiting for the other to perform a certain action before either process can proceed. This problem is even more critical in a distributed system, where time delays due to inter-processor communication may alter the state of a locking variable or semaphore. An exhaustive report on deadlock detection and resolution in distributed databases can be found in [KNA87]. Numerous algorithms and approaches for deadlock detection and prevention are included in this reference.

4. *Heterogeneous System.* Special problems are encountered in distributed systems that consist of heterogeneous processors with different word lengths and data representations. Database requests must translate the data required from the server node representation into the format of the client. A standard intermediate format may be used to minimize the translation procedures. To circumvent some of these problems, it is not uncommon (or unreasonable) to specify certain restrictions for how data should be distributed. Examples of these restrictions include sharing of data only among processes within a physical node, or among homogeneous processors, and the parameter passing mechanism specified to be only *by reference.*

7.4   Data Replication with Voting

One mechanism used to provide fault tolerance in a distributed system is replicating the data on different processors and performing independent operations on the data at each processor. This removes the single point of failure if data is only available at one processor, but it adds to the complexity of managing the data, since a reliable and efficient fault detection system must also be implemented. It also increases the overall cost of the system. In this section we describe a voting scheme suggested in [PIT87] for fault detection and recovery in a database scheme with triple redundancy.

The steps of the transaction processing are illustrated in Figure 7-3, where each column of circles represents the processing that takes place within each of the three nodes. A user request for access to the database is handled by one scheduler and forwarded to the schedulers in the other two nodes. The same sequence of transactions T_1, T_2, . . . , with corresponding time tags t_1, t_2, . . . , are generated at all three nodes. Physical clocks are used in the three nodes for synchronization of the sequence of events. Synchronization algorithms can be found in [DOL84 and LUN84]. The scheduler shown in Figure 7-3 generates the sequence of transactions and passes them to the transaction manager, which executes the transactions in the given order. Each node executes these transactions independently, as it would in a uniprocessor system, and no locking mechanisms are required to synchronize the parallel executions. There is, however, a pre-arranged order for the transactions in all of the three nodes.

When the set of transactions have been completed, a single set of results is returned to the user, and a database "signature" of the results is sent to the voters in step 5 for failure detection. Each voter compares the results of the other two processors to its own results to determine a local failure. If a failure is detected, local recovery procedures are initiated. The local recovery consists of requesting a snapshot of the uncorrupted database from one of the other nodes and processing of the transactions with a timetag greater than the snapshot. The sequence of steps performed during the recovery processing is illustrated in Figure 7-4. As soon as a failure has been detected, the voter sends a notice to the local recovery manager (step 1). In step 2 the recovery manager sends a snapshot request to the local scheduler, which passes the request to the other two remote schedulers (step 3). A snapshot transaction is scheduled with the other transactions and executed (step 4) on all the three nodes (only one non-recovering node is shown in Figure 7-4) to maintain synchronization of the pre-arranged sequence of steps. The transaction manager stores a snapshot of its database and sends a notice and the snapshot to the recovery process (step 5). The recovery manager on the failed node sends its signature to both of the non-recovering nodes, who determine which pages should be sent to the recovering node (step 6). The recovering node compares the pages received from the two nodes and determines which ones should be installed. An additional failure detection mechanism has been included by having

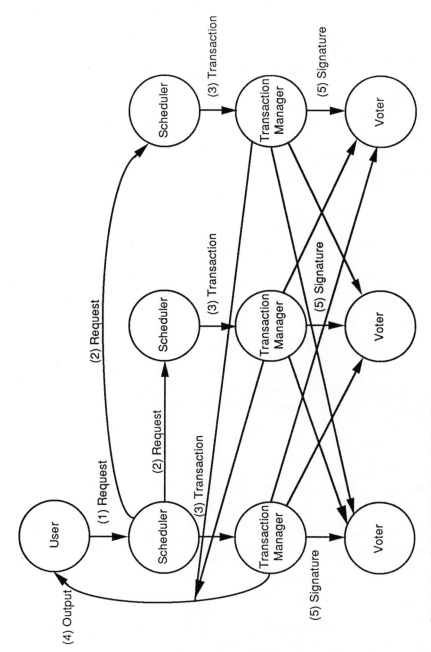

Figure 7-3. Triple Replication with Voting

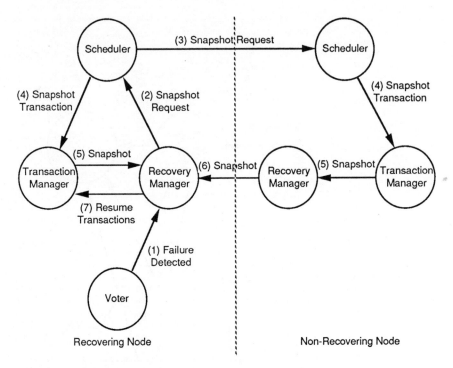

Figure 7-4.   Recovery Processing

both the non-recovering nodes send the replacement pages; a failure
on one of the non-recovering nodes could have taken place after the
recovering node detected an inconsistency in its local database. In
the final step (step 7), the recovery manager on the recovering node
notifies the transaction manager that normal transaction processing
may continue.

Data replication with voting is only one mechanism for implementing fault tolerance of databases in distributed systems. Other
schemes may be implemented more efficiently with regard to resource utilization. Alternative implementations using only two copies
of the database are reported in [NOE87].

7.5   Database Machines

Special database machines can be used in time-critical applications
where the traditional database approaches would be too inefficient.
The database processor is dedicated to database operations and does

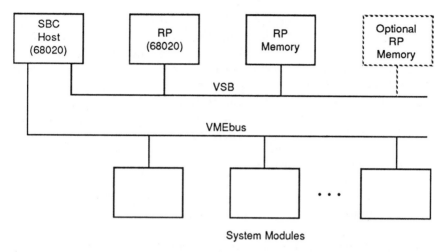

Figure 7-5.   Database Machine Architecture

not perform any other functions of the real-time application. A typical implementation will support query accesses via a standard query language (e.g., Structured Query Language (SQL)), and have the data structure organized in a relational data model. Indexing and searching schemes are usually highly optimized with the instructions implemented in firmware. An example of such a database machine is the Relational Processor (RP) created by the English company Ferranti International [DIX88]. The RP is intended for efficient access to databases used in military Command, Control and Communication systems. It employs an SQL interface and implements a relation data model. SQL statements can be embedded in the source code (e.g., Ada or C) of the application program. A preprocessor translates the SQL code to the equivalent low-level procedure calls that represent requests for the data organization and the queries. The instructions that implement the relational database are coded in firmware for maximum efficiency.

The architecture of the RP is shown in Figure 7-5. The RP processor is a Motorola 68020 with 8 Mbytes of memory. Additional memory boards can be added for a total of 40 Mbytes. The RP operates in conjunction with a single board computer (SBC) interface processor over a high-speed VME Subsystem bus (VSB). The SBC (also a M68020) interfaces with the rest of the system over a VMEbus and acts as host for the RP processor. The operations between the host and the RP are transparent to the application programmers and are handled automatically by the interface procedures and run-time support functions.

Functions are included for declaring relations and attributes, deleting relations, and inserting, updating, and deleting tuples. Operations on relations are available for creating unions, intersections, cartesian products, and joins. Selections can be made by specifying attribute values that lie between upper and lower bounds, e.g., finding a set of tracks that lie within a certain geographical region.

Only a single example of a database machine has been included here to provide the flavor of a typical architecture and the operations they perform. Further details of relational models and database machines can be found in [BER88 and GIL87].

7.6 Summary

The proper distribution of data in a distributed system will place the various data elements as closely as possible to the processor that needs them. This will minimize the amount of communication overhead incurred for inter-processor data exchanges.

Any DDB design with replicated data areas must provide for a data consistency mechanism to prohibit data corruption when simultaneous updates take place. This can be accomplished by selectively locking out all but one copy of the data to be updated.

A general purpose DBMS is probably too inefficient to be used in a real-time system. An efficient DBMS can be tailor made for a given application, or a database machine hosted on a separate processor can be used. This chapter has only touched on some of the most important aspects of designing distributed databases for real-time systems. Details of the implementation of these and additional features can be found in [LIE85, KNA87, CAR87, NOE87, and RAY88].

Chapter

8

Support Environment for Distributed Real-Time Systems

The problems encountered in creating a suitable environment for distributed systems are significantly more complex than for non-distributed systems. Examples of the higher complexity include multiple code generators for heterogeneous processors, different data representations for objects of the same type, inter-process communication, and symbolic debugging on multiple target machines. The support environment must provide facilities for distributing software modules among the processors identified for a given architecture. It should also support reconfiguration of the hardware architecture and reallocation of the software modules in case of hardware faults.

This chapter describes the general features required for supporting the development, implementation, and execution of real-time distributed systems, regardless of the implementation language, and is not tailored to Ada. The emphasis is on the construction of multi-microprocessor systems connected via buses or LANs, and not on large computer networks using WANs. We are assuming that the basic building block for designing these systems is the virtual node (VN) — a set of closely coupled software modules — and that the VNs are distributed over a given set of processors. Communication between the processors is performed via computer buses or LANs. Inter-process communication within a VN is performed with shared memory or a synchronization mechanism such as the rendezvous of Ada and

Concurrent C. Communication between VNs is provided by remote procedure calls, remote entry calls, or asynchronous message passing. The paragraphs that follow contain a description of the basic requirements for a support environment of distributed real-time systems in terms of real-time executive services and some commercial implementations, software development with regard to programming language features and distribution specifications, code generation for homogeneous and heterogeneous architectures, debugging and library management, linking and loading, and run-time execution support.

8.1   Real-Time Executives

Real-time executives must provide a wide range of run-time features to support the critical functions required by real-time systems. These features include task scheduling, queueing and dispatching, interrupt handling, exact timing support, memory management, fault handling, bus arbitration, and multiple-processor operation. The multiple-processor operations include support for several processors on the same bus, multiple buses, or LANs, inter-processor communication, and management of system wide resources. Some of the executive features may be implemented as *controller* functions on special processors, e.g., a bus controller or memory management unit.

Global support for distributed systems is usually limited to shared memory systems, where the executive determines the distribution of processes to processors and the scheduling of processes. Process communication in this case is programmed without concern for the distribution, and inter-processor communication is transparent to the application programmer. The common approach for loosely coupled processors (that do not share memory) is to have a real-time kernel residing in each processor, with the application program using the communication primitives provided by the kernel, i.e., the applications programmer must be aware of the specific distribution configuration.

Some of the early executives for real-time systems were implemented in a Unix environment but did not provide the services required for hard real-time systems. Special real-time executives such as VRTX and MTOS [FAL88] were developed as kernels to be used with bare machines or in cooperation with other operating systems. A "kernel" can be described as a minimal portion of an operating system that provides special services for real-time programming applications. Some of these services include: (1) rapid response to asyn-

Figure 8-1.   Run-Time Kernel as Part of the Operating System

chronous events; (2) interrupt handling; (3) task scheduling and dispatching; (4) response to timed events; and (5) provision for mutual exclusion. An example of a typical kernel for real-time applications is shown in Figure 8-1. The kernel services may be accessible directly from a high-order language module or only from modules coded in assembly language.

The development of Ada run-time support for embedded real-time systems has made a significant contribution to the advancement of the technology of real-time executives. Numerous real-time executives are currently available for microprocessor systems programmed in Ada, C, and occam. Some of these executives also provide support for distributed systems. The characteristics of some of the more common real-time executives and their implementations are described in the following paragraphs.

8.1.1 Executive Services

The executive services described in the following paragraphs are the ones of primary interest for real-time features and support for distributed systems.

1. *Process scheduling.* Even though we are dealing with distributed multiprocessor systems, it will be rare that only a single process will execute on each processor. In most cases there will be multiple processes competing for the use of each processor. This requires some form of process management and scheduling, which may include event driven preemptive, cyclic, or round-robin scheduling. Process queueing, dispatching, and context switching would be part of the process management functions required.

2. *Synchronization points.* If synchronized message passing or mutual exclusion for shared memory are used for communication between processes, a synchronization mechanism must be provided for the concurrent elements. The use of synchronization points imply that at least one process is suspended during the period of synchronization. If this is not acceptable, a different mechanism such as asynchronous communication via queues or mailboxes must be provided.

3. *Real-time clocks.* Services must be provided for initiating an immediate event and to measure the expiration of delayed events for systems with specific time constraints. It must also be possible to translate real-time from one processor to another. This may involve the calculation of a relative offset between the real-times of two different processors. Special considerations must be given to the meaning of "immediate" and "delayed" events for inter-processor communication, i.e., the time spent purely for communication must somehow be accounted for. The resolution of the real-time clock is important, as well as how the applications programmer can specify timed events. Both absolute time and a time interval specification should be available.

4. *Process primitives.* Primitives must be provided for the creation, activation, and termination of processes and for communication between them. This may be implemented with specific executive service requests (ESRs) such as send/receive/reply, or

a tasking model such as the Ada and Concurrent C rendezvous for the communication primitives. The other primitives may also be implemented with ESRs or an implicit task elaboration mechanism such as is used in Ada.

5. *Process distribution.* It must be possible to distribute a set of processes among a given set of processors. This may be done statically with a fixed configuration for the duration of the system operation or dynamically with or without load balancing.

6. *Interrupt handling.* Interrupts for asynchronous events must be handled as efficiently as possible. Features must be included for disabling and queueing of multiple interrupts, and latency and disabling times must be minimized. Interrupt handlers must be directly associated with the hardware, and if priorities are used, the hardware devices must automatically receive the highest possible priority.

7. *Exception handling.* If exception handling is included in the language constructs, the run-time features must be implemented efficiently to support the design of fault tolerant systems. Special considerations must be given to local vs. remote exception propagation. If only local exception handling is implemented, remote propagation is only possible via the interprocessor communication mechanism. This may not be sufficiently efficient to support fault tolerance for hard real-time systems.

It is important that the real-time services and features listed above are implemented efficiently, and the efficiency should preferably be determined by the potential users with suitable benchmarks. Vendors usually claim extraordinary fast execution speeds of their implementations, but the quoted values do not necessarily represent worst-case conditions which may occur in hard real-time systems. Some of the execution times to scrutinize include (1) interrupt latency, i.e., the time from an interrupt is received and the corresponding handler starts to execute; (2) preemption latency, i.e., the time delay before a process with a higher priority than the currently executing process will start to execute; and (3) context switching time, i.e., the time to switch the CPU from executing one process to another. The context switch time can be related directly to the rendezvous latency of Ada and Concurrent C, where, on the average, each rendezvous with parameter passing requires two context switches.

8.1.2 Implementations

In the following paragraphs we discuss the implementations of some real-time executives.

1. *Real-Time Unix.* The Unix operating system was not originally designed to support real-time systems. It was primarily intended for time-sharing systems and did not have a preemptive scheduling mechanism. As the requirements for real-time system support continued to grow, two different approaches to Unix emerged [SIM89]. One approach included a real-time kernel grafted on to Unix, the other a real-time Unix redesigned from the ground up. The first approach does not provide a very efficient run-time environment, and some vendors thus chose to redesign their own efficient version of Unix for real-time applications. The strong selling point of (non–real-time) Unix has always been its portability, although that has been a source of controversy with at least the two different "official" versions from AT&T Bell Labs and Berkeley. The real-time implementations make Unix applications much less portable than before, with each vendor using a different applications interface for the real-time services. An IEEE standards committee (P1003, referred to as Posix) has been given the task to develop a set of real-time Unix extensions and a standard interface between the real-time kernel and Unix. The potential user of a real-time implementation of Unix should carefully evaluate the services provided and their efficiency. The real-time Unix implementations are intended to be used with applications written in C, and most of these applications conform to the *de facto* standard specified by Kernigan and Ritchie [KER78]. Some recent C implementations have extended the language specification to include concurrent constructs, e.g., the version specified at AT&T Bell Labs [GEH88]. This requires special run-time services to be included in the executive to support process creation and management. Some of the real-time Unix products available include Regulus (Alcyon), pSOS (Software Components Group), D-Nix (Diab Systems), RTU (Concurrent/Masscomp), IDRIS (Whitesmiths), and VxWorks (Wind River Systems).

2. *RTAda / OS.* This operating system is produced by Ready Systems and provides support for real-time systems implemented in Ada. A typical application includes multiple single board

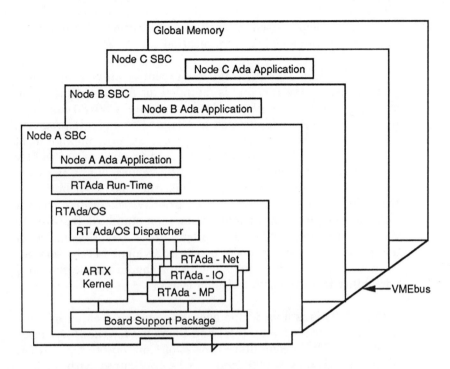

Figure 8-2.   Multiboard VMEbus Computer with Shared Memory

computers (SBCs) that communicate over a system bus (e.g., VMEbus), and that have access to shared global memory as shown in Figure 8-2. ARTX is a kernel that supports the Ada tasking model; RTAda-MP provides services for shared memory multiprocessing; and RTAda-Net provides services for multi-processor communication over LANs. The SBCs connected by the system bus to the global memory, form a *cluster*, and each SBC in the cluster may have its own local memory. Each processor and its environment (i.e., usually an SBC and associated software) form a node. Nodes within a cluster communicate via RTAda-MP over the system bus using remote procedure calls, whereas nodes in different clusters communicate via RTAda-Net over Ethernet. An Ada task that needs to send data to a remote node within the cluster may acquire a block of global data, write to it, and pass only a pointer to that block via an RPC. Adequate memory locks are provided by the OS for mutually exclusive access to the shared data areas. The Ada rendezvous mechanism is used for task communication within a node, and RPC for inter-node communication.

3. *MTOS-UX/Ada*. This is a run-time executive created by Industrial Programming Inc. and is intended for Ada real-time applications on Motorola's 680x0 family and Intel's 80x86 family of processors. An Ada application is designed as a single program, regardless of the number of processors (up to a maximum of 16) used to distribute the Ada tasks. The processors are tightly coupled on a system bus, and the Ada rendezvous is used exclusively for task communication, i.e., the task distribution is transparent to the application. A priority scheduling mechanism is available as an addendum (non-standard feature) to the Ada tasking model. The programmer has the choice of using the Ada tasking model or the equivalent MTOS services for deterministic scheduling. The latter should not be chosen if portability is an important design issue.

4. *BiiN/OS*. This is a real-time operating system created by BiiN (a joint venture between Intel and Siemens) for the BiiN series computers. These computers consist of from one to eight RISC processors (Intel's 80960) and can be configured with various levels of fault tolerance. The OS supports symmetric multiprocessing for a single Ada program, and the only communication mechanism required is the Ada rendezvous. This means that the distribution of Ada tasks is transparent to the applications programmer, and the tasking model is used regardless of how many processors are configured for the hardware architecture. A queueing mechanism and task priority scheme is used to distribute the tasks among the processors, and thus provides for automated load balancing. Multiprocessing and synchronization is supported at the hardware level, and provides for an efficient run-time implementation. Programs written in C and other languages are also supported by this OS.

5. *Miscellaneous*. Numerous other executives and kernels have been developed to support real-time applications. *Harmony* is marketed by Taurus Computer Products and includes support for synchronous message passing between processes using the *send/receive/reply* primitives. A collection of processes within a single program can be distributed transparently over multiple processors. The usual other real-time features are also sup-

ported. *VRTX* is produced by Ready Systems and is comprised of an executive kernel that can support real-time systems on a bare machine. It can also communicate with a host that executes under Unix. The *C-Executive* by JMI Software Consultants is tailored to C applications and includes support for context switching, task scheduling and interrupt handling. *VAXELN* by DEC provides support for real-time systems on various bare VAX configurations, i.e., without VMS or Unix. FlexOS from Digital Research is designed with a modular structure, and only the real-time services specified will be included in the load module to be executed.

8.2 Software Development System

A suitable software development system for distributed real-time systems will consist of a high-order modern programming language that includes constructs for specifying multiple processors, will support the specification of virtual nodes and physical nodes and the mapping of virtual nodes to physical nodes, will create code for the specified target processors, and will provide debugging and program library facilities. These software development features are discussed in the paragraphs that follow.

8.2.1 Programming Language

Desirable features of a modern programming language include not only constructs to support a special application such as real-time systems, they also include support for design paradigms such as object-orientation, process abstraction, data abstraction, stepwise refinement, information hiding, and deferring of design decisions. Building reusable software components should be possible using the features of the language, even though it may not be supported directly with specific constructs. Very few modern programming languages include constructs for distributed systems, but distribution can usually be accomplished by building the necessary services as part of the communication system, or using existing (or expanded) development environment functions and executive functions. The following list includes the desirable features of a programming language we would want to use for our distributed real-time systems:

1. Modular program structure, including separate compilation.

2. Structured and consistent control statements for similar constructs, e.g., all compound statements terminate with an "end."

3. Strong typing (and consistency checking by the compiler).

4. Facilities for program development methodologies (e.g., creation of source and object libraries for use of PDL).

5. Advanced data structures (e.g., variant records).

6. Assignment, expressions, and loop structures.

7. Specification of processes, process priorities, and process communication.

8. Input/output facilities.

9. Exception handling.

10. Facilities for reusable code generation.

11. Real-time features, including interrupt handling.

12. Low-level programming features.

13. Constructs for distributing the software modules and for specifying inter-processor communication.

Very few modern programming languages have all of these features built in. In the next chapter we will focus on Ada and analyze how well it is suited for developing distributed real-time systems.

Some mechanism must exist for the specification of the virtual nodes, the physical nodes, and the mapping of virtual nodes to physical nodes. These features must not necessarily be contained within the real-time programming language and are treated separately in the paragraphs that follow, independent of any specific programming language.

8.2.2   Specifying Virtual Nodes

The abstraction of the software elements that will be distributed among the available processors is referred to as a set of *virtual nodes.* Each node performs a specific part of the application, and is created from the software modules that will perform the partial application function. The complete set of distributed virtual nodes will cooperate as concurrent elements to perform all of the requirements specified for the application. Each node will usually consist of closely coupled processes that share memory. One or more virtual nodes will reside on each processor, or physical node, and there will normally be a requirement for the nodes to communicate during the operation of the distributed system. The communication may be by remote procedure calls, remote entry calls, or message passing (see Part 4 for a discussion of communication between virtual nodes in an Ada environment). When the virtual nodes are identified, great care must be taken to make them as independent as possible. A loose coupling between the virtual nodes will facilitate reconfiguration to support load balancing and fault tolerance, and will make the program easy to port to another hardware architecture.

The actual specification of the virtual nodes may be entirely logical by simply identifying (manually) a grouping of software elements that will subsequently be (manually) allocated to a physical node. The preferred method is to have programming language constructs or compiler directives that can manage the specification as part of the development environment. This may require the services of a special preprocessor prior to the compilation phase. The syntax could be as follows:

```
Virtual_Node (VN_Id, Module_1, Module_5, . . . Module_N)
```

The preprocessor would create a table of virtual nodes and their corresponding software modules. This table would be accessed by the appropriate code generator after the mapping between virtual and physical nodes is completed in a later step.

A methodology for creating virtual nodes in an Ada environment is described in Part 4.

8.2.3 Specifying Physical Nodes

The distributed architecture will usually consist of a set of heterogeneous processors and their associated memory, peripherals, and the connecting links between the hardware elements. The target configuration will be selected to support the distribution of the virtual nodes and is specified for the chosen architecture in terms of *physical nodes.* Each node is described by a symbolic name, the type of processor associated with the node, and a data port or link to facilitate inter-processor communication. This could be done by invoking a preprocessor or interpreter and specifying the pertinent information by use of keywords. This information would be collected in a table that would later be accessed by a preprocessor or compiler to determine the correct code generator for a given virtual/physical node combination. How much information is included depends on how detailed the configuration is specified with respect to type and size of memory, communication links, data port names, interrupt port names, etc.:

```
processor      PN_1     68030
               PN_2     68020
               PN_3     80386


memory         PN_1     dual-ported     1M      32-bit
               PN_2     single-ported   32K     16-bit
               PN_3     single-ported   1M      32-bit


interrupt-id   PN_1     Sensor_1     ID_21
               PN_1     Keyboard     ID_18
               PN_3     Sensor_2     ID_8
```

This is just an example of the kind of information that would be collected for the hardware configuration. The information would be used in the later development and execution steps for compilation, linking, loading, and communication.

If fault tolerance is required by the problem specification, dynamic reconfiguration of the virtual and physical nodes may have to be designed into the application. For most of the real-time systems we are considering, there is a requirement to abort, recreate, or restart processes when hardware faults are detected. The implementation of these requirements is greatly simplified if the specifications of virtual and physical nodes are automated by the programming environment.

8.2.4 Mapping Virtual Nodes to Physical Nodes

The software development environment for a distributed system must support the mapping of virtual nodes to physical nodes. Until such a mapping takes place the two sets of nodes are simply logical, unrelated entities. The virtual nodes must be associated with a given processor such that code can be generated for the given target. In a heterogeneous system this means different code generation for the different processor architectures.

In general, the later the binding between virtual and physical nodes, the more flexible the system becomes, and the less complex it becomes to implement fault tolerance. The binding could be done as early as during compilation with a compiler directive (pragma) to specify the mapping:

```
pragma Virtual_to_Physical_Node_Map (VN_1, PN_3)
```

which signifies that virtual node VN_1 is to reside on physical node PN_3. The compiler or preprocessor would determine the type of processor from the table created during the specification of the physical nodes and would bring in the code generator for the processor PN_3. This would create a rigid system that could not easily be reconfigured for fault tolerance during execution where a virtual node would have to be moved to a processor with a different architecture than the one that failed. One way to avoid having to halt the system and recompile the virtual node for the new target architecture, would be to keep load modules for all the possible virtual/physical node combinations on a disk or in memory. The problems with this approach would be the large amount of memory required, and how to maintain consistent data values for the idle images.

8.2.5   Code Generation

Code generators must be available for every target configuration in the distributed system. This will most likely include heterogeneous processors with widely different architectures. One approach is to compile the virtual nodes that reside on a physical node as a separate program for each target. Compilers for uniprocessors can be used unmodified, and this does not require any special support tools, but it becomes a manual effort.

The preferred approach for compilation of distributed programs is to have an automated tool, e.g., a preprocessor that can identify the code generators required for the various virtual nodes. A library management program will collect the load modules as they emerge from the code generators and place them in a library. A tag is included with each object module name that identifies its processor. The front end of the compiler can handle the intermediate language forms that are processor independent, whereas a separate back end will be invoked for the code generation for each dissimilar processor. This means that compilers used for uniprocessor systems have to be modified for use with distributed programs.

8.2.6 Debugging

It is essential that a sophisticated debugger be available for distributed systems. The complexity of isolating software errors is considerably higher than for uniprocessor systems. It is difficult to determine in which processor a particular event is taking place and to synchronize the complete system such that the cause of an error can be investigated. A typical symbolic debugging session will involve the specification of breakpoints for a set of processors, and it must be possible to isolate the execution of a single processor at a time, or a set of processors linked to specific communication media. The best solution for determining communication problems may be to have a separate debugging monitor with its own processor and memory that can be attached to a particular bus or LAN.

Two basic methods has been developed for supporting distributed debugging: (1) event recording, with a graphical display of messages recorded [LEB85]; and (2) run-time state monitoring, with dynamic testing for the occurrence of certain conditions [HEL85]. These two methods can be implemented either by (1) source transformation: the application source code is altered to send data to a special task that collects the data and displays it; or (2) placing a monitor function in the run-time support. General requirements of a symbolic debugger for distributed systems include the following:

1. *Execution control.* The progress of the execution is controlled with breakpoints, step commands, and a resume command to continue normal execution. This may include selective execution of a given process in isolation from the other processes and processors.

2. *Display information.* Process states, including scheduling information and priorities, and process relations must be readily available. A split screen should simultaneously show source code and the corresponding machine code to facilitate the interpretation of the various step commands.

3. *Execution history.* A history of the execution events should be recorded. This may include a trace of all local and remote procedure and process calls.

4. *Repeatable executions.* An environment must be provided for repeatable executions. If non-deterministic events are part of the language semantics, e.g., the scheduling mechanism, alter-

native deterministic mechanisms must be available for the debugging session. An example is the selection of a time sliced or event driven scheduler instead of a non-deterministic preemptive "fair" scheduler.

5. *Remote debugging.* A host/target environment must be available. This is especially important for distributed systems where the target consists of multiple processors.

In addition to the basic requirements listed above, a powerful debugging environment may include features to allow programming at break points and insertion points in the execution stream and functions to access the run-time environment.

8.2.7 Library Management

Library utilities must be available to support the management of source and object files. Depending upon the particular programming language used, and the level of program distribution, this support could be quite extensive. If the programming language has constructs for separate compilation or importation clauses, the library facility must account for the management of the correct dependencies among the object modules, and should warn the user about obsolete units that need to be recompiled. It should also provide support for multiple sublibraries that will facilitate groups of software developers working on individual parts of a large system. These features are desirable regardless of whether or not the system is distributed.

The library facility in a distributed system may not require any features in addition to those for a non-distributed system. This is especially true if the granularity of the distributed elements is at the program level. Individual libraries can be created for each program, and the linker/loader utility will locate the modules on the correct processors. For a single program, however, information is required for a mapping of an object module to a specific processor.

8.3 Linking and Loading

The linking process of a distributed system assumes that a set of compiled object modules have been prepared and placed in one or more libraries. The linker program needs information about the size of the object modules and the physical node they are associated with.

The physical node specification must include information pertaining to the physical memory where the objects will be loaded. This information can be kept as part of the libraries, or in separate tables generated when the objects are compiled and when a software module is linked to a specific physical node. A global naming scheme can be used where each compilation unit contains an identification of a physical node and a virtual address. The linking step transforms the virtual addresses to absolute addresses of the memory locations associated with the given node. A call to a remote process will be interpreted by the run-time support as a call to process P on physical node N.

The linker should have sufficient intelligence to investigate the dependencies between the library modules and optimize the importation such that only those modules that are actually referenced will be linked. A portion, or all of this functionality may be placed in the compiler as part of a global optimization scheme. The binding of processes to processors can be made during the linking step for static process allocation but will have to be postponed until run-time for processes allocated dynamically. Run-time binding is used with massively parallel systems, for dynamic load balancing, and for dynamic reconfiguration to support fault tolerance.

The loader must resolve the relocatable addresses created by the linker and determine the absolute locations for loading the object modules in their respective physical address spaces for each node. The address space may include shared memory or be restricted to the local memory for each processor. The loader also builds the binary images that are downloaded to the various physical nodes.

8.4 Run-Time Support

Fundamental to the construction of the run-time support are the considerations for the functionality and size of the kernel, whether or not the kernel is implemented on top of an existing operating system, and how many processors require a copy of the kernel. We only consider the functions of a multi-tasking kernel here, where each microprocessor in the system will run under a local kernel supporting the execution of multiple processes.

The application program is usually written in a single programming language, although interfacing functions may be provided to access reusable modules in a different HOL (e.g., pragma Interface in Ada) or assembly language routines for the given processor. The run-time support provides loading, execution, and debugging of distributed systems. It also supports dynamic memory management, handles interrupts and process scheduling on each processor, exception handling, synchronization for inter-process communication, and inter-processor communication via physical channels or ports.

8.4.1 Interrupt Handling and Process Prioritization

Whereas multi-tasking is a requirement for the RTS, the handling of priorities is not an essential feature. Those processes identified to represent critical processing functions (and would normally be assigned a high priority in a uniprocessor system) can be assigned to separate processors and do not need to compete in a preemptive, multiprocess environment. Even though priorities are not formally assigned, interrupts must automatically receive preferential treatment, i.e., at a higher "priority" than the other processes in the given processor. The interrupts must be serviced immediately and should not have to wait for a synchronization point or completion of the task currently executing.

8.4.2 Process Scheduling/Dispatching

A real-time application usually has more inherent parallelism (number of concurrent processes) than the number of processors available, i.e., there will be more processes than processors. Whenever processes share processors, *context switching* takes place as a new process image is made ready to execute. This has an overhead associated with it; the more context switches, the higher the overhead (see [BUR87]). Also, the more information contained in a process control block, the more overhead for each context switch.

The run-time execution of context switching must be implemented as efficiently as possible, and the total number of switches must be minimized. This can be done by identifying two kinds of processes: (1) the usual processes with normal context switching, and (2) *lightweight* processes, which do not have data of their own [VIS88]. The latter exist within a conventional process and share data with that process. The lightweight processes do not require a context switch, and the usual synchronization point (e.g., a rendezvous) can be replaced with a procedure call. Special compiler directives can be employed to specify a lightweight process. In Ada, for example, the existing Ada pragma *Shared* can be used to identify shared memory (restricted to scalar and access types) between a conventional process and a lightweight process existing within it. A new pragma (in the task body) can be used to identify an Ada task as a lightweight process:

```
pragma Lightweight_Process
```

This will signal the compiler that this task can be implemented in the thread of the caller, and the RTS will not perform a context switch prior to the execution of the task. A problem with this approach is that tasks created from a task type must all be either lightweight or normal tasks, since we can only associate the compiler directive with the task type and not with the task object created from the type. Another problem is that code using special compiler directives not specified in the language standard is non-portable. Some compiler vendors may support the directives, others may not.

8.4.3 Process Synchronization

The synchronization of remote entry calls is fairly straightforward when no time constraints are involved. This was illustrated in an earlier chapter for Ada, Concurrent C, and occam. The problems arise, however, when conditional or timed entry calls are allowed within the distributed communication structure. For a conditional entry call, what does it mean that a process is "immediately" available for a rendezvous? And for a timed entry call, which time is used to calculate the expiration of the specified delay? The time spent during the communication between the processors must somehow be accounted for if these calls are allowed, or special buffer processes must be introduced to absorb the timing uncertainties.

8.4.4 Parameter Passing

Parameters in subprograms and task entry calls can be passed by reference or by copy. Reference semantics can only be used across homogeneous processors since the address reference may be to memory associated with the calling module residing on a different processor. In a heterogeneous environment, byte ordering may be reversed between two processors in a client/server relation, and a call by reference will be erroneously interpreted by the server process.

A compiler will generate code with reference or copy semantics for a given target processor, and this code may not correspond to that generated for a processor of a different architecture, e.g., with a different word length. Remote copy semantics can only be used if the data values are converted to the proper format of the called module on the receiving processor. This may be the only safe solution to guarantee proper handling of data between different processors. A related problem is the potentially different byte ordering for different machines, and bytes may have to swapped before the data is used by the called module.

If a programming language with strong typing is used, a type conversion may also have to be done, since the types of the same entities, e.g., Integer, will represent two different data types on two different machines. Both the type conversion and the copying of the data values will add to the run-time overhead of remote communications.

One way to implement the data conversion is to adopt a standard format and to always convert to and from this standard. The values of the client parameters are first converted to the standard format, and the standard value is then converted to the format of the server module. This would always involve the overhead of the dual conversion, even between homogeneous processors, but the conversion mechanism would be transparent to the application software. Some loss of precision of floating point values may be experienced for each set of conversions.

8.4.5 Exception Handling

Real-time systems may use the detection of errant conditions to support fault tolerance, or certain operational conditions such as reaching a certain percentage of the available track store to send alerts to an operator. The two primary mechanisms for handling these conditions is the traditional parameter passing, or setting of flags, and exception handling. Exception handling is usually implemented by raising an exception at the point in the application code where the special condition is detected and transporting the exception to a handler for further processing.

In a system that has code generated for exception handling, it is not guaranteed that a semantic definition is included for remote propagation of exceptions. When an exception is raised in a process residing on a given processor, it may be considered a program error if a handler is not provided within the virtual node residing on that processor. Special run-time support facilities will have to be provided to cope with remote exception handling. A global table could be built that would map exception handlers to specific processors. If a handler could not be found on the local processor for a raised exception, the run-time support would next scan the global table; if a match was found in this table, a remote propagation would take place. This would add to the run-time overhead, but may be tolerable in a system requiring fault tolerance.

8.4.6 Mutual Exclusion

Some mechanism must exist for creating mutually exclusive access to data or critical regions. This is usually supported by providing semaphores [DIJ68a] or executive services as part of the operating system kernel, or it can be provided by special programming constructs such as the *accept* body in Ada and Concurrent C. Shared data must be protected from simultaneous access by two or more processes. A typical mechanism is to create a monitor [HOA74, NIE88] as a module encapsulating the data, and mutually exclusive operations to give access to the data. No special run-time services are required for providing mutual exclusion in a distributed system; protection against simultaneous access by multiple processors will have to be designed into the application. Remote communication would have to be supported across processors, e.g., remote procedure calls could be used for remote access to the shared data.

8.4.7 Inter-Processor Communication

The run-time support must keep track of the processes residing on each processor and local and remote inter-process communication requirements. The inter-process communication mechanism must also be known, since this can be different for local and remote communication. This can be established prior to execution if processes are not declared dynamically, or during execution for dynamic task allocation. The specific communication method can be by remote procedure call, remote entry call, or asynchronous message passing. This will be implemented with a given protocol, e.g., TCP/IP, and the required services will have to be provided as part of the programming environment. Multiple communication links may be available between various processors, and dedicated links between processes may be specified during process allocation.

The complexity of the link specification depends upon the routing mechanism between the processors, e.g., connectionless or datagrams (packetizing) vs. virtual circuits [STA88]. If the processor connections are provided via a LAN, the run-time support may include tables for the physical links between the processors and the routing mechanism used for each link. For processors connected via high speed buses, the interconnections should be handled by the control program, and the links should be transparent to the application program. This kind of transparency is also highly desirable for the difference between local and remote communication mechanisms, such that different design methodologies are not required for local and remote modules.

8.4.8 Real-Time Clocks

Support must be provided for the programming of timed events. This includes events that take place within a single processor, as well as events that depend on the response from processes on remote processors. This is usually provided in the form of an interval timer on each processor. Global time must be available, but should be invisible to the applications programmer. The primary problem with controlling timed events in a distributed system is the considerably longer time spent in inter-processor communication compared to local events. Not only does remote processing take longer than a comparable local event, it is highly non-deterministic. It is very difficult to determine accurately how much time will be spent in remote communication, and a distributed real-time system should never be based on assumptions about inter-processor communication times.

A global, common time-of-day clock should be available to all the processors for system synchronization, and an individual interval timer for each processor for local events. The local timers can accommodate task scheduling and expirations of events for each processor. The combination of the global and local clocks can be used for inter-processor timed events. This is of particular importance for systems that implement conditional and timed calls. The concept of what constitutes an "immediate" response must be clearly defined for remote conditional events. Similarly, for a timed remote event, a semantic definition must be established for whether the elapsed time is measured on the client or server processor.

8.5 Summary

The support environment for distributed real-time systems is quite extensive and considerably more complex than for a uniprocessor system. Multiple code generators must be available to create the appropriate code segments for modules distributed to heterogeneous processors. Support must be available for the creation of virtual and physical nodes, for the mapping of virtual nodes to physical nodes, and for the linking and loading of the software modules in the virtual nodes.

Sophisticated debugging tools will allow remote debugging from a development host. Multiple windows will be used to simultaneously display source code and associated machine instructions, an execution history, and the current state of processes and processors.

Some of the distributed features required for the run-time services include inter-processor communication primitives, remote propagation of exceptions, and accurate timing for remote conditional and timed entry calls.

In this part we have discussed the general requirements and characteristics of system software support for distributed real-time systems, independent of a specific programming language. In the next part we discuss how parallelism and distribution can be expressed in Ada, and Ada implementation issues that pertain to distributed systems.

Part

3

Ada and Distributed Systems

The preferred approach to designing real-time systems that are distributed across a set of loosely coupled physical nodes is to have a single distributed program, and a single mechanism for both local and remote inter-process communication. The design of a single program assumes that adequate support tools are available for specifying the distribution of virtual nodes, and that the run-time support includes services for local and remote inter-process communication. If these two assumptions are not valid, our real-time systems are quite likely to consist of multiple programs that employ different mechanisms for local and remote process communication. Several commercial implementations have been developed for tightly coupled Ada systems with shared memory, but very few, if any, are available yet for loosely coupled Ada systems in a heterogeneous environment.

The language specification of Ada does not include specific constructs for expressing a distribution of Ada modules among a set of processors. In this part we examine the Ada language and associated run-time support to determine its advantages and shortcomings for use in distributed systems. It is our premise that Ada has many features that support the design and implementation of distributed systems, and we need to determine the additional support facilities required to provide a complete distributed development and implementation environment.

The first chapter in this part examines the Ada tasking model in terms of asynchronicity, and the provision of synchronization points for inter-task communication using the Ada rendezvous and other mechanisms such as remote procedure calls. Various forms of non-determinisms are described within the context of Ada semantics and are extended to distributed systems. The proper distribution of Ada tasks in a multi-microprocessor environment is discussed with respect to the inclusion of special compiler directives (pragmas) or the addition of a special processing language independent of Ada.

The last chapter investigates Ada syntax and semantics issues as presently specified, and how they may be extended to support distributed systems.

In the previous parts of this book we have used the language-independent term process *to describe a design abstraction for a concurrent element of a real-time system. Ada uses the specific programming construct* task *to describe a concurrent element, and this will be used in an Ada context. We will still use the term* process *if it refers to a general design abstraction.*

9

Parallelism and Distribution in Ada

Ada was designed in accordance with a U.S. DoD specification for the implementation of real-time embedded systems [DOD78]. Embedded systems are similar to industrial real-time systems, e.g., process automation, robotics, and signal processing, and Ada is also used extensively in the implementation of these real-time systems. Ada was, however, not designed for distributed systems, and special features have to be provided when the functionality of a real-time system is distributed over two or more processors. Restrictions may also have to be imposed on the designers if the support environment has certain limitations, e.g., the Ada rendezvous may only be allowed among tasks that reside on the same processor.

In the discussion that follows we analyze the parallel features specified in the ARM [DOD83] and their implementations for distributed and non-distributed real-time systems. The basic premise for the discussion is to accept the language specification as it is specified in [DOD83] without any extensions.

9.1 Asynchronous Tasks

Ada includes statements for the declaration of tasks as independent modules that can execute asynchronously:

```
task Interrupt_Handler is
   entry Interrupt;
   for Interrupt use at Interrupt_Address;
end Interrupt_Handler;
```

After this task is elaborated and activated [SHU88], it will execute asynchronously with the other tasks declared within the same program. A single, sequential thread of control will govern the execution of the algorithm specified within the task body (not shown here). A typical strategy for interrupt handlers and device drivers is to put the algorithms within infinite loops so the tasks continue to execute until the program is halted.

In many cases the tasks created for a real-time application have a requirement to communicate. Asynchronous Ada tasks may communicate by sharing memory, but great care must be exercised to prevent the creation of erroneous programs from interleaving (non-atomic access) of the shared data structures. Ada tasks may also remain asynchronous and communicate via message passing. This mechanism is used in many distributed systems where a global operating system does not provide services for distribution. The communication mechanism is provided by a set of services such as a send/continue mail operation. A message is passed to a central facility, and the sending task continues to execute in an asynchronous fashion without waiting for a reply. If a reply is required, the calling task will interface with the mailbox function later, at the convenience of the calling task.

Asynchronous message passing is the most common form for interprocessor communication between multiple programs dispersed over a set of distributed processors. It is also used for communication between processes residing on the same processor, but that is not of importance for the type of real-time systems we are concerned with. The communication facilities are usually provided in the form of a set of procedures that implement a specific communications protocol. The application programs must interface with these procedures at certain levels, e.g., transport level. Remote processes are identified as "sockets" or "ports" [SUN86] and are unique for a given target processor. Distributed Ada programs that require remote asynchronous operation of tasks will use this same communication mechanism.

Communication via asynchronous message passing is in direct contrast to Ada tasks using the rendezvous model with synchronization points provided. Asynchronous, communicating Ada tasks can be implemented by the introduction of intermediary tasks (e.g., a buffer task) and still use the rendezvous, but this becomes part of a design methodology and is not included in the semantics of the rendezvous model. The next section describes the synchronization of communicating Ada tasks.

9.2 Task Communication and Synchronization

The rendezvous mechanism in Ada provides for synchronized communication between tasks (this was discussed in Chapter 6). The visible synchronization point is called an entry, and the rendezvous starts when the entry call is accepted by the called task. The calling task is suspended from the time it makes the call until the called task has completed its set of instructions on behalf of the caller. Entry calls include the passing of parameters, just like procedure calls. The synchronization between the two tasks in the rendezvous represents various levels of coupling depending on the combination of parameter modes used [NIE86, NIE88]. A parameterless entry call has a small amount of coupling, and may be implemented as a procedure call. A mixture of *in* and *out* mode parameters represents the highest degree of coupling between the two tasks where the caller is waiting for a reply.

Ada synchronization semantics does not include remote entry calls for distributed tasks. Special communication services will have to be provided if tasks are going to use the rendezvous for inter-processor communication. If a single Ada program is distributed, these services will be provided with the run-time support, and a remote rendezvous will be transparent to the application. If multiple Ada programs are distributed, services will have to be provided just as for asynchronous message passing, i.e., a set of subprograms implementing a given protocol.

Regardless of whether we can distribute a single Ada program or multiple programs, an added complexity of remote entry calls is experienced for conditional and timed entry calls. For a conditional entry call, the semantics of the called task being "immediately" available for a rendezvous is not defined for remote communications. Considerable latency time may be involved in the communication mechanism, independent of whether or not the called task is ready to accept an entry call. The time spent during the communication must be accounted for before the conditional call is cancelled. If this is not done, a considerable polling effect [NIE88] may reduce the throughput of the system.

The time spent in communication must also be accounted for in remote timed entry calls. The overhead of the communication may take longer than the delay expression that specifies the expiration of the timed event, and may thus signal a false unavailability of the called task.

9.3 Non-Determinism

Two primary areas of non-determinism exist for non-distributed Ada real-time systems:

1. *Selection of open entries.* The ARM does not specify the order of selection of open entries in selective wait statements within a task body. The consensus among developers and application programmers alike is that the selection algorithm should be "fair" such that certain entries should not be favored, and none of the entries should be starved.

2. *Task scheduling.* No semantics is specified in the ARM for the selection of the next task to execute when multiple tasks of the same priority are competing for the use of the same processor. This gives freedom to the run-time support developer to implement any algorithm that seems reasonable, such as preemption, round-robin, or time slicing. Higher priority tasks have preference over those with lower priority, but nothing is said about how called tasks inherit the priority of the calling task. This can lead to the so-called "priority inversion" mechanism [COR87], where a higher priority task (the caller) is forced to wait because a lower priority task was not ready to rendezvous.

Additional forms for non-determinism are present in distributed systems. One of these is the accounting for the time spent during remote communication as described above. We would not want to have to estimate this time and attempt to "pad" the expressions given in delay statements for timed events. The accounting of the communication time should be transparent to the application programmer to allow proper implementations of conditional and timed entry calls. The programming of these features should be the same regardless of whether they are used for distributed or non-distributed designs.

One of the problems with a distributed system on a set of hetero-geneous processors is the different representations of the same data types residing on the different machines. The required type conversions of data elements passed between the distributed processors should be transparent to the application programmer. These conversions should be a part of the remote communication services and hidden from the programmers.

9.4   Task Distribution

There are no language constructs in Ada for distributing tasks among a set of processors. A note in the ARM (page 9-1) alludes to the use of Ada tasks on distributed systems:

> Parallel tasks (parallel logical processors) may be implemented on multicomputers, multiprocessors, or with interleaved execution on a single *physical processor*. On the other hand, whenever an implementation can detect that the same effect can be guaranteed if parts of the actions of a given task are executed by different physical processors acting in parallel, it may choose to execute them in this way; in such a case, several physical processors implement a single logical processor.

This implies that the Ada run-time system developers are given the freedom to implement Ada on either loosely coupled or tightly coupled distributed systems, but nothing is specified about distribution semantics.

For loosely coupled multicomputers or multiprocessors, an explicit distribution will have to be specified either via pragmas or with a special support tool to map tasks to specific processors. For tightly coupled multiprocessors (e.g., an array or hypercube architecture) executing the functions of a single program, the task distribution will be completely transparent to the application program. Ada has no programming statements for specifying parallelism within a given algorithm for massively parallel systems.

Several schemes have been devised for distributing real-time Ada programs among a set of processors in loosely coupled systems [VOL89, JHA89, TED84, and ATK88]. All of these efforts are supported as research projects, and none of them have yet been implemented commercially. There is no question about Ada's suitability in distributed real-time systems, and it is simply a matter a time before commercial support becomes available for the distribution of a single Ada program in loosely coupled systems. In the meantime we must carefully design our systems using available communications packages, and adopt design methodologies that anticipate future support for the distribution of a single Ada program with transparent remote rendezvous. Ada's suitability for distributed real-time systems is discussed further in the next chapter.

10

Ada Implementation Issues

In this chapter we consider specific language and run-time issues for distributed systems written in Ada. Language issues include the features available to a programmer using the Ada constructs in creating a solution for a given real-time system. Run-time issues concern the support of the execution of the real-time system during the operational phase, and how efficiently the Ada semantics have been implemented.

The initial consideration facing a designer of real-time systems is how the application should be distributed to maximize the throughput of the parallel system. Ada does not specify any units for distribution among a set of processors, and reasonable assumptions must be made. Related design guidelines are provided in this chapter. The language definition also does not include a specification syntax for a distribution notation, and alternative mechanisms for a specification scheme are discussed.

Even though, as designers and programmers, we are only creating the software solution to a specific application, it is important to understand run-time issues and how efficiently they are implemented. We may have to choose between several different commercially available run-time implementations. A good understanding of the issues will help us make the right choice for our application.

10.1   Language Issues

The following paragraphs contain a description of various language
issues that pertain to the use of Ada for distributed systems with the
syntax and semantics specified in the ARM.

10.1.1   Granularity of Distributed Units

The proper granularity for the distribution of Ada components is
probably the most important design decision that must be made even
before the design process starts. Since no distribution is specified or
suggested in the ARM, it is up to the designers to determine this
granularity as part of the design methodology. This design decision
is highly dependent upon the availability of a distributed run-time
support and inter-process communication facilities. It also depends
upon whether or not the designer is expected to be aware of the
target architecture and specify the distribution. The following classifications have been suggested [TED84, ATK88] for the specification
of distributed Ada components:

1. *Full Ada, single program.* Full Ada is used, without any restrictions, to write the system as a single Ada program. Since
   there are no distributed facilities available in the language, the
   system is being designed without any consideration for the distributed target configuration. This approach can be used on
   systems residing on parallel processing supercomputers (tightly
   coupled systems), but not for the type of real-time systems we
   are concerned with here.

2. *Full Ada, multiple programs.* Full Ada is used, without any
   restrictions, to write the system as multiple Ada programs. The
   designer is aware of the distributed target and determines the
   distribution of Ada components. The system is also designed
   with specific interfaces between the programs. An artificial
   "main" program may have to be added for each program distributed to a specific processor.

3. *Uniformly restricted Ada, single program.* The system is written as a single Ada program, accepting the same restrictions
   on the use of Ada for all the components. An example of a
   uniform restriction could be that no tasks would be allowed to

share variables. This would permit the tasks to be allocated to any one of the target nodes.

4. *Non-uniform restrictions of Ada, single program.* The system is written as a single Ada program, with restrictions on the use of Ada at the interfaces where the system components may be split for the distribution to the hardware nodes. The system will be designed with a possible distribution in mind, but is not closely tied to a specific target configuration. An example of a possible restriction is the use of entrance procedures in a package specification as the only means of interfacing with tasks declared within that package. This will facilitate the construction of virtual nodes, and simplify the implementation of remote entry calls.

The second approach is the one most commonly used with current programming languages and could also be used for Ada. The methodology we will describe in later chapters, however, uses elements of both the second and fourth approaches. Non-uniform Ada restrictions are accepted in the creation of virtual nodes, and these nodes will form individual communicating Ada programs that are mapped to the distributed architecture with one program per physical node (assuming that no facilities are available for the distribution of a single program). The Ada components that make up a virtual node will typically consist of tasks encapsulated in library packages and dependent packages and subprograms. Shared memory may be allowed within a virtual node, but not between these nodes.

10.1.2   Use of Pragmas

Special compiler directives (pragmas) can be used to specify the distribution of a given module within the Ada source code. This does not require modification of the compiler, but the pragmas will be sprinkled throughout the Ada application code. The code is also likely not to be portable, since the pragmas are not part of the standard language specification, and various Ada vendors will implement their own versions of these pragmas.

The use of pragmas for distribution specification is not the preferred method for Ada programs, but is probably the easiest to implement for the Ada compiler vendors. Pragmas are discussed further in Chapter 14.

10.1.3   Representation Clauses and Attributes

Ada includes the following set of representation clauses that reflect the architecture of the target hardware:

1. *Address clause.* Used to link an interrupt address to a task entry or to locate code or data at specific addresses in memory.

2. *Length specification.* Controls the amount of storage associated with objects of a given type.

3. *Enumeration type representation.* Used to specify the actual numerical values of symbolic enumerations (e.g., hexadecimal values of symbolic machine instructions).

4. *Record type representation.* Specifies the bit-by-bit layout of the components within a record structure.

The use of any of these representations ties the software to a given target configuration, and in a distributed system they must be specified for each physical node. To reduce complexity, we may wish to adopt certain restrictions as part of our design methodology. One such restriction may be, for example, that interrupt handlers and I/O drivers must reside on their associated physical nodes. If this is not done, the address clause for an interrupt or I/O channel would have to include a processor identification. Similar restrictions could be applied such that memory is not shared between processors. This would make the representation clauses that reference memory unique for a physical node and would not require any additional specifications for the clauses. This is another way of saying that the designer is keenly aware of the target configuration, rather than assuming that the distributed architecture is transparent. This is commensurate with our basic software-first design philosophy for real-time systems, and will be expanded further in the chapters on design methodology.

The use of some of the predefined Ada attributes will make a virtual node target dependent. Storage_Size for access types will refer to the local part of a heap reserved for objects of the type, and for task types it will refer to the activation size of a local task object. Machine_Emax refers to the maximum value for an object on a given hardware floating point unit. The 'Address attribute must be interpreted correctly for any given processor/memory configuration that will execute the task object on that processor. An Ada vendor may

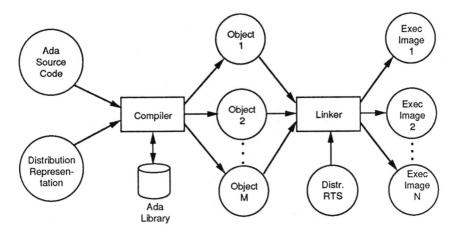

Figure 10-1.   Compilation and Linking in Distributed Environment

choose to include implementation-dependent attributes (ARM, 4.1.4) for distributed systems. This will tie the virtual nodes that use these attributes closely to the target architecture and to the compiler used.

The primary problem with target dependent virtual nodes is how to implement dynamic reconfiguration as part of a fault tolerant system. In general, we accept the responsibility of distributing virtual nodes to physical nodes as part of the design decisions.

10.1.4   Distribution Specification and Preprocessors

The distribution of virtual nodes to physical nodes can be made using a separate (non-procedural) distribution specification language. This has the advantage that the Ada application code will not contain any alien syntax, and no preprocessor is required. A separate tool must be available, however, to support the specification, and the representation must be in a suitable format for input to the compiler. An example of such a tool is the Ada Program Partitioning Language (APPL) as reported in [JHA89]. The process of creating images for a set of physical nodes is illustrated in Figure 10-1, where the Ada source code and the distribution representation (after the distribution specification) are introduced to the compiler along with the Ada library modules. Object code is created for each virtual node based on the distribution representation, and information about where the object code is to be loaded is kept with the object file. The linker

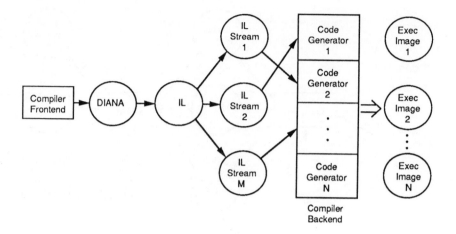

Figure 10-2.   Creating Executive Images in Heterogeneous Distributed Environment

creates code images for the various physical nodes based on the information kept with each object file. Code required for run-time support is included with the images for the physical nodes.

The distribution can also be specified with a special syntax that is alien to an Ada compiler. The special code segments must be interpreted by a preprocessor and transformed to Ada-compatible statements, typically procedure calls to subprograms that will implement the distribution semantics. The advantage of this approach is that the compiler does not have to be modified, but the disadvantage is that a separate preprocessor is required.

Regardless of the method used to specify the distribution of virtual nodes to physical nodes, creating executable images for a set of heterogeneous processors requires special compilation and code generation techniques. One approach has been suggested in [JHA89] and is illustrated in Figure 10-2. The compiler front end is first invoked and creates the intermediate form Descriptive Intermediate Attributed Notation for Ada (DIANA) [PER84]. The DIANA notation is transformed to an intermediate language (IL) form that is used to create a set of IL code streams for each virtual node. The compiler back end is invoked with the code generator for a given physical node, such that the proper executable image is created for each physical node. A different code generator is required for each unique processor, and information must be available to match a virtual node to its corresponding physical processor.

10.1.5 Packages Standard and System

The packages Standard and System are supplied with each Ada implementation system for a given target processor. Package Standard defines certain types such as Integer and Float, and the generation of efficient code requires that the lengths of the values of these types be directly supported by the instruction set for the given target processor. The definitions of maximum and minimum sizes of integers and floating point values assume a single type of memory or floating point unit.

The package System defines a type Address (assuming a single type of processor/memory combination), the length in bits of a Storage_Unit (assuming a single type of memory), and a Memory_Size (assuming a single memory).

A set of related pragmas (System_Name, Storage_Unit, and Memory_Size) can be used to redefine the entities of the same name in package System. The use of any of these pragmas causes the implicit recompilation of package System, and makes any compilation units in the library that are dependent on System obsolete. These pragmas are intended to provide a controlled modification of the predefined package System for the target environment only, and can thus be used to specify System entities for a given target in a heterogeneous architecture.

10.1.6 Language Extensions

Distribution specifications could be included in the Ada language. This would require a modification to all existing Ada compilers used for uniprocessor systems, and the language standard would have to be changed. A vehicle for making changes to the language standard is the Ada 9X working group [ADA89, AND89]. This working group evaluates suggested modifications to the Ada language standard and makes recommendations about which modifications should be adopted. No modifications are expected to be approved until the mid-1990s, and this approach is currently not viable.

Associated with the possible modifications to the language is the specification of a standard set of packages and interfaces that can provide remote communication primitives. The use of these primitives could result in portable systems, where only recompilation of the application code is necessary when it is moved to a new target architecture. (We would, of course, also have to modify the few modules that contain hardware dependencies.)

10.2   Run-Time Issues

The paragraphs that follow include a discussion of the implementation of the Ada semantics, and how the run-time support functions may have to be modified for distributed systems.

10.2.1   Global vs. Local Copies

The distributable units described above as virtual nodes were considered in the context of the application code to be designed for a given real-time system. There is also a distribution of code at a lower level: the run-time support functions. The distribution of these functions is dependent on the hardware architecture chosen for the system solution.

In a loosely coupled system each processor will have its own local copy of a complete set of the run-time services. This includes functions for local task scheduling and dispatching, timing services, elaboration, activation and termination, exception handling, and remote communication. The local copy of the RTS will essentially function as it would in a uniprocessor system, and is not concerned with the overall task distribution. Primitives must be available, however, for remote communication services, and the application code would be designed for a specific distribution.

In a tightly coupled system only a single copy is required for all the run-time services. Each individual processor would need some run-time services such as message passing to the global RTS, local exception handling, and local timing functions. Task scheduling and dispatching, global time handling, elaboration, activation and termination, remote exception handling, and remote communication functions will all reside in the single copy of the global RTS. Task distribution and remote communications are transparent to the application code, and a single Ada program can be designed as it would be for a uniprocessor system.

10.2.2   Task Scheduling

A specific scheduling mechanism is not specified in the ARM. This leaves the choice up to the implementers who usually select one or more alternatives of preemption based on task priority, round-robin, or time-slicing. If multiple alternatives are available, the programmer picks the method that best fits the application prior to compilation. If none is chosen, the default mechanism specified by the developer is used. In a loosely coupled system a copy of the scheduling algorithm is included with the RTS in each processor, and task management is performed just as in a uniprocessor system. We are assuming that tasks created dynamically are assigned to the same processor as their respective masters and are not migrated to a different processor. Similarly, if tasks are reconfigured to support fault tolerance, we assume that tasks and their children are migrated together. If these assumptions are not valid, the scheduling mechanisms will have to be modified to account for remote task scheduling with a considerable increase in complexity.

Task scheduling in tightly coupled systems is usually associated with load balancing. A global scheduler assigns tasks to processors to maximize the overall throughput of the system, and to ensure that time critical functions get the proper attention. The assignments can be made by allocating the tasks with the highest priorities to the processors that have the least load. By "load" we mean the number of tasks competing for the use of the same CPU. If a sufficient number of processors is available, each high priority task can be assigned its own processor for optimum response time. This can be done, for example, with interrupt handlers that receive time critical input values. If multiple tasks are assigned to the same processor, a local scheduler can perform task management until a reconfiguration is performed by the global scheduler.

The scheduling mechanism is expected to support periodic tasks which are usually programmed in Ada with the *delay* statement.

10.2.3 Inter-Node Communication

We have already seen that one of the most important issues facing the application programmer is how the software should be distributed among the processors chosen for the system solution. The preferred design object is a virtual node that may consist of Ada packages, tasks, and subprograms. Virtual nodes are the distributable software units, and one or more of these units will reside on each processor. Virtual nodes normally have a need to communicate, and run-time support must be available to satisfy this requirement.

Ada program units within each virtual node make subprogram calls and entry calls. If these calls are made among nodes residing on the same processor, the run-time support required is the same as for a uniprocessor. The parameter passing mechanism is the same, and no changes need to be made for the Ada rendezvous. Some extra table space is required to associate each callable unit with a processor, such that the executive can determine whether a call is local or remote.

To support remote subprogram calls and the entry calls associated with the Ada rendezvous, inter-processor communication services must be available. This includes message passing between the processors via low level protocols. Sufficient services should be provided such that the details of the remote communications are made transparent to the application programmers. If this is not the case, the application code must detect the remote calls and include explicit code to implement the communication protocols. This is not desirable since the Ada code becomes dependent on the specific communication mechanism and the application program is not portable to other systems.

A tightly coupled system is expected to have support for transparent remote subprogram and entry calls. This would be implemented with the global run-time support package, and would be used by single Ada programs where the distribution is transparent.

A single Ada program implemented as a loosely coupled system should be designed for transparency of remote subprogram and entry calls. In this case, the communication services would be duplicated on each processor and include a table to associate callable units with a processor.

Multiple Ada programs distributed as a loosely coupled system will have to have the remote communication protocol built into the application code. Remote subprogram and entry calls are definitely not transparent in this case, and a communication mechanism such as RPC or TCP/IP will have to be used. The distribution of multiple Ada programs is, of course, the least preferred distribution approach, but it may be the only one available for a loosely coupled system.

10.2.4 Task Priorities

The ARM includes an optional specification of the pragma Priority for the declaration of a task. It is implied that a preemptive scheduling mechanism should be implemented for competing tasks based on the given set of priorities. This is particularly important in a uniprocessor real-time system, where multiple tasks are usually competing for the use of a single CPU, and there is a considerable difference in the time critical nature of the various tasks. An interrupt handler, for example, should have a higher priority than a display task to prevent loss of incoming data. A periodic task may also be assigned a high priority to ensure being serviced quickly when its period expires.

The use of priorities is less important in a distributed system, since time critical functions can be identified early in the design phase and assigned to a separate processor in a loosely coupled system. The RTS must still implement the support for priorities to provide portability of Ada code between uniprocessor and multiprocessor systems. Priority inheritance and the avoidance of priority inversion for remote rendezvous should be handled just as for uniprocessor systems [COR87 and LEV88].

In a tightly coupled system, priorities can be used by the global RTS to assign the highest priority tasks to the processors with the lightest loads for automatic load balancing. Local priority handling could be implemented when multiple tasks are assigned to the same processor. This would result in less message passing than would be required if it was all handled by the global scheduler.

10.2.5 Shared Memory

The run-time handling of shared memory depends upon how it is used in the real-time system. State variables, for example, are typically defined in Ada package and task bodies. These variables are visible only to the subprograms, packages, and tasks nested within the package or task containing the state variables. If we accept the restriction that each finite state machine resides within a single virtual node, there is no run-time problem associated with the state variables for that FSM (see [NIE88] for the construction of FSMs in Ada). Ada packages and tasks are non-reentrant, and only a single copy of the data is kept in the memory associated with the virtual node. If several nested tasks have access to a state variable, mutually exclusive access must be provided, as discussed earlier. The latter situation is not unique to distributed systems, however, since we have the same concern for a multiprocessing system on a uniprocessor architecture.

The primary problems of shared data in distributed Ada systems is where we allow sharing between physical nodes. Some mechanism must then be provided for remote updating of variables, and for protection of remote access, i.e., a global rather than a local monitor. If memory is not directly addressable, for example, in a remote entry call, we may have to restrict parameter passing to call by reference and to eliminate call by value. This would make it relatively straightforward to implement a locking mechanism at the point of data access. The problems become compounded in distributed systems with heterogeneous processors. Ada representation clauses must then be used to specify the data for each physical node, and the run-time system must provide conversion functions for the different data representations.

10.2.6 Interrupt Handling

Interrupt handling is not a function of the Ada language specification, and it is up to the application programmer to implement it. Interrupt handlers can be written in Ada using the normal task specification and the address representation clause:

```
task Interrupt_Handler is
   entry Interrupt;
   for Interrupt use at Interrupt_Address;
end Interrupt_Handler;

task body Interrupt_Handler is separate;
```

The only run-time support to implement this is a correct transfer of control from the interrupt to the handler. We are assuming that the handler will always reside on the processor that accepts the interrupt, and services for remote transfer are not required.

10.2.7 Exception Handling

The semantics of Ada's exception handling is fairly straightforward and is supported with existing Ada run-time systems for most of the modern microprocessors. The ARM does not, however, specify separate semantics for distributed systems. Exception propagation is defined within the context of a single Ada program, and we should not expect the support for remote propagation between multiple distributed programs. If a run-time support system is available for a single Ada program with distributed virtual nodes, we will expect the current propagation semantics to be valid, and remote exception propagation would be transparent to the application.

If we require that exceptions be propagated among multiple Ada programs residing on distributed processors, it could be done by introducing a new pragma and by modifying the RTS. The new pragma could be

```
pragma Remote (Exception_Name [, Exception_Name]).
```

The RTS would have to be modified to accept and propagate both local and remote exceptions. A table of the exceptions and their handlers could be constructed from the compilations, and subsequently made available to the RTS on every processor during execution.

It is clear from the above discussion that the use of exception handling in distributed systems is highly dependent upon the available run-time support. An early design decision may be, for example, to restrict exception handlers to the exceptions raised within a virtual node, or within virtual nodes residing on the same processor.

An additional complexity occurs when the calling task is aborted. A message must be sent to the called processor to cancel the rendezvous if it has not already started. If it is already in progress, the called task is allowed to complete the rendezvous, and no exception is propagated.

Further discussion of remote exception handling is deferred to the chapters describing the design methodology.

10.2.8 Real-Time Clocks

Timing support must be available for programming of conditional and timed entry calls using the Ada rendezvous, and for expressing timed events with the *delay* statement. This assumes that each processor has at least an interval timer for measuring relative time. As was discussed in an earlier chapter, the primary problem with measuring timed events between distributed processors is the non-deterministic latency associated with inter-processor communication. This implies that a global clock must also be available for measuring absolute time to synchronize inter-processor timed events. The synchronization of multiple processors with a single global timer may, however, be subject to drift [CLA89], and would not be reliable for hard real-time systems.

To safely implement remote conditional and timed entry calls with the rendezvous model, two clocks will be required: an interval timer and a time-of-day clock. Time associated with the start of the rendezvous can be measured on the called processor. The calling processor sends a message to the remote processor and waits for a reply message regarding the status of the rendezvous. In the case of the timed entry call, the calling processor includes the time delay in the message.

When the time is measured on the called processor, the communication latency does not enter into the determination of "immediately available" in the case of the conditional entry call, or the expiration of the delay interval for the timed entry call. There is, of course, the additional overhead of the message passing between the two processors.

A general problem associated with real-time clocks is that time cannot be measured any more accurately than the granularity of the clock tick. If, for example, a real-time clock advances by 5 ms for each tick and a delay statement specifies a period of 3 ms, the minimum interval for the expiration of the delay is 5 ms. This problem occurs regardless of whether we are designing a system for a uniprocessor or a distributed system.

10.2.9   Task Elaboration, Activation and Termination

Task elaboration, activation, and termination have a specified semantic definition in Ada [SHU88]. Tasks are not explicitly activated and terminated, except for the use of the *abort* statement. Tasks are elaborated in a certain order in an Ada program, depending upon the location of their declarations. All library units referenced by the main program and their bodies, if any, are elaborated before the main program starts to execute. As soon as a task (in the main program or encapsulated in a library unit) has been fully elaborated, it is activated by the run-time support and starts to execute. Each task continues to execute until its logical termination or until it is aborted by another task (it can also abort itself). The main program does not terminate until the tasks that depend on it have terminated. Termination rules are not specified in the ARM for tasks encapsulated in library packages.

If our application consists of multiple, communicating Ada programs, task activation and termination take place just as if each program executed independently on a uniprocessor. When a single program is distributed over several processors, the task activation and termination process becomes more complex. The executable images are loaded on each processor, and they have to be elaborated in some order. The main procedure resides on one of the processors and can be considered an "environment" task. We assume that run-time support for the elaboration mechanism is available on every processor, and that it has been modified slightly to accommodate remote elaborations.

The elaboration order of a uniprocessor system can also be used in a multiprocessor system. This order starts with the environment task and is dependent upon the *within*g relations of the virtual nodes. When the elaboration function for the environment task detects an importation of a remote virtual node reference, it halts its elaboration and sends a message to the elaboration function on the remote processor. Elaboration proceeds on the remote processor until it is either completed, or another remote reference is detected. When it is completed, the remote elaboration function sends a completion message to the environment processor, whose elaboration continues until completion or until another remote reference is detected. If a remote elaboration function detects another remote reference, it halts its elaboration and sends a message to the new remote processor. This scheme continues until all the virtual nodes on all the distributed processors have been elaborated, in the same order as if they were located on the same processor. The additional complexity arises with the message passing required between the elaboration functions residing on the different processors and the availability of a mapping of virtual nodes to processors.

Cyclic dependencies can be handled in the same manner as for uniprocessor systems by raising the predefined exception Program_Error, and the pragma Elaborate can be used without any restrictions to force a specific elaboration order.

The normal Ada task termination rules can be implemented with a similar scheme by incorporating message passing into the run-time termination function. The additional one-time overhead associated with task elaboration, activation, and termination in a distributed system is of little concern in most real-time systems. These systems are usually started infrequently and execute for long periods of time before they are halted.

10.2.10 Portability

The Ada implementation issues discussed in this chapter are based on the language standard that was specified in ANSI/MIL-STD 1815A-1983 [DOD83]. This standard does not specify any language constructs for distributed systems. It merely makes some weak references to distribution [DOD83, page 9-1].

The design methodology described in the next part is based on the current standard and available Ada compilation and development systems. The language extensions discussed in this chapter are not anticipated in the methodology, since it will not be known for some time which of the extensions will be included in the next version of the standard. The working group for Ada 9X will not make its recommendations until the mid- or late 1990s, and we are concerned here with how we can implement distributed real-time systems for current problems. Designing an application based on expected language extensions will make the code non-portable, especially if the extensions are never implemented.

The proposed methodology includes design guidelines that make the code portable to other systems, and is easily adaptable to new implementations as they become available.

10.3 Summary

The granularity of distributable Ada modules is one of the most important design decisions that must be made, and is directly related to the level of support available for the distribution. This decision becomes a part of the design methodology for a given application.

The current Ada language definition does not include any constructs or semantics for the distribution of Ada modules. Possible distribution mechanisms include the use of pragmas, representation clauses, or preprocessors with a separate distribution specification.

The run-time support required for distributed systems is considerably more complex than for uniprocessors. It is important to understand the run-time issues and how efficiently they are implemented. We may have to choose between several different commercially available run-time implementations. A good understanding of the issues will help us make the right choice for our application.

This part of the book has discussed Ada's suitability as a programming language (including the run-time support) for distributed real-time systems. Even though Ada does not have specific constructs for expressing a distribution of modules to processors, it has numerous real-time features that are quite useful also in distributed systems. The run-time support found in most uniprocessor implementations must be modified or extended to include the added services required.

An appropriate design methodology for distributed real-time systems implemented in Ada must include certain restrictions on the use of the language. These restrictions are made to match the distributed services available. Such a design methodology is described in the next part.

4

Design Methodology

The design methodology described below for distributed real-time systems is based on a software-first approach. This approach makes no a priori assumptions about the hardware architecture in terms of a specific supercomputer or set of microprocessors. The software is designed first, with the highest possible correspondence to the problem specification. The hardware is then chosen to support the software architecture. In our case this will be a distributed architecture with the set of virtual nodes dispersed across the chosen processors. The first chapter in this part describes the traditional software design methodology where the hardware architecture is specified by the customer because it is already acquired or available, or the software must reside on standard processors such as the 1750A for U.S. Air Force contracts or AN/UYK-43 for U.S. Navy contracts. The remaining chapters in this part describe the recommended software-first Ada design methodology for distributed real-time systems.

The proposed methodology is an extension of the real-time approach described in [NIE88] for single processor systems and is based on a two-phase approach. During the first phase we determine the process abstraction that represents a concurrent model of the system. This model is expressed as a set of cooperating Ada tasks embedded in virtual nodes. In the second phase we select a suitable set of processors and map the virtual nodes to the processors in a distributed configuration.

One of the most important design decisions to be made for distributed real-time systems is the communication mechanism to be em-

ployed within and between virtual nodes. Various mechanisms available and suitable for use by Ada programs are described.

The functionality contained within each of the Ada tasks may be sufficiently complex to warrant a decomposition of a task into a set of packages and subprograms. The Layered Virtual Machine/Object-Oriented Design (LVM/OOD) approach is used to perform this decomposition. Most distributed real-time systems have a requirement for a high reliability of operation, and a discussion is included about Ada and the design of fault tolerance.

This part concludes with a summary of suggested design guidelines for distributed real-time Ada systems.

11

Hardware-First vs. Software-First

Most traditional software design methodologies are based on the hardware-first approach. This is where the hardware is either chosen by the system engineers who wrote the requirements specification, the customer already has the hardware suite that will be used for the application, or the target consists of standard processors for the given application. The software design becomes burdened with hardware restrictions or limitations that are unrelated to the actual functioning of the application. These restrictions or limitations of the target architecture may be in terms of the word size of the processor (e.g., 16- or 32-bit), the amount of memory available (e.g., 64K maximum, or virtual memory), and the operating system or run-time support available.

Whenever the hardware dictates the software design approach, we should expect a suboptimal correspondence of the software solution for the problem specification. The software has to be designed within the limitations of the hardware and operating system support. If, for example, a programming language that supports multiprocessing does not exist for the chosen processor, a concurrent system has to be designed using artificial multiprocessing components supported by the executive. A standard processor may represent an old-fashioned architecture and would not take advantage of state-of-the-art processing. Such a system has built-in obsolescence, and will most likely be hard to maintain since a certain amount of "tricky" programming, or "work-arounds" will be included in the design.

A software design that is closely coupled to a given hardware architecture is non-portable. Changing either the hardware configuration or the distribution of virtual nodes for such a system will require considerable redesign and reprogramming.

Distributed real-time systems designed with a hardware-first approach should be expected to be less efficient than those designed with hardware tailored to support a carefully designed software-first system. Experimentation and rapid prototyping on various hardware architectures is made difficult and costly by the hardware dependent software, and prohibits an optimal design solution. In the rapidly changing field of state-of-the-art hardware architectures, it is important that the software be designed to take advantage of more powerful processors and parallel configurations as they become available.

The methodology outlined in the following chapters assumes a software-first approach. It is based on a two-phase design strategy where the software solution is designed during the first phase for the real-time application without concern for a hardware configuration. The hardware architecture is chosen during the second phase, and the virtual nodes designed in the first phase are distributed among the chosen processors. This approach is expected to reduce the cost of studying alternative hardware architectures that can best support the system solution. Software redesign is not required to experiment and evaluate prototype architectures; the only changes required are in the distribution of the virtual nodes that have already been designed.

The design and distribution of virtual nodes is highly dependent on the tools and primitives available for expressing and modeling distributed elements in a real-time system. The methodology described in the chapters that follow is tailored to the use of Ada in a variety of distributed real-time applications. It is based on the current language specification ANSI/MIL-STD-1815A [DOD83]. The methodology utilizes some design restrictions and design conventions to model Ada distributed system solutions without relying on any modifications to the programming language. The primary emphasis of the approach is to produce efficient, portable software that does not have to be redesigned as the support for distributed Ada systems becomes more mature.

12

Process Abstraction and Distribution

A distributed program that satisfies the requirements of a particular real-time application is typically specified in two separate phases:

1. The software is designed in terms of processes, data abstractions, data structures, and algorithms, and associated with a set of virtual nodes.

2. The target hardware configuration is specified as a set of physical nodes that can best support the functionality defined by the virtual nodes. The virtual nodes of the application system are mapped to the physical nodes, i.e., the virtual nodes are configured to reside on specific processors. A reconfiguration may take place after normal execution if faults are detected, and if fault tolerance is implemented by the hardware or built into the application.

Before the virtual nodes can be specified, we need to determine the inherent concurrency of the real-time system and to express it as a model of process abstraction. This abstraction will be represented by a set of Ada tasks and the required support modules (packages and subprograms). The detailed steps for designing real-time Ada uniprocessor systems are contained in [NIE88]. A set of heuristics is included to ease the transitioning from the design decisions made in one step to the start of the next step.

Every effort should be made to make the virtual nodes as independent as possible, i.e., with a minimum amount of coupling between them. This will facilitate the implementation of the communication mechanism between remote nodes, and provide portable code. The actual communication protocol should be invisible to the application modules in the virtual nodes and implemented at a lower level.

The following paragraphs give only an overview of the steps involved in creating the process abstraction (which is the same for both uniprocessor and multi-processor designs), and focuses on the details of the expanded methodology for designing distributed systems. The term *process* is used here as a general language-independent abstraction for a concurrent element that can operate in parallel with other processes. This is distinguished from an Ada *task*, which is a real software entity specified with Ada constructs that will be implemented on a given target machine.

12.1 Allocation of Requirements

The starting point for our methodology is a *requirements specification* document. This may be a formal document, e.g., specified under U.S. DoD Military Standard 2167A [DOD88], or it may be in some unspecified format. In either case, we assume that this document will adequately specify the requirements for the real-time system to be designed and implemented. It is recognized that these requirements may change somewhat during the development cycle and that some of the design steps may be repeated, but this is considered normal for a long development cycle of large software systems.

During the analysis phase, a context diagram is used to describe the interfaces to the external devices as shown in Figure 12-1 for a (simplified) robot controller. The rectangles represent the devices, the circle illustrates the program controlling the devices and the implementation of the requirements for the application, and the directed graphs show the interfaces between the devices and the control program.

The application requirements are allocated to functional entities and described with data flow diagrams (DFDs). Each function is represented in the DFD by a circle ("bubble"), and annotated directed graphs show the interfaces between the bubbles. Both data and control flows are included in the DFDs as described in [MEL86 and HAT88]. An example of a DFD for the robot controller is shown in

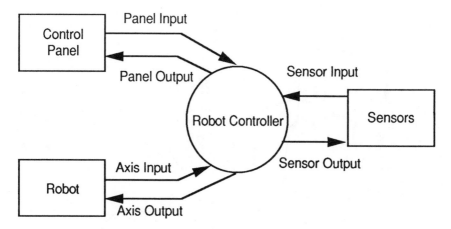

Figure 12-1.   Context Diagram

Figure 12-2. This figure presents a functional view of the system, and will be used to determine a proper set of communicating sequential processes.

Another tool used during the analysis phase is the state-transition diagram, as shown for the robot controller in Figure 12-3. The circles in this diagram represent the various states the system can attain, and the annotated graphs the conditions that cause state changes. This diagram can be used to create finite state machines for the complete system or for portions of the system.

After a thorough analysis of the requirements, we use the DFDs, the state-transition diagrams, and a set of heuristics to determine the processes that represent the abstraction of the parallel solution to the application. How we perform the selection of the concurrent elements is described in the next section.

12.2   Process Selection

The DFDs created during the analysis phase form the basis for our process selection procedure. This procedure has in the past been perceived as intuitive and based on "black magic." A set of process selection rules has been developed to simplify the selection and to remove the magic [NIE88]. The processes we select represent the set of communicating sequential processes that reflect the inherent concurrency of the requirements. Great care and considerable time and at-

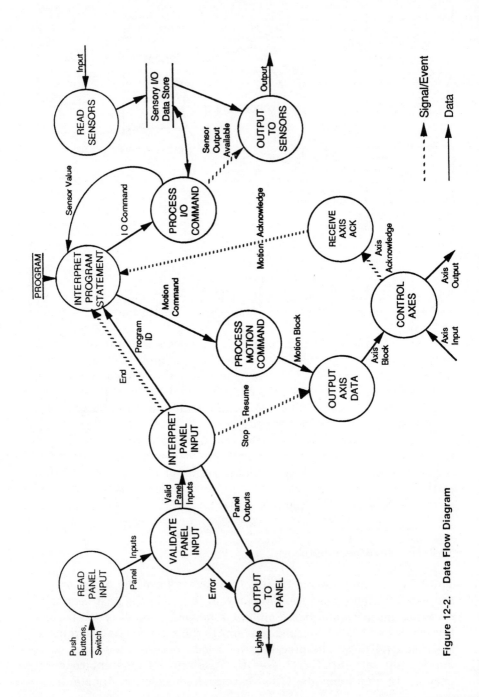

Figure 12-2.   Data Flow Diagram

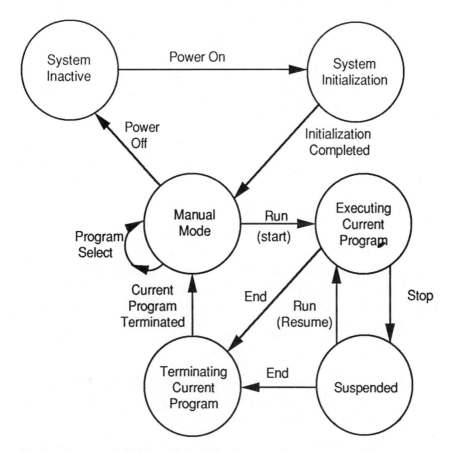

Figure 12-3.   State-Transition Diagram

tention should be expended during this step. The concurrent model selected is the process abstraction of the real-time system and represents our first major design decision.

The heuristics intended to simplify the selection procedure include the following:

1. *External Devices.* These devices normally run at widely differing speeds and usually require a separate process for each device or channel. These processes should be designed as simple device drivers with a minimum of executable instructions.

2. *Functional Cohesion.* Transforms with closely related functions can be combined into a single process if this will reduce the overhead compared to having each function as a separate process. The implementation of the set of functions as separate modules within the single process will contribute to functional cohesion (highly desirable) both within each module as well as within the process.

3. *Time-Critical Functions.* Certain functions must be performed within critical time limits, and this implies a separate (high priority) process for such functions.

4. *Periodic Functions.* Periodic functions should be implemented as separate processes that are activated at the proper time intervals. Such functions should not be combined into a single process, because it would quite likely be difficult to program more than one periodic function within the suspend/resume conditions of the process. In Ada, for example, we can specify a periodic interval with a delay statement. The Ada task will be suspended for (at least) the period specified, and it will be difficult to have more than one delay statement representing (accurately) different periodic functions within the single task. If periodic tasks compete for the use of a processor, they can be specified with a high priority to ensure a minimum latency for the expiration of the period.

5. *Computational Requirements.* Transforms that are not time critical (and often computationally intensive) can be designed as background processes (low priority) that will consume spare CPU cycles.

6. *Temporal Cohesion.* Transforms that perform certain functions during the same time period, or immediately following certain events, can be combined into a single process. Each function should be implemented as a separate module or set of instructions within the process. This contributes to functional cohesion at the module level, but only temporal cohesion within the process.

7. *Storage Limitations.* Virtual storage limitations may dictate the creation of additional processes by splitting up any process that is found to be too large. This limitation may apply to processors that use only 16 bits (or fewer) for virtual address cal-

culations. Although not a conceptual issue of concurrent processing, this is frequently a vitally important practical issue for older, standardized processors. For our software-first approach, this will not be a problem since we will simply choose a modern 32-bit processor that has sufficient memory.

8. *Database Functions.* Functions that need access to a shared database can be collected in a single process with mutual exclusion for the access mechanism, and the structure of the database hidden. This is the concept of a monitor [HOA74, NIE88], and can be implemented in Ada with a package that specifies the access routines, and a task and the use of a selective wait statement for providing mutual exclusion.

9. *Asynchronous Functions.* Functions (other than the external device drivers mentioned in 1 above) that appear independently and sporadically throughout the operation of the system should be separate processes. Examples of this type of function include (1) data recording that is activated and terminated at irregular intervals by an operator; and (2) an alert function that manages the queueing and display of alerts as they are received from the various processes

10. *Minimizing Communication.* The combination of functions into processes should be made such that the overall communication between the processes is minimized. When the processes are later distributed among a set of processors, this design consideration will result in a lower overall remote communication latency for the system. (This consideration is also brought up to a higher level when we later develop the virtual nodes.)

As a result of using these selection rules, the bubbles encapsulated by the polygons in Figure 12-4 represent a set of eight concurrent processes for the robot controller example.

12.3   Layered Development of Objects

The object orientation of our development approach is layered, i.e., different sets of objects will appear as we complete each step of the design methodology. The result of each (layered) step can be considered a virtual machine with a set of design objects as the product of

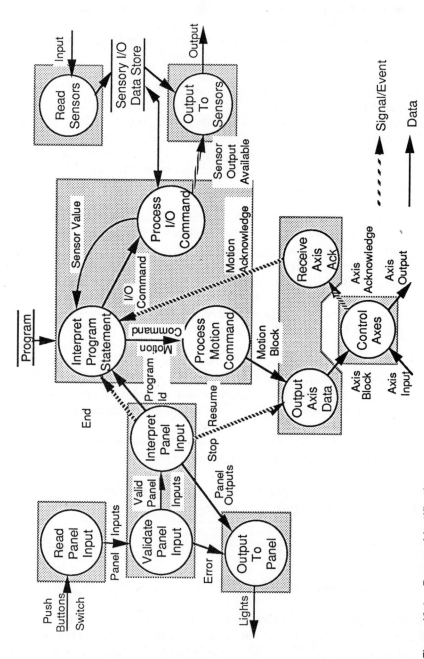

Figure 12-4.   Process Identification

that step. The objects we describe for the upper layers are abstractions, and are not entities in the traditional object-oriented sense of properties such as encapsulation, inheritance, binding, and message passing. At the lower layers, traditional objects will appear in the form of abstract data types, instantiations of generic Ada packages and subprograms, and the creation of data structures and variables from type definitions.

The processes shown in Figure 12-4 are the design objects for the first virtual machine, and can be traced directly back to the requirements specifications. These objects and their interfaces are illustrated in the process structure chart in Figure 12-5. The circles are no longer functions (as they were in Figures 12-2 and 12-4); they now represent a set of (abstract) sequential communicating processes that can operate in parallel in a concurrent system. The different types of interfaces between the processors are also shown in Figure 12-5. The piston shaped interface represents a loose coupling between two processes, whereas the "stair step" (between Axis Manager and Robot Handler) represents tight coupling, where the sender is expecting a reply. The open box (Program Id) depicts the passing of data where the sender does not expect a reply, and the lightning bolt represents the passing of a signal. The annotations on the interfaces describe the type of data passed or the name of a signal.

The process abstraction shown in Figure 12-5 is language independent, and must be implemented for a target hardware configuration with a specific compilation system and run-time support. This could be C and Unix or, in our case, Ada and whatever run-time support is supplied for a given target. The interfaces must be implemented using the available primitives and services. Loose coupling in Ada, for example, may be implemented with a buffer task, and in C/Unix with a mailbox.

The next layer in the design approach will consist of a set of Ada tasks which have been derived from the process abstraction. The interfaces between the tasks are determined using a set of heuristics for the caller/called decisions. A thorough analysis of these interfaces is extremely important since they determine the degree of coupling between the Ada tasks. Inefficient polling, for example, should be eliminated during this analysis step. Additional Ada tasks may be included to implement interface functions such as buffers, transporters, and relays. The heuristics for making the caller/called decisions for a uniprocessor system are described in [NIE88]. Additional considerations for distributed systems are included in a later section in this chapter.

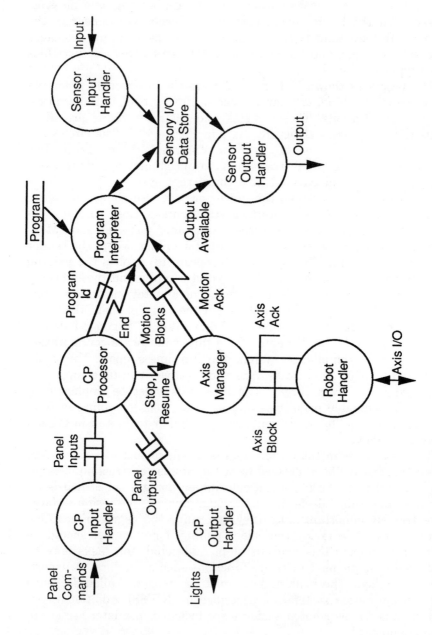

Figure 12-5.   Process Structure Chart

The transformation to Ada tasks for the robot controller is shown in the Ada task graph in Figure 12-6. The design objects in this layer are the Ada application tasks and the communication tasks needed to implement the proper interfaces between the application tasks in a non-distributed system. These interfaces will have to be reconsidered after the tasks have been allocated to virtual nodes in a distributed system. Some of the Ada rendezvous may have to be replaced with another communication mechanism if remote rendezvous are not supported. Such other mechanisms include remote procedure calls or message passing.

The next layer of virtual machines will contain design objects in the form of Ada packages created within the context of the taxonomy shown in Figure 12-7. The Ada tasks shown in Figure 12-6 will be encapsulated in packages using the packaging rules described in [NIE88]. Additional packaging considerations are discussed below in connection with the creation of virtual nodes.

The objects created in this step are shown in Figure 12-8. These are objects of the type described by Booch [BOO86 and BOO87], and are encapsulations of the communicating sequential Ada tasks. These objects will form the units that will be combined and distributed among a set of virtual nodes. Additional Ada packages and tasks may have to be included in the distributed system solution to support remote inter-node communication mechanisms.

12.4   Virtual Node Specification

The virtual node structure is created by combining the objects determined in the previous step (see Figure 12-8) and allocating each combination to a virtual node. Memory can be shared by the objects contained within each virtual node, but not between the nodes since the virtual nodes may be allocated to different processors, and we are designing for loosely coupled distributed systems. Groups of tightly coupled objects are identified and assigned to the same virtual node. These objects are Ada packages, tasks, and subprograms that encapsulate the application and communication tasks. Tight coupling refers here to objects that share memory, and to tasks that rendezvous with a combination of *in* and *out* mode parameters in the same entry call. Interrupt handlers (interfaces to external devices) have, typically, no need to communicate directly and should be placed in different virtual nodes. These nodes should end up on the

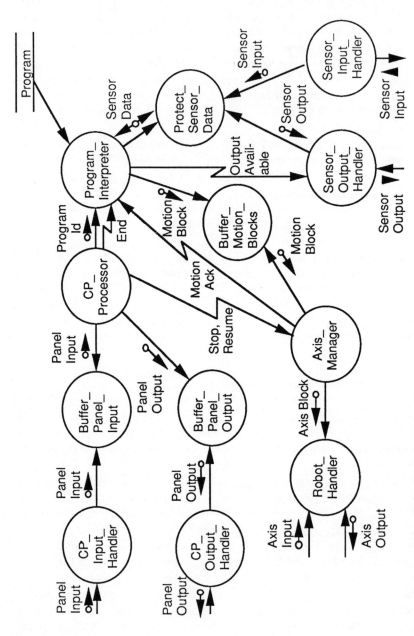

Figure 12-6.   Ada Task Graph (after caller/called decisions)

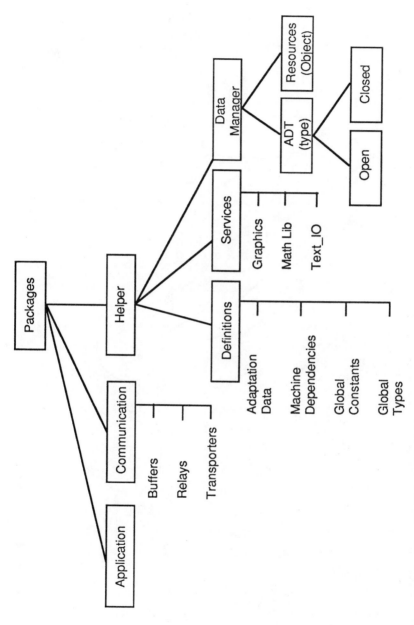

Figure 12-7.   Classification of Ada Packages

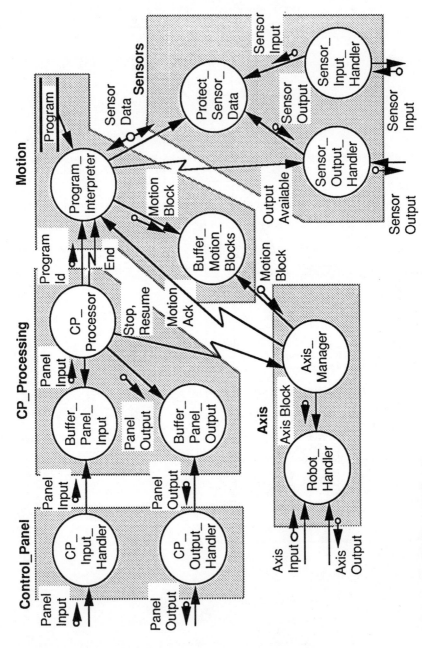

Figure 12-8.   Ada Package Graph

physical node that represents the external device being handled, as we are not advocating remote propagation of interrupts.

Every effort should be made to make the virtual nodes as independent as possible in anticipation of a possible reconfiguration of the mapping of virtual nodes to physical nodes in a fault tolerant architecture. This also promotes the portability of programs that can be rehosted on systems that implement a different inter-processor communication mechanism.

Since a distributed design must be supported by adequate runtime services, the design methodology may include restrictions as a result of lacking services, for example, for a remote rendezvous. The use of conditional and timed entry calls may be restricted and (by convention) only allowed within a virtual node. This will simplify the interfaces between the virtual nodes that end up on different processors. Task specifications are made in the encapsulating package body, and inter-package entry calls can only be made via the *entrance procedures* specified in the package specification. This is recommended regardless of whether the package is on a node boundary or internal to a node.

An example of a set of entrance procedures in the package specification of Motion for the robot controller is shown in Figure 12-9. This is one of the major application packages and provides four interfaces to the other application packages. The procedure Start_Program is called with the parameter Program_Id to start the execution of a given (preprogrammed) motion program. The procedure End_Event is called to signal the end of execution of the current. The procedure Motion_Ack is called to signal an acknowledgement of the completion of a set of motions. The procedure Dequeue_Motion_Block is called to provide the next set of motion commands.

```
with Definitions;   use Definitions;
package Motion is
    procedure Start_Program (Id  :  in Program_Id);
    procedure End_Event;
    procedure Motion_Ack;
    procedure Dequeue_Motion_Block (M  :  out Motion_Block);
end Motion;
```

Figure 12-9.   Use of Entrance Procedures for Information Hiding

All of the procedures in Figure 12-9 act as entrance procedures, and hide the implementations of the various functions. The information hiding includes the structure of the application function, e.g., a procedure or task, and local or remote communication. A virtual node called by the entrance procedures may be co-located on the same processor, or it may be on a remote processor; this is invisible to the caller and provides a layered design approach with portable code. This design hides an actual implementation of local or remote entry calls, and can use the most efficient model for the given target configuration without redesigning the application program.

Similar restrictions to the ones suggested for virtual node interfaces may be applied to exception handlers. This is especially true if the distribution to physical nodes is of multiple Ada programs. There are no semantics specified for propagating exceptions between Ada programs, and all exception handlers must be local to a given program. If remote propagation of exceptions is allowed between multiple, communicating Ada programs, a message passing mechanism must be implemented, and all exceptions must be tagged as local or remote. If a single program is distributed across processors, the propagation is transparent and in accordance with the normal propagation semantics.

Whenever restrictions are applied to the methodology used to select the virtual nodes, every effort should be made to anticipate future implementations of the missing services. The programs should be structured such that a minimum amount of redesign is required when the services become available. An example is the use of entrance procedures to hide the implementation of remote entry calls.

12.5   Selecting Active and Passive Tasks

In the creation of the task interfaces shown in the Ada task graph in Figure 12-6, we used a set of caller/called heuristics [NIE88] to provide a properly balanced concurrent design for a uniprocessor solution. The heuristics are summarized here and expanded with considerations for multi-processor solutions:

1. *Device drivers.* Device drivers can be pure servers or hybrids for interrupt driven devices. These drivers will contain entries for the interrupt handling, and, possibly, an entry for the interface with other application tasks. It may alternately make a call to the interfacing application tasks, and thus become a hybrid. For devices that require polling, hybrid tasks or pure cal-

lers are the most likely choice. These drivers will poll the devices via calls to see if they are ready for input or output. They may contain entries for the interfaces with the other application tasks, or they may make calls to these tasks.

2. *Controlling tasks.* Tasks that need to control a rendezvous are called. The control is typically implemented with guarded entries, nested rendezvous, exception handling with inner frames, and the use of the Count attribute.

3. *Busy tasks.* Busy tasks are called. "Busy" is here referring to tasks that can interact with several other tasks, i.e., there are several entries specified within a single task. If a busy task is allowed to make calls to other busy tasks, severe delays could be experienced for the calling task.

4. *Complex tasks.* Algorithmically complex tasks are callers. This will reduce their complexity compared to making them called tasks. A call within a task represents an abstraction of a portion of the algorithm, and thus reduces the complexity of that task body.

5. *Service tasks.* Tasks with functions that provide the equivalent of executive services should be pure servers, like a buffer task used to store input or output data.

6. *Avoid hybrids, if possible.* If the choice (in conjunction with the heuristics given above) is between a hybrid or a pure caller or server, avoid the hybrid. This will enforce the notion of active or passive tasks discussed above and advocated by Pyle [PYL85] and Burns [BUR85].

7. *Minimize inter-processor communication.* A buffer task and data analysis task may be included with an I/O device driver to reduce message passing between processors. This could effectively reverse the caller/called direction of entry calls derived for a uniprocessor design. The additional processing performed by the analysis task could be to strip off message headers and to check error codes. The amount of data crossing the communication medium could thus be substantially reduced.

8. *Allow polling.* In a uniprocessor design, polling implies "busy wait" which usually wastes resources. Active and passive tasks

are carefully constructed to only allow polling where it cannot be avoided. In a distributed design, however, polling is of much less concern because there are fewer tasks per processor and busy wait is less important.

These heuristics will promote the overall design goals for a distributed design that is free of deadlock and cyclic dependencies, and that will minimize the amount of inter-processor communication for maximum throughput.

The determination of active and passive tasks is an iterative operation as the design progresses. The first attempt is made just as for a uniprocessor design in the creation of the Ada task graph. These decisions are revisited after the virtual nodes have been determined, and additional considerations can be made for a distributed solution.

12.6   Identifying Time-Critical Events

It is important that real-time critical events be identified as early as possible during the analysis phase, and that adequate measures be planned for their implementation as the design progresses. The events should be known and understood before the processors are selected and the virtual nodes are mapped to physical nodes. The following design features can be assigned to critical events to ensure proper execution behavior during system operation:

1. *High priorities.* Tasks that contain critical events are identified during the design phase and are assigned the highest priorities in the system. This will normally include device drivers, interrupt handlers, and periodic events.

2. *Fixed communication links.* Fixed, high bandwidth communication links can be specified between inter-communicating processes that contain critical events. The remaining (non-critical) processes will have to contend for the other communication links.

3. *Increased number of processors.* Processes containing critical events can be assigned to their own processor. This increases the number of processors and the parallelism of the system, but with an associated increase in the hardware cost. (The selection of processors is discussed further in a later chapter.)

The identification of critical events can start as early as the requirements analysis phase and noted on DFDs. This information is carried through the various design steps and used whenever appropriate, e.g., assigning a high priority to a periodic task that must expire with a finite latency.

12.7 Summary

The first phase of the overall design methodology is to determine the concurrent elements of the system and to combine Ada modules into virtual nodes. This is done with a step-by-step approach and the use of a set of heuristics to ease the transition from one design step to the next. At every step of the design we create a layered virtual machine that contains the design objects of that step.

The concurrent elements of the real-time system are determined just as they would be for a uniprocessor implementation. The process abstraction created is language independent and must be implemented with a specific programming language and run-time services in mind. In our case the processes are transformed to Ada tasks, which are encapsulated in Ada packages. These application packages form the basis for the creation of the virtual nodes that will be distributed to the processors.

The distributed design is determined without regard for a specific hardware configuration. The steps of the methodology support a software-first approach with the identification of a set of virtual nodes that will be distributed among processors that can best support the software design.

Certain restrictions may have to be applied to the methodology because desired programming tools or run-time services are not available for the distributed solution. The design should be made with the anticipation of future implementations of the missing services. The programs should be structured such that a minimum amount of redesign is required when the services become available. An example is the use of entrance procedures to hide the detailed implementation of remote entry calls.

Whereas this chapter has focused on the creation of processes, Ada application packages, and virtual nodes, the next chapter describes various mechanisms and programming techniques used for communication between the nodes.

13

Node Communication

The communication mechanism specified in the ARM for Ada tasks is the synchronous rendezvous mechanism. Application tasks will be encapsulated in Ada packages that will be distributed with virtual nodes to different processors. The ARM does not include a semantic specification for remote rendezvous, and this may be implemented by other communication mechanisms such as the remote procedure call (RPC) or message passing. It is preferable that the communication mechanism be transparent to the applications programmer. If the run-time services are not available for such transparency, however, the communication mechanism has to be built into the application. These mechanisms are discussed in the following subsections.

13.1 Ada Rendezvous and Remote Entry Calls

The Ada rendezvous implements a synchronous communication mechanism where the calling task is suspended during the rendezvous. Parameters can be sent and received just as in procedure calls, and the modes *in*, *out*, and *in out* determine the direction of the parameters. The ARM includes a specification for a timed entry call, where the calling task is suspended while a rendezvous is attempted. If the time interval expires before a rendezvous is initiated, the calling task resumes execution. A conditional entry call is also specified, where the rendezvous will only take place if the called task is immediately available for the initiation of the rendezvous. An example of a timed entry call for reading the temperature of a furnace is the following:

```
   . . .
   loop
      select
         Furnace.Read_Next (Temperature);
         . . .
         -- process new temperature reading
         . . .
      or
         delay Furnace_Timeout;
         raise No_Response_From_Furnace;
      end select;
   end loop;
   . . .
```

If the rendezvous does not take place within the expected response time (Furnace_Timeout), the exception No_Response_From_Furnace is raised, and the task continues its normal execution. If the task that normally reads the furnace temperature is located on a different processor, this example constitutes a remote timed entry call.

The ARM does not include a specification for how either remote (simple) entry calls or remote timed and conditional entry calls should be implemented by the run-time support. The required remote services may not be available with the run-time support supplied by a particular Ada vendor (or from any vendor!), and the distributed application software will then have to include these services. By including the services, the distributed solution can use the Ada rendezvous without restrictions, and remote inter-node communication becomes transparent to the rest of the application. A distinction may have to be made between a simple rendezvous and timed or conditional rendezvous. The latter two cases require timing services to properly interpret the global meaning of the expiration for the timed entry call, and the "immediate" condition for the conditional call. The simple entry call does not require any global timing services. If global timing services are not available, timed and conditional entry calls may have to be restricted to local virtual nodes.

13.1.1 Remote Entry Call Model

Remote entry calls can be implemented as suggested in [ATK88] for the Distributed Ada Demonstrated (DIADEM) project. A layered communication model for Ada remote rendezvous is shown in Figure 13-1. The application layer of the calling task environment includes the context of the remote entry call (REC), which could be from within a task body or a subprogram executing in the same thread as the task it supports. The remote rendezvous layer of the calling task includes the services required to transport an ordinary entry call to the standard communication interface (SCI). The services provided include functions to prepare and send messages to the output port of the SCI, and to interpret replies received via the input port of the SCI. The prepared messages include the parameters of the original entry call. The services of the rendezvous layer are implemented as subprograms encapsulated in Ada packages. The communication layer consists of the ports included in the SCI of the calling and called rendezvous layers, and the low level inter-processor communication protocol. This protocol can be TCP/IP or UDP, and should be invisible to the application virtual nodes.

The remote rendezvous layer of the called task environment includes an entry port task which receives all incoming messages. When this task detects a remote entry call to one of the visible entries, it creates a local agent task and passes all the entry parameters to the agent. The entry port task then loops back to receive the next message. The dynamically created local agent task acts as a surrogate for the calling task and issues an entry call on its behalf. If the rendezvous between the agent and remote task is successful, the agent passes back the values associated with the *out* or *in out* parameters to the entry port task and then terminates.

With this approach to the remote entry calls, the only layer visible to the calling task environment of the application program is the remote rendezvous layer. The other layers are implemented at a lower level and can be replaced without changing the application code. In a heterogeneous architecture, all of the processors will include the identical services of the remote rendezvous layer of both the caller and called environments. The functions of the communications protocol are included as required for each processor and may be tailored for efficient execution.

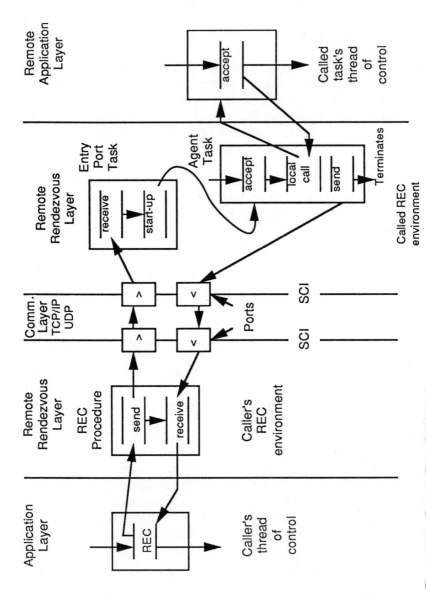

Figure 13-1.   Remote Entry Call Model

13.1.2   Remote Entry Call Services

The REC approach can be used with the distribution of virtual nodes of a single program among a set of loosely coupled processors (provided the required remote elaboration services are available). The entrance procedures on the boundary of the remote rendezvous layer of the calling task will transport the entry calls to the REC procedure. An example of a set of REC services as suggested in [ATK88] is illustrated in Figure 13-2 for the standard interface to the communication layer.

```
with Global_Defs;

package Std_Comm_Interface is
    type Std_Node_Id    is new Natural;
    type Return_Address is private;
    type Header_Type    is private;

    generic
        Node : Std_Node_Id;
    package Caller_Ports is
        generic
            type Request_Packet is private;
            type Reply_Packet   is private;
        package Primitives is
            type Ref_Request_Packet is access Request_Packet;
            type Ref_Reply_Packet   is access Reply_Packet;
            procedure Allocate_Packet (Addr : out Ref_Request_Packet);
            procedure Deallocate_Packet (Addr: in out
                                            Ref_Reply_Packet);
            procedure Send_Msg (Addr : in Ref_Request_Packet);
            procedure Receive_Msg (Addr : out Ref_Reply_Packet);
        end Primitives;

        procedure Close_Ports;
    end Caller_Ports;
```

```
generic
    Node : Std_Node_Id;
    type Remote_Entries is (< >);
    type Request_Packet is private;
    type Reply_Packet (Rem_Entry : Remote_Entries) is private;
package Server_Ports is
    type Ref_Request_Packet is access Request_Packet;
    type Ref_Reply_Packet   is access Reply_Packet;
    procedure Allocate_Packet (Addr :        out Ref_Reply_Packet;
                               Rem_Entry : in  Remote_Entries);
    procedure Deallocate_Packet (Addr : in out
                                              Ref_Request_Packet);
    procedure Send_Msg (Addr : in Ref_Reply_Packet);
    procedure Receive_Msg (Addr : out Ref_Request_Packet);
    procedure Close_Ports;
    end Server_Ports;
private
    type Return_Address is new Global_Defs.Address_Types;
    type Header_Type    is new Global_Defs.Header_Types;
end Std_Comm_Interface;
```

Figure 13-2.   REC Standard Interface Services

The package Std_Comm_Interface contains type definitions for a
standard node, return address for the request message packets received by the entry port task, and a packet message header. Nested,
generic packages are declared for the caller and server ports. The
package Caller_Ports is instantiated in the REC procedure and generates a pair of ports for sending request packets and receiving reply
packets. The package Server_Ports is instantiated in the entry port
task, and generates a similar pair of ports for receiving request packets and sending reply packets. The receiving server port must reside
at a fixed network address that is known to the sender of the request
packet. A correspondence is maintained between the identification of
a software node and physical node, and the associated port address
as shown in Table 13-1.

13.2   Remote Procedure Call

If there is no mechanism available for distributing the virtual nodes
of a single Ada program, the virtual nodes must be combined into

Table 13-1.   Node Name/Port Address Association

Virtual Node	Physical Node	Port Address
VN (1)	PN (r)	Addr (a)
VN (2)	PN (s)	Addr (e)
. . .	. . .	. . .
VN (n)	PN (q)	Addr (g)

multiple programs that are compiled, linked, and loaded independently. Each program is executed on a separate processor, and the virtual nodes have the same communication requirements they would have if they were part of a single distributed program.

The semantic specification of the Ada rendezvous does not extend past the boundaries of a single program, and the remote entry call model described in the previous section is not appropriate for inter-program communication. Alternate communication models include the remote procedure call (RPC) specified in [SUN86] or some form of message passing. We consider the RPC model here and message passing in a later section.

13.2.1 RPC Model

Whenever we are forced to artificially create multiple programs to implement a single application, we must carefully design the system in anticipation of reconfiguring the virtual nodes for a future single program distribution. The necessary layers should be provided for the RPC services such that only a minimum of redesign is required to change from multiple communicating programs to a single distributed program.

An illustration of the RPC communication environment is shown in Figure 13-3. This is the basic client/server model, where the client task on processor A makes a call to the remote services and waits for a reply. The message that is passed to the server side contains the identification of the remote procedure that is called. A demon task on the server side waits for an execution request made by the server on behalf of a client. When a request is accepted, the demon passes the request to the appropriate server functions and waits for a reply.

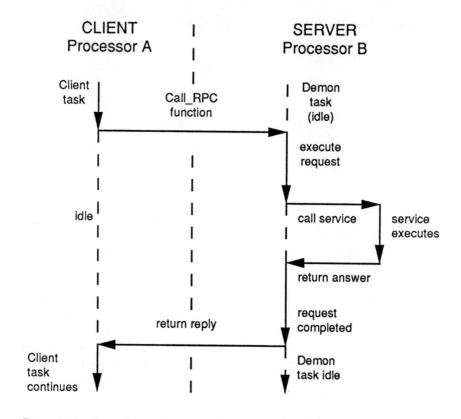

Figure 13-3.   Client/Server Model for Remote Procedure Call

When the reply arrives, the demon returns the reply to the client and waits for another client request.

As a layered approach, the RPC has replaced the remote rendez-vous layer in the REC method as was shown in Figure 13-1. The actual communication protocol is invisible in both mechanisms, but the RPC requires knowledge of the remote processor, the RPC program and version number, and the remote procedure identification, all of which are passed as parameters in the RPC call. These parameters are not required in the REC mechanism, and the application program is thus better shielded from the details of the remote communication. The C version of a call to RPC created by Sun Microsystems has the following form:

```
callrpc (host, prognum, versnum, procnum, inproc, in, outproc, out)
    char   *host;
    u_long prognum, versnum, procnum;
    char   *in, *out;
    xdrproc_t inproc, outproc;
```

This calls the remote procedure on the *host* machine associated with the program *prognum*, and version number *versnum*. The parameter *in* is the address of the remote procedure's arguments, and *out* is the address for returning the results. The parameter *inproc* is used to encode the procedure's parameters, and *outproc* is used to decode the procedure's results. The latter two parameters reflect the added complexity present with the RPC approach, as a translation is required for the proper data representation as parameters are passed between heterogeneous processors. The RPC services specified in [SUN86] include the External Data Representation (XDR) functions with data types and operations for the required data transformations. If the underlying communication services are not available with the RPC/XDR functions, these services will have to be furnished as a part of the communication protocol. Specifications will then have to made for the *domain*, i.e., an environment such as Unix or Internet; the socket *type*, e.g., stream (TCP/IP) or datagram (UDP); and the *protocol*, e.g., TCP/IP, Internet Control Message Protocol, or UDP. A socket is defined in terms of a domain, socket type, and protocol:

```
s = socket (domain, type, protocol);
```

A process name on a given processor is bound to a socket with the call:

```
bind (s, name, namelength);
```

where the format of the name is dependent on the domain. In Unix, for example, the name associated with a socket is the path name, whereas in Internet the name consists of an Internet address and a port number [SUN86].

The RPC model couples an application much tighter to the communication mechanism than the REC approach, but it has less run-time overhead. The REC approach is preferable, if the extra overhead can be tolerated, since it provides a more portable solution.

13.2.2   RPC and Ada

The RPC services are readily available in the C language and can be accessed by Ada systems that implement the pragma Interface for C routines, for example:

```
pragma Interface (C, callrpc);
```

How well this will work on a particular Ada implementation depends on the compatibility of the parameter passing conventions between C and Ada data structures. Modifications to the Ada compiler may have to be made to accommodate the differences of, for example, the *struct* type in C and *record* type in Ada. If the pragma is not available, or the C and Ada calling conventions are not compatible, the equivalent communications services will have to be programmed in Ada.

A set of RPC services and lower level communication protocols for Ethernet (TeleAdaLAN) have been implemented in Ada by the Swedish company TeleLogic [TEL88]. The services are implemented as Ada library packages to be used with TeleSoft's TeleGen Ada compiler. The system is implemented with a layered approach as shown in Figure 13-4. The real-time application program interfaces with the RPC services in the process layer, or directly with the task-to-task communication layer (TTC). RPC uses logical names to refer to network addresses; TTC maps the logical names to sockets on the local and remote machines. Sockets are assigned to individual tasks which may communicate directly with each other. The lower layers in TeleAdaLAN include the protocol, Internet, and network layers. Some of the library packages available in AdaLAN are listed below:

```
AdaLAN_Error_Handler
AdaLAN_Types
AdaLAN_Socket
AdaLAN_RPC_Types
AdaLAN_RPC_Client
AdaLAN_RPC_Server
AdaLAN_Authent
AdaLAN_XDR_Memory
AdaLAN_Std_XDR
AdaLAN_Portmap_Server
```

The use of sockets for remote message transfer, for example, can be done with procedure calls to services included in the package AdaLAN_Socket:

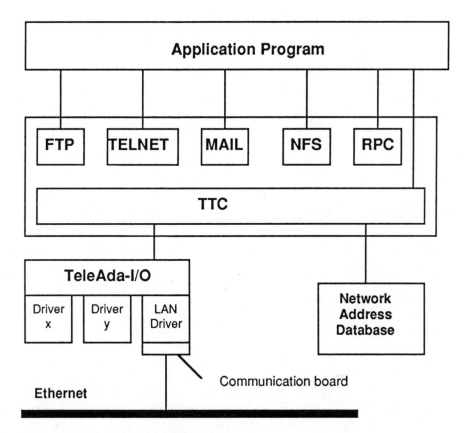

Figure 13-4.   Design of AdaLAN Services

```
.  .  .
package AS renames AdaLAN_Socket;
.  .  .
AS.Create_Socket (Error_Status, Socket, Internet, Stream_Socket);
AS.Bind (Error_Status, Socket, " ", Port_Number);
AS.Accept_Direct (Error_Status, Socket, Peer_Name,
                  Peer_Name_Length, Peer_Port);
AS.Receive (Error_Status, Socket, Buffer, Buffer_Length);
AS.Send (Error_Status, Socket, Buffer, Buffer_Length);
AS.Close (Error_Status, Socket);
```

The first call creates a socket in the Internet domain with a stream socket (TCP) protocol. The next call associates a port number (specific program or task) with the socket. The third call creates a connection between the peer port (client program) and the socket.

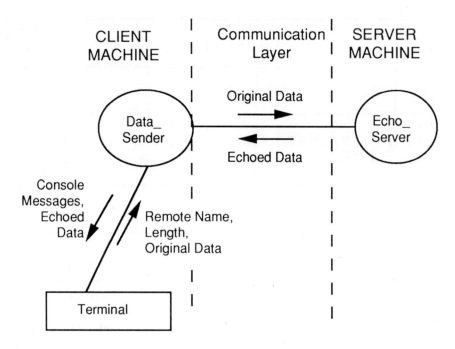

Figure 13-5.   Client/Server Model of Echo Server

Messages are received from and sent via a buffer of a certain length at the socket address. When the communication is completed, the socket is closed.

A model for the use of the standard Arpanet Echo Server is illustrated in Figure 13-5. The echo server can be used for testing of networks and act as a simulator for remote communication. The main program (Data_Sender) shown in Figure 13-6 creates a socket on the client machine, and makes a connection between the client socket and the remote server machine. Data is read from the input terminal and sent to the remote server. When the data is echoed back from the server machine, it is displayed on the client console.

```
-- Main procedure (Data_Sender) on the client machine reads
-- data from the terminal, sends the data to the echo
-- server program on the server machine, and waits for data
-- to be returned from the echo server.  Data returned is
-- displayed on the console.
```

```
with Text_IO;
with AdaLAN_Socket;
with AdaLAN_Types;
with AdaLAN_Error_Handler;

procedure Data_Sender is          -- Main
   package EH  renames AdaLAN_Error_Handler;
   package ATY renames AdaLAN_Types;
   package AS  renames AdaLAN_Socket;

   Error_Status : EH.Status := EH.Allocate_Status (0);
   Socket       : AS.Socket;

   Line         : String (1 .. 256); -- Holds data sent and
                                      -- received
   Line_Length : Natural := 0;        -- Length of data

   Remote_Name         : String (1 .. 80); -- Name of remote
                                            -- node
   Remote_Name_Length : Natural := 0;      -- Length of
                                           -- remote name

begin                 -- Data_Sender
   Text_IO.Put_Line ("Start Data_Sender");

   loop          -- New connection
      Text_IO.Put ("Establish connection with ");
      Text_IO.Put_Line ("remote node with name:");
      Text_IO.Get (Remote_Name, Remote_Name_Length);
      Text_IO.New_Line;
      --
      -- Domain is Internet and socket type is stream
      -- (TCP/IP).
      -- Establish connection
      --
      AS.Create_Socket (Error_Status, Socket, AS.AF_Inet,
                    AS.Sock_Stream);
      AS.Bind (Error_Status, Socket);
      AS.Connect (Error_Status, Socket,
                 Remote_Name (1 .. Remote_Name_Length),
                 AS.P_Echo);
      --
```

```
      -- Read data from the terminal and send it to the
      -- remote node until "END" is entered
      --
      loop          -- Read data until "END" is entered
         Text_IO.Put_Line ("Enter text to send:");
         Text_IO.Get_Line (Line, Line_Length);
         exit when Line_Length >= 3 and then Line (1 .. 3) = "END";
         --
         -- Send the line to the echo server
         --
         AS.Send (Error_Status, Socket, Line (1 .. Line_Length));
         --
         -- Receive a string from the echo server
         --
         AS.Receive (Error_Status, Socket, Line, Line_Length);
         Text_IO.Put_Line ("String received from echo server:");
         Text_IO.Put_Line (Line (1 .. Line_Length));
      end loop;          -- Read data
      --
      -- Close connection
      --
      AS.Close (Error_Status, Socket);
      Text_IO.Put_Line ("Connection closed");
   end loop;           -- New connection
   EH.Deallocate_Status (Error_Status);
exception            -- error handling from AdaLAN
   when EH.Error =>
      EH.Report (Error_Status);
      begin
         AS.Close (Error_Status, Socket);
      exception
         when others =>
            null;
      end;
      EH.Deallocate_Status (Error_Status);
end Data_Sender;
```

Figure 13-6.   Data_Sender (Main) on Client Machine

The remote echo task shown in Figure 13-7 is created with the pragma Elaborate and the call to the procedure Start in the package body. An attempt is first made to create a stream socket (for the

TCP protocol). If the attempt fails, the task is completed (the exception handler is outside the main loop). The socket is associated with a local (server) host address and default echo port. The task waits for a remote client process to connect with the server socket. After a connection is established, the server task will read data from the local buffer and echo the same data back to the remote client. With this implementation, only one client can be serviced per connection, since the Accept_Direct call is inside the main loop. When the connection is broken either by a status error or by closing a socket, the task returns to establish another connection.

```
-- (c) TeleLogic AB Sweden 1988
--      All rights reserved

package AdaLAN_Echo_Server is
end AdaLAN_Echo_Server;

with AdaLAN_Error_Handler;
with AdaLAN_Socket;
with AdaLAN_Types;
package body AdaLAN_Echo_Server is

    package EH renames AdaLAN_Error_Handler;
    package AS renames AdaLAN_Socket;
    package AT renames AdaLAN_Types;

    task Echo;

    task body Echo is
        Error_Status      : EH.Status;
        Socket            : AS.Socket;
        Peer_Name         : String (1 .. 80);
        Peer_Name_Length  : Natural;
        Peer_Port         : AS.Ports;
        Buffer            : AT.Byte_Buffer (1 .. 1024);
        Buffer_Length     : AT.Size_in_Bytes;
    begin
        loop
            AS.Create_Socket (Error_Status, Socket, AS.AF_Inet,
                              AS.Sock_Stream);
            begin
                AS.Bind (Error_Status, Socket, " ", AS.P_Echo);
```

```
        AS.Accept_Direct (Error_Status, Socket, Peer_Name,
                          Peer_Name_Length, Peer_Port);
        loop      -- read data from remote machine (in local
                  -- buffer) and echo back
          AS.Receive (Error_Status, Socket, Buffer,
                      Buffer_Length);
          exit when Buffer_Length = 0;
          AS.Send (Error_Status, Socket, Buffer,
                   Buffer_Length);
        end loop;
      exception
        . . .
      end;
    end loop;
  exception
    . . .
  end Echo;
end AdaLAN_Echo_Server;
```

Figure 13-7. Echo Server Task

13.2.3 RPC and External Data Representation (XDR)

In a heterogeneous environment, data representations differ from
processor to processor. A particular distributed architecture may include processors with different word lengths and byte ordering. Appropriate conversion routines must be available to accommodate
these different data representations. The original RPC services specified by Sun Microsystems include a set of External Data Representation (XDR) functions to support the required data transformations.
These services are also included in AdaLAN.

A model of the transformations required between the various representations is shown in Figure 13-8. Data on the client machine is
transformed to the XDR standard representation before a remote
procedure call is made. Data received by the server machine is in the
XDR standard format, and is converted to the server representation
before any operations take place on parameters passed from the client to the server. Similar conversions are performed on result parameters returned to the client machine. Parameters transmitted

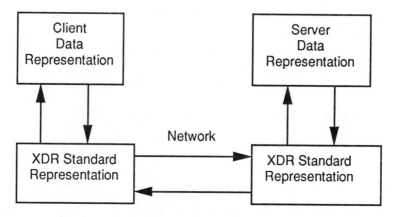

Figure 13-8.   Transformation to/from Standard Data Representation

across the network are always in the format of the XDR standard representation. If the data representation of a particular machine is the same as the standard format, compiler switches can be set to prevent needless data conversions.

An example of the kind of conversions required for the addition of two integer values and the return of the result and possible overflow are shown in Figure 13-9(a) and (b).

```
with AdaLAN_XDR_Memory;
with AdaLAN_RPC_Types;
with AdaLAN_Error_Handler;

package XDR_Conversions is
    package XM renames AdaLAN_XDR_Memory;
    package RT renames AdaLAN_RPC_Types;
    package EH renames AdaLAN_Error_Handler;

    Program_Number : constant RT.Prognums := 200_500;
    Version_Number : constant RT.Versnums := 1;
    Add_Proc_Num   : constant RT.Procnums := 1;   -- RPC proc number;

    type Add_In is          -- RPC data in
        record
            First  : Integer;
            Second : Integer;
        end record;
```

```
-- XDR (RPC) in-data conversion routine
procedure XDR_Add_In (Error_Status : in EH.Status;
                      XDR :          in out XM.Xdrs;
                      Data :         in out Add_In);


type Add_Out is        -- RPC data out
   record
      Result   : Integer;
      Overflow : Boolean;
   end record;


-- XDR (RPC) out-data conversion routine
procedure XDR_Add_Out (Error_Status : in EH.Status;
                       XDR :          in out XM.Xdrs;
                       Data :         in out Add_Out);
end XDR_Conversions;
```

Figure 13-9(a).   XDR Conversion Services (package spec)

```
package body XDR_Conversions is

   procedure XDR_Add_In (Error_Status : in EH.Status;
                         XDR :          in out XM.Xdrs;
                         Data :         in out Add_In) is
      procedure XDR_Integer is new XM.XDR_Integers (Integer);
   begin
      XDR_Integer (Error_Status, XDR, Data.First);  -- first
                                                     -- operand
      XDR_Integer (Error_Status, XDR, Data.Second); -- second
                                                     -- operand
   end XDR_Add_In;


   procedure XDR_Add_Out (Error_Status : in EH.Status;
                          XDR :          in out XM.Xdrs;
                          Data :         in out Add_Out) is
      procedure XDR_Integer is new XM.XDR_Integers (Integer);
      procedure XDR_Boolean is new XM.XDR_Enumerations (Boolean);
   begin
      XDR_Integer (Error_Status, XDR, Data.Result);
```

```
   XDR_Boolean (Error_Status, Data.Overflow);
   end XDR_Add_Out;
end XDR_Conversions;
```

Figure 13-9(b). XDR Conversion Services (package body)

The package specification and body is included on both the client and server machines. On the client machine, the procedure XDR_Add_In is used to convert the two input operands to be added from the representation on the client machine to the XDR standard format. XDR_Add_Out is used to convert results returned by the server from the XDR representation to the client representation. On the server machine, XDR_Add_In is used to convert from XDR format to the server representation, and XDR_Add_Out from server representation to XDR format. Instantiations of generic procedures are made for the required types on the respective machines. This ensures the correct data representations in a heterogeneous as well as a homogeneous environment.

The constants Program_Number and Version_Number refer to the utility program on the server that the clients will access. The constant Add_Proc_Num defines a procedure number for the remote Add function. If other remote functions were included, such as, for example, Fast Fourier Transforms or remote entry calls, they would be given different remote procedure numbers. The parameter XDR in XDR_Add_In and XDR_Add_Out refers to a buffer address and is used to locate the converted data elements.

When a task or subprogram makes a call to another procedure or task, the location of the called module should be as transparent as possible to the caller to promote portable Ada code. The main program ("environment task") shown in Figure 13-10 makes a call to the Add procedure specified in package Add_On_Client. The actual implementation of the Add function may be located on a remote machine, and this remoteness is transparent to the caller Test_Example_Client.

```
with Add_On_Client;
with Text_IO;

procedure Test_Example_Client is       -- main
   First          : Integer := 0;
   Second         : Integer := 0;
```

```
    Result          : Integer := 0;
    Overflow        : Boolean := False;
    Line            : String (1 .. 80);
    Line_Length     : Natural;
begin
    Text_IO.Put_Line ("Test of Add_On_Client");
    loop
        Text_IO. Put_Line ("Enter first number");
        Text_IO.Get_Line (Line, Line_Length);
        First := Integer'Value (Line (1..Line_Length));

        Text_IO. Put_Line ("Enter second number");
        Text_IO.Get_Line (Line, Line_Length);
        Second := Integer'Value (Line (1..Line_Length));

        Add_On_Client.Add (First, Second, Result, Overflow);
        Text_IO.Put_Line (Integer'Image (First) &
                          Integer'Image (Second) &
                          Integer'Image (Result) &
                          Boolean'Image (Overflow));
    end loop;
end Test_Example_Client;
```

Figure 13-10.   Main Procedure for Testing Add on Client

If we assume that the call to Add in Test_Example_Client represents an RPC, one implementation of the environment for the Add procedure (Add_On_Client) on the client machine is as shown in Figure 13-11. The package specification is the same regardless of whether the actual Add operation is performed on the client or server machine. The package body, however, will be tailored for a client and the server. The client implementation shown in Figure 13-11 includes local declarations used in the creation of UDP services. The call to RPC.Create attempts to allocate a buffer for the client and checks if the conversion program is on the server. A call is made to the server machine (clerc1) and returns with a port number for access on the server. The client buffer is linked to the port number on the server. The call to AU.Create_Unix makes the client look like a Unix machine with a given user id and group id (the Gids is currently not implemented with the AdaLAN RPC version).

```
-- this package spec and body are placed on the client
-- machine

package Add_On_Client is
   procedure Add (First :  in  Integer; Second :   in Integer;
                  Result : out Integer; Overflow : out Boolean);
end Add_On_Client;


with AdaLAN_Error_Handler;
with AdaLAN_RPC_Client;
with XDR_Conversions;
with AdaLAN_RPC_Authent;
with AdaLAN_Std_XDR;


package body Add_On_Client is
   package EH    renames AdaLAN_Error_Handler;
   package RPC   renames AdaLAN_RPC_Client.UDP;
   package AU    renames AdaLAN_RPC_Authent;
   package SX    renames AdaLAN_Std_XDR;
   package XCON  renames XDR_Conversions;


   Null_Gids     : AU.Unix_Grouparr := null;
   Local_Machine : SX.Access_String := new String'("clerc2");
   Retry_Delay   : constant Duration := 5.0;


   -- only one task at a time may use package Add_On_Client
   Client       : RPC.Clients;
   Error_Status : EH.Allocate_Status (1024);


   procedure Add (First :  in  Integer; Second :   in  Integer;
                  Result : out Integer; Overflow : out Boolean)
                                                 is separate;

begin
   RPC.Create (Error_Status,
               Client,
               XCON.Program_Number,
               XCON.Version_Number,
               Retry_Delay,            -- time between retries
               "clerc1");              -- server machine
```

```
AU.Create_Unix (S         => Error_Status,
                Auth      => Client.Auth,
                Machine   => Local_Machine,
                Uid       => 1,
                Gid       => 17,
                Gids      => Null_Gids);
exception
   . . .
end Add_On_Client;
```

Figure 13-11.   Specification and Body of Add Environment on Client Machine

---

The implementation of the Add procedure on the client is shown in Figure 13-12. The generic RPC is instantiated with the Add procedure number, types for *in* and *out* parameters, and the conversion routines for the *in* and *out* parameters. The parameters in the RPC_Call_Add include error status to be returned, the buffer address of the client which is linked to the port address on the server, the input parameter which will be converted to XDR format before the call, and the output parameter containing the result.

```
separate (Add_On_Client)
   procedure Add (First :  in  Integer; Second :   in  Integer;
                  Result : out Integer; Overflow : out Boolean) is

       package XCON renames XDR_Conversions;
       In_Param  : XCON.Add_In := (First, Second);
       Out_Param : XCON.Add_Out;

       procedure RPC_Call_Add is new RPC.Call
                     (XCON.Add_Proc_Num,
                      XCON.Add_In,
                      XCON.Add_Out,
                      XCON.XDR_Add_In,
                      XCON.XDR_Add_Out);
   begin
       RPC_Call_Add (Error_Status, Client, In_Param, Out_Param);
       Result   := Out_Param.Result;
```

```
    Overflow := Out_Param.Overflow;
  exception

       . . .

  end Add;
```

Figure 13-12.   Implementation of Add on Client Machine

The modules to be loaded on the server machine include the same conversion functions as were loaded on the client machine, the various server functions and the actual implementation of the Add procedure. The server functions shown in Figure 13-13 include the procedure Dispatch and an instantiation of the RPC.UDP services. The procedure Dispatch is called from a low level port server (not included here), and is used in converting input parameters from XDR standard format to the server format, and from server format to XDR representation for the output parameters for the given function, i.e., Add in our case. The instantiation of RPC.UDP creates a task that waits for client calls. After this task is started, it calls a port mapping function to inform it that the RPC program exists and which port the task will wait on. Clients will find the server task via the RPC calls. The system will choose a port for the waiting server task (RPC.Anyport).

```
package Server_Functions is
end Server_Functions;


with AdaLAN_Error_Handler;
with AdaLAN_RPC_Types;
with AdaLAN_XDR_Memory;
with AdaLAN_RPC_Server;
with XDR_Conversions;


package body Server_Functions is
    package EH    renames AdaLAN_Error_Handler;
    package RT    renames AdaLAN_RPC_Types;
    package XM    renames AdaLAN_XDR_Memory;
    package RPC   renames AdaLAN_RPC_Server;
    package XCON  renames XDR_Conversions;

    Stack_Size : constant := 4000;
```

```
procedure Dispatch (Error_Status :   in EH.Status;
                    Proc_Num :       in out RT.Procnums;
                    XDR_In :         in out XM.Xdrs;
                    XDR_Out :        in out XM.Xdrs;
                    Accept_Status :  in out RT.Accept_Status)
                                             is separate;


package Example_RPC_Server is new RPC.UDP
                (XCON.Program_Number,
                 XCON.Version_Number,
                 RPC.Anyport,           -- system chooses port
                 Stack_Size,
                 Dispatch,
                 RPC.Authenticate_Default);
end Server_Functions;
```

Figure 13-13.   Server Functions (spec and body)

The implementation of the Dispatch procedure is shown in Figure 13-14. This procedure is called from the low level RPC services and provides for the required data transformations for a given function. The only function included in the case statement is for a procedure number that corresponds to the Add function. The case statement can be expanded to include other functions by adding procedure numbers. Conversions from XDR format to server format are provided by calling XDR_Add_In. A call is made to the actual Add function, and results are returned in server formats. Parameters to be returned to the client are converted to XDR format before they are placed on the network. The implementation of the actual Add function is shown in Figure 13-15. This is identical to the implementation on a uniprocessor.

```
with Add_On_Server;
separate (Server_Functions)

    procedure Dispatch (Error_Status :   in EH.Status;
                        Proc_Num :       in out RT.Procnums;
                        XDR_In :         in out XM.Xdrs;
                        XDR_Out :        in out XM.Xdrs;
                        Accept_Status :  in out RT.Accept_Status) is
```

```
      begin
         case Proc_Num is
            when XCON.Add_Proc_Num =>
               declare
                  In_Param  : XCON.Add_In;
                  Out_Param : XCON.Add_Out;
               begin
                  XCON.XDR_Add_In (Error_Status, XDR_In, In_Param);
                  Add_On_Server.Add (In_Param.First,
                                     In_Param.Second,
                                     Out_Param.Result,
                                     Out_Param.Overflow);
                  XCON.XDR_Add_Out (Error_Status, XDR_Out, Out_Param);
               end;
            when others =>
               Accept_Status := RT.Procedure_Unavailable;
         end case;
      exception
         . . .
      end Dispatch;
```

Figure 13-14.   Dispatch Procedure Body

```
package Add_On_Server is
   procedure Add (First  :  in  Integer; Second :   in  Integer;
                  Result : out Integer; Overflow : out Boolean);
end Add_On_Server;

package body Add_On_Server is
   procedure Add (First  :  in  Integer; Second :   in  Integer;
                  Result : out Integer; Overflow : out Boolean) is
   begin
      Overflow := False;
      Result   := First + Second;
   exception
      when Numeric_Error =>
         Overflow := True;
   end Add;
end Add_On_Server;
```

Figure 13-15.   Routine to Add Two Integers and Return the Result (package spec
and body on Server Machine)

The mini-design for the Add function illustrated in Figures 13-16 and 13-17 represents the calling hierarchy on the client and server machines, respectively. The required data transformations are shown by calls to XDR_Add_In and XDR_Add_Out. This design can be used as a model for implementing more complex RPC functions, such as remote entry calls used with the Ada rendezvous.

13.3 Message Passing

If neither REC nor RPC services are available, message passing can be implemented and accessed directly from the application layer. Message passing may also be used to implement the lower communication layers of either REC or RPC. It should be noted that message passing primitives are usually part of the run-time services used to support the Ada rendezvous on uniprocessors, completely invisible to the application code.

The emphasis in this section is to describe a message passing mechanism that can be used to support the communication of multiple Ada programs, as well as a possible implementation of an efficient communication kernel.

A message passing layer can replace the remote rendezvous layer of the REC approach or the RPC layer to keep the application code reasonably uncoupled from the communications protocol. In general, however, the application code is more tightly coupled to the communications protocol than in either of the other two models, and the code is less portable.

The choice of a specific set of message passing primitives is dependent on considerations such as whether sending and receiving messages should be blocking (synchronous) or non-blocking (asynchronous) operations, the naming conventions for source and destination tasks and node addresses, the message formats, and the detection and handling of communication failures.

A message passing mechanism for Ada has been suggested in [ROS87] using the model shown in Figure 13-18. The run-time executive services include a set of communication primitives, and are loaded on each of the processors that make up the distributed configuration. The Ada application tasks make blocking (synchronous) calls to send/receive primitives that transport messages between the tasks

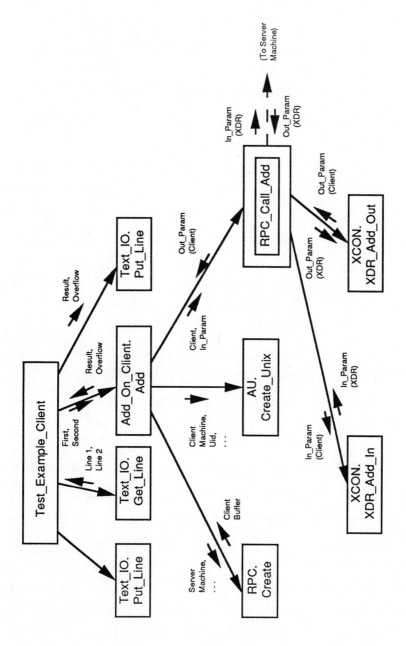

Figure 13-16.   Calls on Client Machine

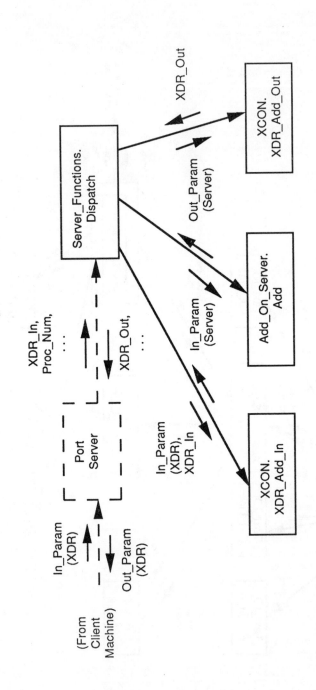

Figure 13-17.   Calls on Server Machine

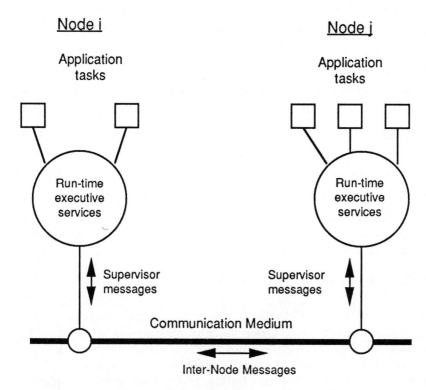

Figure 13-18.   Multi-Processor Message Passing

residing on the physical nodes i and j (the other nodes are not included in the figure).

A possible specification of message formats using a variant record
is shown in Figure 13-19. All of the messages will contain uniform
fields regardless of the message type, and another set of fields that
depend on the specific message. The variable fields are implemented
using the message type as the discriminant in the variant record.

```
package Global_Defs is

    . . .

    type Message_Types is (REC, Timed_REC, Conditional_REC, RPC);

    type Message_Format (Message : Message_Types) is
```

```
   record
       Msg_Source                : Task_Name;
       Msg_Dest                  : Task_Name;
       Msg_Source_Node           : Node_Address;
       Current_Senders_Master    : Task_Name;
       case Message is
          when REC =>
             . . .
          when RPC =>
             . . .

             . . .
       end case;
   end record;
   . . .
end Global_Defs;
```

Figure 13-19.   Message Formats

An implementation of a task to send messages is outlined in Figure 13-20. This solution assumes that the run-time services are included on each processor and that each processor stores a (partial) global view of the task states for the tasks residing on that physical node and (at least some of) the remote tasks they communicate with. The use of partial global views will minimize the amount of updates that will have to be made for communicating task states. It is also assumed that each task will initialize itself with a unique global identifier which can be used as a reference during execution.

```
with Global_Task_Map;
with Local_Task_Map;
with Global_Defs;

task body Send_Message is
   Temp_Msg : Global_Defs.Message_Format (RPC);
   . . .
begin
   Temp_Msg.Msg_Source      := <source task name>;
   Temp_Msg.Msg_Dest        := <destination task name>;
   Temp_Msg.Msg_Source_Node := <current node address>;
   . . .      -- other Temp_Msg fields
   if Temp_Msg.Msg_Dest has an entry in the Global_Task_Map then
```

```
    if Node_Address (Temp_Msg.Msg_Dest) = <current node address>
       then
       -- Msg_Dest is a local task
       Put Temp_Msg in local task map for Temp_Msg.Msg_Dest
    else
          -- Msg_Dest is not a local task.  Forward message
          -- to Msg_Dest
          Send (Temp_Msg, Node_Address (Temp_Msg.Msg_Dest));
    end if;
  else        -- Msg_Dest is not in global task map
       -- Set the value of the Current_Senders_Master field
       Temp_Msg.Current_Senders_Master :=
          Global_Task_Map.Master_Task (Temp_Msg.Msg_Source};
       while Node_Address (Temp_Msg.Current_Senders_Master) =
          <current node address>  loop
          Temp_Msg.Current_Senders_Master :=
             Global_Task_Map.Master_Task
                        (Temp_Msg.Current_Senders_Master);
       end loop;
       Send (Temp_Msg, Node_Address
                        (Temp_Msg.Current_Senders_Master));
  end if;
end Send_Message;
```

Figure 13-20.   Sending Algorithm

Data structures are maintained on each processor that describe the states of all the tasks with a global view (defined in package Global_Task_Map), as well as the tasks residing on each processor (defined in package Local_Task_Map). Definitions are made for source and destination information, and other values pertaining to the local message.

For the sending algorithm shown in Figure 13-20, a search is first made to see if the destination task has an entry in the global task map, and to determine if the communicating tasks reside on the same processor. If the destination is a local task, the message is entered in the local task map for the destination task. If the destination is not a local task, the message is sent to the node address listed in the global task map. If the destination task is not in the global task map, the sending task's master is located (this information about the source task is kept in the global task map; it is the destination task that is not in the global task map). The fact that the destination task is not yet in the global task map implies that it was created on another node. The lack of updating could be because the task is in the process of becoming activated, or migration may have taken place. When the remote node address of the sending task's master is found, the message is sent to the processor where the master is located. There is a high probability that the master of the source and the destination task will reside on the same processor, since the source task must have visibility to the destination task, and they may both be dependents of the same master.

The receiving algorithm shown in Figure 13-21 acts as both a receiver and forwarder. The global map is first updated with the node address of the source task. If the destination task is listed in the global map, a determination is made whether it is local or remote. If it is remote, the message is forwarded to the destination node address. If the destination task is not in the global map, it cannot be local to this node. A new location for the sender's master is found, and the message is forwarded to that node, and the forwarding continues until the node of the destination task is found. This method of updating the global task map as each new task is created and as a message is received, provides for a "self repairing" system, unless frequent migrations occur. With sporadic migrations the system gets a chance to catch up, and the amount of forwarding is minimized.

```
with Global_Task_Map;
with Local_Task_Map;
with Global_Defs;

task body Receive_Message is
    . . .
begin
    loop
        Receive (Temp_Msg);
        Update the global map with an entry for Temp_Msg.Msg_Source
            using the value of Temp_Msg.Msg_Source_Node;
        if Temp_Msg.Msg_Dest has an entry in the Global_Task_Map then
            if Node_Address (Temp_Msg.Msg_Dest) = <current node
                                                              address>
            then
                -- Msg_Dest is a local task
                Put Temp_Msg in local task map for Temp_Msg.Msg_Dest;
            else
                -- Msg_Dest is not a local task.  Forward
```

```
                -- message to Msg_Dest
                Send (Temp_Msg, Node_Address (Temp_Msg.Msg_Dest));
            end if;
        else      -- Msg_Dest is not in global task map
            -- Set the value of the Current_Senders_Master
            -- field
            Temp_Msg.Current_Senders_Master :=
                Global_Task_Map.Master_Task
                            (Temp_Msg.Current_Senders_Master};
            while Node_Address (Temp_Msg.Current_Senders_Master) =
                        <current node address>  loop
                Temp_Msg.Current_Senders_Master :=
                    Global_Task_Map.Master_Task
                        (Temp_Msg.Current_Senders_Master);
            end loop;
            Send (Temp_Msg, Node_Address
                        (Temp_Msg.Current_Senders_Master));
        end if;
    end loop;
end Receive_Message;
```

Figure 13-21.   Receive Algorithm

13.4 Summary

Some of the possible communication mechanisms between remote Ada virtual nodes include REC, RPC, and message passing. The specific mechanism employed for a given application depends on the communication services available for the chosen target configuration. The preferred mechanism is the REC since the Ada rendezvous can then be used without any restrictions, and the code will be portable between distributed systems, and it can also be readily ported from a uniprocessor system.

If the REC is not available, it can be created in Ada with a remote rendezvous layer that implements the lower level protocols. An alternative to the REC is the RPC mechanism made for Unix systems by Sun Microsystems. The RPC layer can replace the remote rendezvous layer of REC, or it can be used to implement the lower level protocols of the REC.

Synchronous or asynchronous message passing represent other alternatives for providing remote communication between virtual nodes. A set of general message passing primitives written in Ada are not readily available, and such an approach would probably be derived "from scratch" and closely tailored to a specific application.

Every effort should be made to shield the application nodes from the communication services. This provides a portable design that can be adapted for different targets and communication models. The REC approach provides the loosest coupling between the application code and the communication mechanism. If the application makes direct use of RPC services, the code is less portable than what we can accomplish with the REC. The least portable solution will occur with the use of message passing, since the application code will be making direct calls to the message passing services. These services will be target dependent, and the application code will have to be modified as the system is ported to another architecture.

The choice of a remote communication scheme will not be based entirely on the desire for creating portable code. An important design consideration for real-time systems is efficiency, and the available communication options must be evaluated with this in mind.

Up to this point in our design methodology we have focused on the creation of virtual nodes and the possible communication mechanisms between them. This represents the first phase of the software-first approach. In the next chapter we describe the selection of processors to support our software design, various distribution specifications, and the mapping of virtual nodes to processors. This represents the second phase of our overall design methodology.

14

Distribution Configuration

The basis for our software-first design methodology is that we first determine the architecture that has the highest possible correspondence to the requirements specification. For the kind of real-time systems we are considering, this architecture contains elements that will execute in parallel, and the solution is inherently concurrent. In a non-distributed environment a concurrent software architecture is implemented with apparent concurrency, where the parallel processes compete for the use of the same processor. The processes in a non-distributed environment reside in a single computer with sufficient resources to support the given application. In a distributed environment, however, we choose a set of processors that can best support the set of virtual nodes that have been identified. The system solution will exhibit real concurrency as the chosen processors execute in parallel during the operation of the application.

This chapter contains a discussion of how we choose a set of processors that will support the set of virtual nodes that represent the concurrent solution to the real-time system, and how we can map the virtual nodes to the chosen hardware configuration.

14.1 Processor Selection Rules

Each virtual node was created as a set of closely coupled tasks encapsulated in Ada packages. Other packages and subprograms were included in the virtual node to support the functionality of the tasks, and were designed for the maximum possible amount of modularity. Each virtual node is loosely coupled to the other virtual nodes via a message passing mechanism, REC, or RPC, but not through shared data. Some applications may be implemented with tightly coupled virtual nodes that share memory. In this case a mapping function may not be available (or even necessary), and the distribution is completely transparent to the application code.

The primary inefficiency in a distributed system is the amount of message communication that takes place between processors. The more data passed between the processors, the more overhead associated with the overall efficiency of the system. As the set of processors is chosen, it is not sufficient that they support the performance characteristics of their respective virtual nodes, they must also minimize the amount of data transfers between the processors. An underlying assumption in our selection process is that it is cost effective to include several processors and associated memory, and the necessary hardware links between them, compared to a single large computer. The choice of a distributed system has been based (aside from cost) on extensibility, modularity, ease of maintenance, and implementation of fault tolerance. The following criteria can be used as a guide in the selection of suitable processors for a given real-time system:

1. *Device drivers.* The external devices in a real-time system typically operate at widely differing speeds, and processors should be chosen to match these speeds. It is not cost effective to choose all the processors based on the fastest external device. Other considerations include the I/O mode of the device, i.e., whether it is an interrupt driven or a polling device. Interrupts must be handled immediately to prevent loss of data, whereas a polling function is less critical. A separate processor can be used to support each device driver.

2. *Special functions.* Some of the virtual nodes may represent special functions such as digital signal processing or a database application. Processors may be available that are optimized for these functions. That may include special RISC architectures that are tailored to these applications. A separate processor can be used for each function, or functions can be combined on the same processor.

3. *Time-critical functions.* Virtual nodes that contain time-critical functions require a fast processor that can accurately and effi-

ciently handle the starting and ending of timed events. This may be an executive with a low overhead for context switching and message passing in Ada rendezvous. We assume that the designers have minimized the number of Ada tasks that reside in these virtual nodes to keep the run-time overhead to an absolute minimum. A critical factor in the choice of processor is the timing accuracy of the executive for the expiration of a delay, and the termination and reactivation of tasks.

4. *Performance requirements.* Certain functions may be computation intensive, and a processor with the required MIPS or MFLOPS rating must be chosen. The required speed rating can usually be calculated from the given requirements.

5. *Processor homogeneity.* A typical distributed real-time system will usually consist of a mixture of heterogeneous processors of different word lengths and processing powers. If a reasonable choice can be made between homogeneous and heterogeneous processors, the former should be chosen to simplify the compilation, linking, and loading phases, and the communication interfaces. Where only different processing speeds are required, a family of processors can usually be chosen such as the Motorola 680x0 or Intel 80x86. The software development environment will most likely be uniform for all the processor elements within a given family. It is also likely to be easier to interface between the processors in a family than between heterogeneous processors made by different manufacturers. Another consideration that may weigh against heterogeneous systems is the added overhead of the transformations between the various data representations.

6. *Fault tolerance.* If fault tolerance is to be designed into the application, great care must be exercised in choosing the processors. Considerations must be given to redundant processors, redundant buses or LANs, and how difficult it will be to reconfigure the virtual nodes within the context of the run-time support and/or operating system. Tasks must be created and activated dynamically, and virtual node images must be reconfigured either to the redundant processors or to the remaining processors that have not yet failed.

7. *Expandability.* The capability of expanding the functionality of a system may influence the selection of processors and their

interfaces. A system using standard buses or LANs such as VMEbus, Multibus II, Futurebus, or Ethernet are easier to expand in a modular fashion than a system using customized buses and LANs. Here is another example of the advantage of using a processor family. An existing 68030 or 80386 processor, for example, may later be replaced by a 68040 or 80486, respectively, with only minimal impact on the real-time software architecture. The impact on the code generators and run-time support will depend on how different the next member of the family is, e.g., if it changes from a 16-bit to a 32-bit processor.

8. *Interfacing capabilities.* The interfacing capabilities between the distributed processors are extremely important characteristics in a real-time system. The bandwidth for data transfers between the processors must be sufficient, and there must be adequate control programs to prevent bus contentions from becoming a constraint in bus-based systems. If a LAN is chosen, not only is a sufficient bandwidth required, the overhead associated with the additional communication services must be within reasonable limits.

9. *Processor/memory compatibility.* The processor/memory combinations must be chosen with care. A fast processor with associated slow memory will most likely result in the processor remaining idle for one or more clock cycles and will not have the effective throughput of the processor's nominal MIPS rating. The tradeoff here is that the faster memory may become disproportionately expensive. Some of the faster processors with extremely high clock rates employ a combination of fast (expensive) cache memory and somewhat slower (less expensive) primary memory for an effective zero wait state operation.

10. *Physical location and size constraints.* It is sometimes desirable to place a processing element physically close to a sensor or actuator, e.g., at an axis where a robot arm is moved or in a heat-seeking missile. The choice of processor and memory may be limited by the restrictions imposed by the physical environment, and the smallest possible configuration with the highest MIPS or MFLOPS to support the performance requirements will be the preferred choice. The physical location of the various processors will also determine how they should be interfaced. If all the processors fit within the same chassis, they can be connected via high-speed buses. If they are distributed

throughout a building, however, one or more LANs will be required.

These selection rules are not all inclusive, but form a good basis for making the proper selection of the hardware configuration. This is not an easy task and should be done in cooperation with hardware engineers who fully understand the characteristics of various microprocessor chip designs and how they should be interfaced.

14.2   Node Specification and Mapping

The method used to specify virtual and physical nodes, and the mapping of virtual nodes to physical nodes, is highly dependent on the software tools available for these functions. This ranges from a completely manual downloading of multiple Ada programs, to an automated distribution and load balancing of a single Ada program. Somewhere between these two extremes is the use of compiler directives (pragmas) and a separate specification language. These two approaches are discussed in the paragraphs that follow.

14.2.1   Use of Ada Pragmas

Pragmas can be used to specify a distributed system without any restrictions on the use of Ada regarding the rendezvous and shared memory. One such scheme has been proposed in [VIS88] for a loosely coupled distributed system (single Ada program using the rendezvous for task communication), where tasks are allocated to processors in a hierarchical order:

1. The first pragma is placed in the main program ("environment task") and specifies the number of processors required for this application:

    ```
    pragma Processor_Allocation (N);
    ```

    where N is an integer value that is less than or equal to the total number of processors available. The compiler keeps track of the number of processors allocated in subordinate tasks, such that the total number allocated can never exceed the total number of processors available.

2. Another pragma is used to specify the possible connections between the processors:

```
pragma Processor_Connection (A, B);
```

where A and B are processor identification numbers (or symbolic names) that can be connected in the topography. The compiler will know whether the connections are bidirectional or unidirectional, and can construct a suitable NxN matrix (only the L or U part of the matrix may be required) from the Processor_Allocation and Processor_Connection pragmas.

The allocation of subnets for dependent tasks is performed hierarchically. For statically declared tasks, the compiler checks if the required subnet can be constructed from the remaining processors. For dynamically declared tasks, the run-time support uses the subnets created at compile time to check if the current subnet can be constructed from the remaining processors belonging to the parent's subnet. If the subnet cannot be constructed, the program is aborted by the RTS. The programmer must ensure that sufficient processors are available for the required connections when tasks are declared dynamically. For static declarations, the compiler will check for processor resources and the required connections between them.

3. A third pragma is used to map the tasks (if tasks are allowed as distributable elements) to the processors:

```
pragma Task_Mapping (T[(i)], P);
```

where T is a task name, and P is a processor identification (or symbolic name). The task name specification may include an instantiation of a task type and an index to an array of tasks. A virtual node can be constructed by mapping multiple tasks to the same processor. The *withing* of packages and subprograms will import the required support modules, and will effectively create a virtual node without an actual specification. Elements of an array of tasks may be assigned to different processors. The same task name cannot appear in more than one Task_Mapping pragma.

The combination of the Processor_Connection and Task_Mapping pragmas will create a complete logical network of the tasks. No specific ordering is required between multiple occurrences of these two pragmas since the complete static topography is determined during compilation. Dynamically created tasks are assumed to reside on the same processor as their respective masters and do not require any mapping specifications.

The above approach is straightforward to implement. The language can be used as currently specified without any extensions or modifications. It is the programmer's responsibility to have sufficient memory associated with each processor. If lack of memory is detected during the loading phase, this phase is aborted with an appropriate error message. When these pragmas are supported for a given target architecture, it is implied that a single Ada program can be distributed as a set of loosely coupled nodes, and that remote entry calls are transparent to the application.

The use of pragmas to specify the allocation of tasks to processors has some serious disadvantages, however. Binding between virtual and physical nodes is performed at compilation time and does not support fault tolerance and load balancing. Reconfiguration of tasks cannot readily be performed dynamically, and when a fault is detected, appropriate alerts and error messages can be created, but the system must be halted to correct the fault. Another disadvantage is that the code is non-portable. Different Ada vendors will support different pragmas, and a given solution can usually not be ported to another hardware architecture (with a different compilation and runtime support) without redesign or reprogramming.

14.2.2 Separate Distribution Specification

Another way to specify the configuration of processors and the mapping of virtual nodes and tasks to processors is to use a separate distribution specification tool. This differs from the use of pragmas by not including any non-portable statements with the application program, and utilizes one of the software development tools (assuming one is available!). Another advantage with this approach is that the language specification does not have to be extended or modified, and Ada code originally designed for a uniprocessor system can readily be used for a distributed system.

Various approaches to separate distribution specification tools have been developed as research projects [TED84, JHA89, and ATK88], but no standard set of specifications has emerged, and no commercial implementations are yet available. The paragraphs that follow contain an outline of the approach described in [JHA89] for the Ada Program Partitioning Language (APPL). This approach will support our two-step software-first design methodology with the distribution of a single Ada program after the software design is complete.

The APPL specification uses a non-procedural notation where the target hardware is viewed as a collection of interconnected physical nodes, and an Ada program is a collection of mutually exclusive virtual nodes ("fragments"). APPL provides facilities for partitioning an Ada program into virtual nodes and for mapping these nodes to the physical nodes. An APPL configuration unit is structured like an Ada package with separate specification and body. The specification part includes the definition of virtual nodes (fragments), and the body maps fragments to physical nodes.

An outline of an Ada program for the "Dining Philosophers" problem [GEH84] is shown in Figure 14-1, and the corresponding APPL program in Figure 14-2. The main program Dining_Philosophers and Text_IO are assigned to the physical node Central_Node. Virtual nodes for the philosopher tasks (Philosophers) are specified with fragment constructs and mapped to separate physical nodes. The package Text_IO is included via the importation clause in the main program. In general, any dependent library unit is implicitly included with the fragment that imports it and does not have to be specified separately as a fragment.

```
with Text_IO;
procedure Dining_Philosophers is
    subtype Id is Integer range 1 .. 5;

    task Host is . . .;
    task type Fork is . . .;
    task type Philosopher is . . .;

    Forks       : array (Id) of Fork;
    Philosophers : array (Id) of Philosopher;
    . . .

end Dining_Philosophers;
```

Figure 14-1.   Skeleton Program of Dining Philosophers

```
-- Configuration specification

with Dining_Philosophers;
configuration Configuration_Example is
   fragment Philosopher_1 is
      use Dining_Philosophers;
      Philosophers (1);
   end Philosopher_1;
   . . .
   fragment Philosopher_5 is . . .;
end Configuration_Example;

-- Configuration body
configuration body Configuration_Example is
   map Philosopher_1 onto Node_1;
   . . .
   map Philosopher_5 onto Node_5;
   map Dining_Philosophers onto Central_Node;
end Configuration_Example;
```

Figure 14-2.   Distribution Specification for Dining_Philosophers

Ada entities that can be assigned to a fragment include packages, tasks, subprograms, static objects, and dynamically created objects. Objects created during execution can be assigned to the same processor that is host for the allocator, or a mapping function can be called to determine the physical node. The use of function calls in the mapping of fragments to processors can facilitate program reconfiguration during execution. Whenever a reconfiguration is required, the entire set of mapping constructs in the configuration body is executed, with a potentially new assignment for a given fragment. For example,

```
map Read_Furnace onto Next_Available_Node;
```

where Next_Available_Node is a function call that will return a physical node result of a suitable type.

14.3 Summary

The second phase of our overall design methodology is to select a set of processors to support the real-time solution, and to map the virtual nodes developed during the first phase to the processors.

A set of processor selection rules can be used as an aid in determining the proper hardware architecture. This will usually require the services of hardware engineers who fully understand the characteristics of various microprocessor chip designs and how they should be interfaced.

The distribution mechanisms described include the use of pragmas and a separate specification. Both of these methods support our software-first design methodology and the distribution of a single Ada program. The primary problem with using these approaches is that they are not yet available as commercial products, and a potential user will have to implement the underlying compilation, linking, and loading services. This is no simple task in a heterogeneous environment where multiple code generators are required to create code from a single program for a variety of processors.

15

Decomposition of Large Tasks

The process abstraction effort culminates with a concurrency model of a set of cooperating Ada tasks encapsulated in Ada packages. Each of these tasks has a single thread of control (although they may declare nested task objects dynamically during system operation). Each application task represents a major portion of the system requirements, and may have too large a functionality to be expressed as code statements within its task body. Each task body will by convention be limited to a certain (approximate) number of lines of Ada code statements, and will have to be decomposed if the approximate line count is exceeded. This chapter describes the Layered Virtual Machine/Object-Oriented Design (LVM/OOD) approach [SHU88, NIE88] to decomposing large Ada tasks into packages and subprograms to support the functionality of a given task. An Ada package taxonomy is used to classify the various types of packages used in real-time systems. The LVM/OOD method is used to create the necessary support packages classified in the taxonomy.

15.1 Ada Package Taxonomy

The package categories shown in Figure 15-1 include all the different types of packages required for the design of a real-time system in

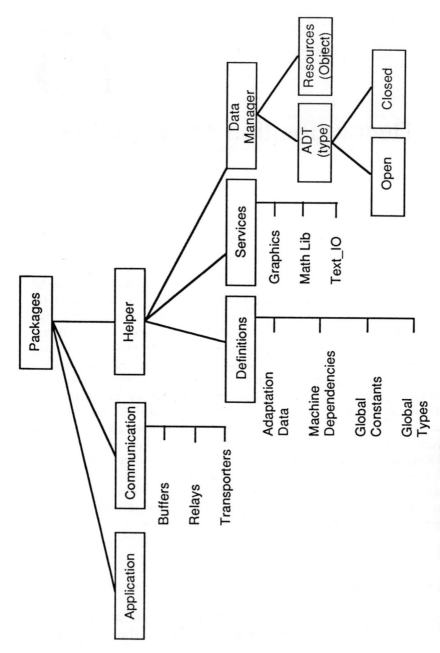

Figure 15-1.   Classification of Ada Packages

Ada. Communication packages encapsulate buffer tasks and various other special communication tasks. Application packages contain the tasks that represent the functionality of the requirements specification, including device drivers and interrupt handlers. Helper packages include special services packages, definitions packages, and data managers. The packages in the latter three subcategories support the functionality of the tasks encapsulated in communication and application packages. Special service packages and data managers are of particular importance in the decomposition of large Ada tasks. Definitions packages are created to support globally visible adaptation data, global constants, global types, etc., and will be imported by *with*ing by the packages, subprograms, and tasks that need these global elements. The details of the construction of the various types of data managers, for example, open and closed Abstract Data Types (ADTs), is covered in [NIE88]. The next section describes the task decomposition approach and the creation of the required helper packages and subprograms.

15.2   Layered Virtual Machine/Object-Oriented Design

The concept of layered virtual machines was first reported by Dijkstra [DIJ68a] for the construction of the "THE" operating system. His notion of a proper software architecture was based on a set of hierarchical layers, where each layer only depended upon the layer underneath. Changes implemented in a given layer should only have a minimal impact upon other modules using the services of the primitives in the changing layer. His discussion also included the incorporation of objects, and the balanced treatment of algorithms and data structures during the early stages of the design phase.

Layered virtual machines can be created at different levels of abstraction. We have already seen examples of layered virtual machines in the form of cooperating sequential processes based on process abstraction and application packages as major design objects (see, for example, Figures 12-5 and 12-8). For the present purpose, we will be employing functional (or procedural) abstraction and data abstraction in the decomposition of the large Ada tasks. The functional abstraction will result in a set of layered high level instructions, i.e., procedure calls and function invocations, that will support a hierarchy of layered virtual machines. A virtual machine in this context will consist of a set of abstract instructions that will solve a given problem, i.e., support the implementation of the functionality of the specific virtual machine. The instructions will consist of lower level virtual machines (subprogram calls), and operations on objects. The operations are, typically, encapsulated in abstract data types.

The layered virtual machines can be expressed graphically with a traditional structure chart as shown in Figure 15-2 for the drawing of an image [NIE88]. A unique feature that applies to Ada designs is the use of "dot" notation for the names of the instructions (operations) that are imported from other packages. As an example, the instructions Mark, Space, and Next_Line are all imported from the package Printer. Similarly, Print, Clear, and Mark_Position are imported from the package Image. We note that operations belonging to the same package may be used at different layers.

Concurrently with the functional abstraction that will create the hierarchy of layered machines, we must also take data abstraction into account. Data abstraction is concerned with data types, data values, and operations on instances of objects of the given types. The instructions that support the functions of a virtual machine use the operations of the objects that represent specific data abstractions. To decompose large Ada tasks we have a parallel concern for functional abstraction with a resulting hierarchy of layered virtual machines, and data abstraction with a resulting set of packages that encapsulate that abstraction. This parallelism is illustrated in Figure 15-3 and shows the intimate linking between the virtual machines and the operations on objects. The left side of this figure shows the layered virtual machines, and the right side the objects that represent the data abstraction. The graphical object representation is referred to as an Ada architecture diagram, and was originally proposed by Booch [BOO83]. The virtual machine instructions make use of the operations visible on the object (Ada package) boundary. A given object may use lower level objects to support its operations, but this would be invisible to the virtual machine instructions.

The approach to the decomposition of large Ada tasks is to develop, in parallel, the hierarchy of virtual machine instructions, and the objects and their operations that support these instructions. The functional decomposition proceeds according to the guidelines of traditional structured design [YOU79], and the resulting hierarchy is illustrated with structure charts. Every effort is made to organize the instructions (Ada subprogram calls) that support a higher level virtual machine in horizontal layers. This will allow only a minimal impact on the virtual machine if any of the instructions are modified.

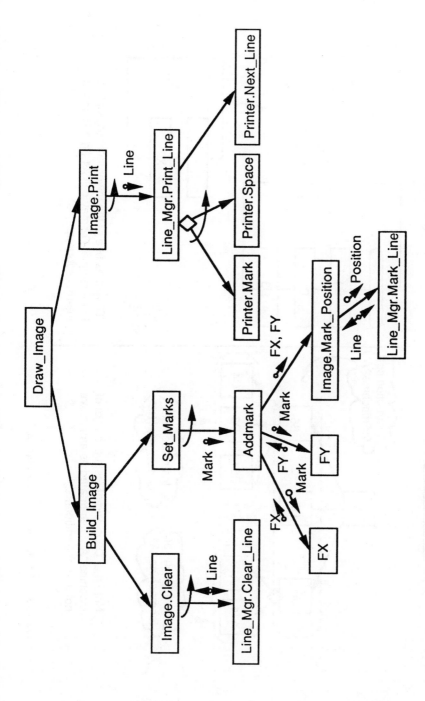

Figure 15-2.   Layered Virtual Machines

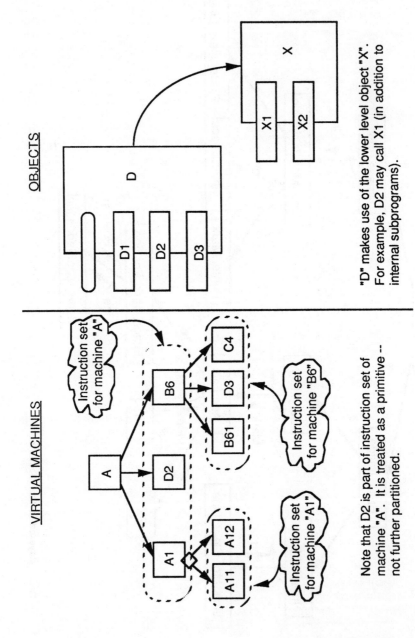

Figure 15-3.   Virtual Machines and Objects

The data abstractions used to support the virtual machine instructions are created with Ada packages in the form of data managers listed in Figure 15-1. Service packages may also be used to support the virtual machine instructions. The operations are declared in the package specification, and the implementations are hidden in the package body. The actual data objects may be internal to the package for object managers (or resources), or declared externally by the user of the object for type managers (abstract data types). The creation of the various types of Ada data managers is described in [NIE88].

To illustrate the decomposition approach, we use the robot controller as an example. The process abstraction model is shown in the process structure chart in Figure 15-4, and the encapsulated Ada tasks are shown in the Ada package graph in Figure 15-5. As a decomposition example, the functional abstraction of the task CP_Processor is depicted in Figure 15-6. The first layer of instructions to support this virtual machine (the task CP_Processor) include Dequeue, Validate_Panel_Input, Send_Input_Command, and Send_Panel_Output. The first instruction is an operation in the generically instantiated package Buffer_Panel_Input, and the remaining instructions are encapsulated in the package CP_Manager. It is important that the instructions be associated with their respective packages in the structure chart, and we have already mentioned the use of dot notation for this purpose. A second layer of instructions has been created to support the virtual machine Validate_Panel_Input. These instructions have been declared as procedures inside the package body of CP_Manager (this is illustrated with Ada PDL below).

The Ada PDL for CP_Processor and its decomposition is shown in Figures 15-7 to 15-9. The package specification and body of CP_Processing shown in Figure 15-7 include declarations for the task CP_Processor and the nested package CP_Manager. In our example, the task CP_Processor is the top-level virtual machine, and the package CP_Manager the object. The (separate) implementation of the task body is described in Figure 15-8, and shows the instructions (procedure calls) that support this task (top-level virtual machine). The package body of CP_Manager is given in Figure 15-9, and includes the two lower level instructions Determine_Command and Validate_Command to support the operation Validate_Panel_Input. An internal state variable is declared and is hidden from users of the operations.

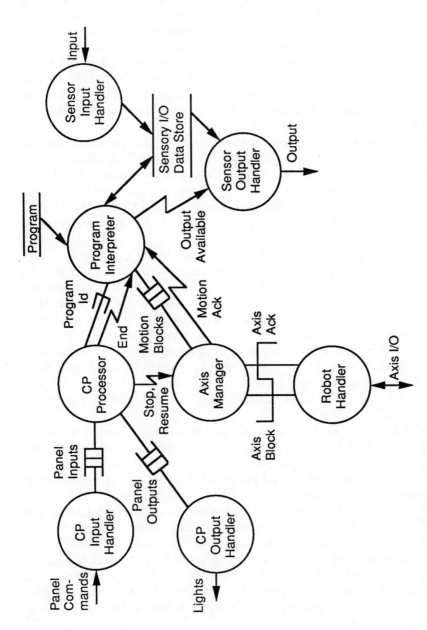

Figure 15-4.   Processor Structure Chart

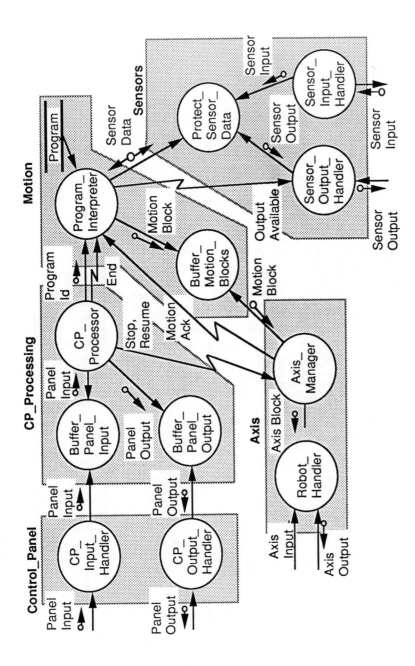

Figure 15-5.   Ada Package Graph

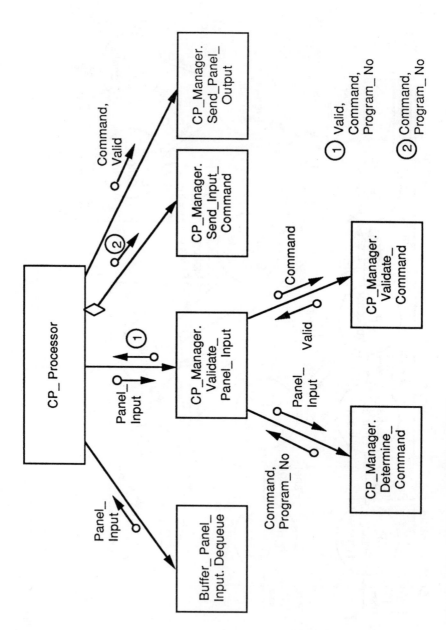

Figure 15-6.   CP_Process Structure Chart

```
with Definitions;   use Definitions;
package CP_Processing is
   procedure Take_CP_Input (T : in CP_Input);
   procedure Provide_CP_Output (CP_Out : out CP_Output_Code);
   -- Calls
      -- Motion.Start_Program
      -- Motion.End_Event
      -- Axis.Stop
      -- Axis.Resume
end CP_Processing;


with Buffer_Overwrite;
package body CP_Processing is
   task CP_Processor is
      -- Calls
         -- Buffer_Panel_Input.Dequeue
         -- Validate_Panel_Input
         -- Send_Input_Command
         -- Send_Panel_Output
   end CP_Processor;

-- Instantiate buffer task for CP input
      package Buffer_Panel_Input is new Buffer_Overwrite
         (Size = Max_CP_Input,
          Item = CP_Input);

-- Instantiate buffer task for CP output
      package Buffer_Panel_Output is new Buffer_Overwrite
         (Size = Max_CP_Output,
          Item = CP_Output_Code);


   package CP_Manager is
      procedure Validate_Panel_Input
                        (Panel_Input : in      CP_Input;
                         Valid       : out     Boolean;
                         Command     : in out CP_Command;
                         Program_No  : out     Program_Id);
```

```
      procedure Send_Input_Command
                     (Command : in out CP_Command;
                      Id      : in      Program_Id);
      procedure Send_Panel_Output
                     (Command : in out CP_Command;
                      Valid   : in      Boolean);
   end CP_Manager;


   package body CP_Manager is separate;
   task body CP_Processor  is separate;


   procedure Take_CP_Input (T : in CP_Input) is
   begin
      Buffer_Panel_Input.Enqueue (T);
   end Take_CP_Input;


   procedure Provide_CP_Output (CP_Out : out CP_Output_Code) is
   begin
      Buffer_Panel_Output.Dequeue (CP_Out);
   end Provide_CP_Output;

end CP_Processing;
```

Figure 15-7.   CP_Processing (package specification and body)

```
separate (CP_Processing)

task body CP_Processor is
   use CP_Manager;
   Panel_Input : CP_Input;
   Valid       : Boolean;
   Command     : CP_Command;
   Program_No  : Program_Id;
begin
   loop
      Buffer_Panel_Input.Dequeue (Panel_Input);
      Validate_Panel_Input (Panel_Input, Valid, Command,
                            Program_No);
      if Valid then
         Send_Input_Command (Command, Program_No);
      end if;
```

```
        Send_Panel_Output (Command, Valid);
    end loop;
end CP_Processor;
```

Figure 15-8.   CP_Processor (task body)

```
separate (CP_Processing)

package body CP_Manager is
    type State_Type  is (Manual, Running, Suspended);
    State_Variable : State_Type := Manual;

    procedure Determine_Command
                    (Panel_Input : in      CP_Input;
                     Command     : in out CP_Command;
                     Program_No  : out     Program_Id) is separate;

    procedure Validate_Command
                    (Command : in out CP_Command;
                     Valid   : out     Boolean) is separate;

    procedure Validate_Panel_Input
                    (Panel_Input : in      CP_Input;
                     Valid       : out     Boolean;
                     Command     : in out CP_Command;
                     Program_No  : out     Program_Id) is separate;

    procedure Send_Input_Command
                    (Command : in out CP_Command;
                     Id      : in      Program_Id) is separate;

    procedure Send_Panel_Output
                    (Command : in out CP_Command;
                     Valid   : in      Boolean) is separate;
end CP_Manager;
```

Figure 15-9.   CP_Manager (package body)

As a summary of the steps of LVM/OOD for decomposing large tasks, we can list the following:

1. Invent a machine, i.e., a set of instructions, that will solve the problem. This is done by employing functional decomposition as suggested by the principles of structured design. Consider the data abstraction in parallel with the creation of the instructions. The virtual machine is expressed as a set of Ada subprogram calls, incorporated with some simple logical expressions. The hierarchical structure of the machine is represented graphically with structure charts.

2. For each instruction of the virtual machine, determine if that instruction is an operation on an object or a lower level virtual machine. If it is an operation, create the corresponding object. If it is a virtual machine, continue the functional decomposition as outlined in step 1.

3. Implement the objects determined in step 2. Lower level objects may become apparent, and the functional decomposition of step 1 can be employed. The objects are expressed as a set of Ada packages and subprograms. The operations are declared in the package specification, with the implementation hidden in the package body. Specific types of data managers (i.e., object managers vs. type managers) depend on the type of support required for the virtual machines (see [NIE88] for details). The structure of the objects is expressed graphically in Ada architecture diagrams.

15.3 Summary

Our initial design efforts of the two major phases (described in earlier chapters) are primarily devoted to the determination of a process abstraction model, the creation of virtual nodes, the selection of processors, and the mapping of virtual nodes to processors. Another major design effort is the determination of the proper decomposition of the Ada tasks that represent the concurrent elements of the real-time system.

The LVM/OOD approach is used as a methodology for the decomposition of large Ada tasks. This approach combines the elements of functional abstraction and the use of structure charts, with data abstraction and the use of Ada package architecture charts. There is thus a parallel concern with the construction of algorithms and the associated data structures. Functional abstraction is used to create the layered virtual machines in the form of a set of instructions at each layer.

The layered virtual machines are represented with traditional structure charts, modified to express the encapsulation of operations in Ada packages. The data abstractions are created with packages that encapsulate operations that manipulate data structures (objects) of a certain type. The data structures themselves are typically hidden within the package body of each abstract data type, and the user (caller) of the operations cannot access the individual data elements. This supports the construction of highly modular systems with loose coupling between the modules. The objects that represent the data abstractions are illustrated with Ada package architecture charts.

16

Fault Tolerance

A general definition of a fault tolerant system is one that can continue to operate (at least partially) after a failure has occurred. A failure can be caused by either a hardware fault or a software error. The degree of reliability required in real-time systems varies considerably, from extremely short operational durations in avionics applications to continuous performance in tracking systems and processing plants. Fault tolerance mechanisms built into the application can reduce the probability of a total failure, but can never eliminate the causes of a failure.

The real-time systems we are considering have a requirement to tolerate hardware failures during their operation to continue the execution and to preserve data integrity. Software errors are another source of failure and represent design or coding errors. They are unrelated to hardware faults and usually require (at least partial) shutdown of the system to determine the cause of the failure, and to repair the software either by "patching" or by a complete reconfiguration.

The probability of a fatal hardware fault occurring in a real-time system can be reduced by designing fault tolerant hardware architectures into the system solution. These approaches include the use of dual buses or communication media and redundant processors. The basic design premise is to avoid a single point of failure in the architecture. Software error tolerance schemes have been described by *recovery blocks* and assertions [RAN75] and *n-version programming* with voting schemes [CHE78]. The approach we describe below is not concerned with how to build fault tolerant hardware architectures, or with making the software fault tolerant. Our primary concern is: given a hardware fault, how to detect the fault, and how to reconfigure the Ada software to continue the operation of the system.

It should be recognized that any one of the schemes introduced below is associated with a certain amount of processing overhead during execution. This may not be acceptable in certain hard real-time systems. The only solution for these systems will be to use a hardware architecture that promotes fault tolerance *and* is efficient enough to satisfy the real-time constraints. No processing overhead due to extra application software is experienced by these systems.

The sections that follow contain some general considerations for building fault-tolerant Ada systems, a discussion of failure detection schemes, some concerns and guidelines regarding Ada failure semantics, and conclude with some specific reconfiguration and data consistency schemes.

16.1 General Considerations

Distributed systems offer excellent opportunities for implementing fault tolerant mechanisms, where functions can be regenerated and relocated to other processors that have not failed. Redundant processors can also be used to replace the ones that are failing (this approach can also be used with uniprocessor systems). The general scheme for providing fault tolerance includes the following steps:

1. *Failure detection.* The failing processor must be identified as soon as possible before the remaining system is corrupted.

2. *Fault diagnosis.* An immediate assessment must be made of the extent of the damage, and data must be generated that can effect a possible recovery.

3. *Recovery.* Based on the data created during the diagnostic phase, an attempt is made to restore the system to its full or reduced operational state. This may include load balancing, aborting and creating tasks, restoring critical data elements, and creating message data for later analysis. The execution of a recovery scheme is based on the implementation of a specific failure semantics. Since the ARM does not include such seman-

tics, the recovery rules become a part of the overall design decisions that must be made for the given application.

Before a suitable failure semantics and recovery scheme can be determined, we need to specify a set of basic assumptions regarding the failure detection. These assumptions include:

1. Failure detection will be limited to one or more failed processors (and associated memory), and does not include the detection of a software error in a specific Ada component. If an expected response from a processor is not received as expected, it is assumed that all the software components on that processor must be reconfigured.

2. Once a processor has failed, it cannot be restarted.

3. Data recovery must be based on data residing in the remaining (healthy) processors.

4. In a tightly coupled system (shared data), all the data for the application is lost if global (shared) memory fails.

5. In a loosely coupled system, only the local data associated with the failed processor is lost.

16.2 Failure Detection

Ada has no failure semantics, and any desired error detection and correction features that will support fault tolerance have to be designed and integrated with the application. Exception handling in Ada cannot be relied upon to provide fault tolerance. Even if exceptions are propagated between processors, an exception intended to detect a processor failure may never be raised because it happens to reside on the failing processor. On the other hand, an exception intended to report a processor failure, and that would normally be propagated to another processor, may never be handled because the destination processor has also failed. Ada exceptions may be used as part of an error detection and recovery scheme, but are only supporting the overall fault tolerance approach.

Ada exceptions can be raised if an expected reply message is not received from another processor within a given time. This could be effected with a *delay* statement using a specified expiration interval or by sending fake messages [KNI87]. The condition of no reply is then used to deduce that the server processor has failed, and recovery procedures will be initiated with the raising of an appropriate user defined exception in the healthy processor. A similar deduction can be made if an exception handler for the predefined exception Tasking_Error is activated in a client task. This would indicate that the attempted rendezvous with the remote server task had failed and, thus, that the processor hosting the server task had failed. The recovery process would be initiated by an appropriate call from the exception handler to the recovery module.

Another failure detection mechanism has been suggested in [KNI87] where the Ada run-time support (RTS) detects a hardware failure and sends an "interrupt" to a predefined task entry. The parameters in the entry call would include the identification of the specific hardware element that has failed. The accept body of the waiting task will then initiate the reconfiguration steps. A variation of this approach is described in [ARE89] and is referred to as the "Death Notice Mechanism." Whenever a task wants to be informed about the death of another task, it specifies a specific entry point to the run-time support, and waits to be called at that entry if the condition occurs. A recovery can then be initiated following the entry call.

16.3 Failure Semantics

Even though Ada failure semantics will be designed uniquely for each application, some general guidelines for the construction of Ada fault-tolerant systems can be given.

Some of the Ada language features that promote good software design actually make the implementation of fault tolerance more complex. An example is the separate specification and body of a task, with potentially different contexts.

The different semantic contexts of a task complicate failure semantics: the creator of the task may be on one processor, its master on another, and the task itself on a third. To fully restore a lost task may require complete knowledge of all three different contexts.

Another complication occurs if the main procedure includes declarations of tasks that are distributed to other processors. If the context of the main procedure is lost, this could imply that the complete program must be recovered since all the tasks whose masters are not in library packages are dependent on the main procedure.

The recovery of a lost task could be made much simpler if we establish a set of guidelines for task contexts and the distribution of tasks. Such guidelines will include:

1. The main procedure should not include any task declarations or global variables, and should only have a *null* statement in the executable part. This implies that we only use the main procedure to start the elaboration process. If the context of this procedure is lost with a faulty processor, it will not affect the context of the rest of the application modules. We only have to recover the tasks that are co-located with the main procedure on the processor that failed.

2. All application tasks should be embedded in library packages. This separates the task masters and aligns them with the major application packages. Library packages and their embedded tasks are then independent of the main program. The fact that task termination is not defined for tasks in library packages is not a problem, since the typical real-time application is intended to run "forever" anyway.

3. Child tasks should be distributed with their masters whenever possible. This will reduce the complexity of determining proper task context for task recovery. It will also support the Ada semantics for the abortion of a master task, which assumes that all the master's children are also aborted.

The guidelines suggested above are fully supported by the design methodology specified in earlier chapters. The application packages we create as major design objects contain the tasks that represent the natural concurrent elements of the system, and these packages are library units (with task masters independent of the main program). The distribution granularity of virtual nodes supports the notion of collecting the masters and their children on the same processor, and thus simplifies the task contexts.

16.4 Task Recovery and Reconfiguration

A general approach (as suggested in [KNI87]) is to have one or more (normally idle) tasks that are dedicated to fault tolerance on each processor. One of these tasks will detect the failure of a neighboring processor, and will send the processor number to other tasks that will attempt the recovery procedures. The deletion or creation of tasks is performed using the abort statement to eliminate tasks on failed processors, and an allocator with access types or declare blocks and task types is used to reconfigure new tasks. If a task is aborted (i.e., removed from the task tables in the RTS) and a new task created with the same name and entries, the callers can continue to make the same entry calls, since the task tables are updated with the new location of the recovered task.

A reconfiguration scheme may be implemented using Ada's exception handling. A calling task will include a handler for the Tasking_Error exception that will be raised in a task that is terminated. The caller issues a call to a configuration manager and gets the identity of a replacement task. This replacement is already running, but is not yet known to the rest of the system. The task tables must be updated with the location of the replacement task such that the other tasks (in addition to the caller who detected the failure) can continue to call the restored task. The name and entries of the restored task should be made the same as the failed task; this makes the restoration transparent to the callers.

16.5 Data Consistency

To retain data consistency when a processor fails requires different approaches depending on whether the distributed system is tightly or loosely coupled.

In a tightly coupled system, no data recovery is required provided adequate redundant backup data is available on a different processor than the one that failed. The location of physical memory is transparent to the tasks and subprograms, which are only referencing virtual memory. The switching of memory areas is handled by the runtime support and not by the application code.

In a loosely coupled system, the data recovery scheme becomes much more complex, and various forms of data redundancy of local data will have to be implemented in the application. Only essential data need to be recovered, and this implies that only a portion of each local memory must be replicated. Data that is frequently updated with sensor inputs, for example, need not be replicated and recovered in the case of a failure. One way to identify essential data elements is to use a pragma [KNI87]:

```
pragma Essential_Data (Data_Element_1, Data_Element_2, . . .);
```

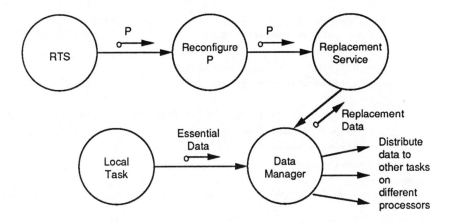

Figure 16-1.   Maintaining Consistent Data Among Processors

and copies of these elements will be maintained by the run-time support on all the processors. This is a straightforward mechanism for maintaining data consistency, but it is potentially inefficient depending on the amount of data specified as essential for a given application.

An alternate approach is to provide a set of programming tools [KNI87] that allow a local task to broadcast the data elements that are deemed essential to the other processors. The tools also include recovery modules that can be used when a failure occurs. The general scheme is illustrated in Figure 16-1. A local task sends its essential data to a data manager, which, in turn, sends the data to the other processors for updating. When a failure occurs, the run-time support sends a message with the identification of the failed processor to the reconfiguration manager. This manager calls a replacement service task which consults a task/processor mapping table to determine the proper data manager to query for recovery data. A skeleton Ada code segment for the local data manager is shown in Figure 16-2, and the replacement service for processor P is shown in Figure 16-3.

```
task body Data_Manager_P is

. . .

begin
    loop
        select
```

```
            accept Receive_Data (Data : in Data_Input_Type) do
               -- receive essential data.
            end Receive_Data;
            -- distribute to the other tasks on the
            -- various (healthy) processors
        or
            accept Provide_Data (Data : out Data_Output_Type) do
               -- provide data to a replacement task
            end Provide_Data;
         end select;
      end loop;
end Data_Manager_P;
```

Figure 16-2.   Local Data Manager

```
task body Replacement_Service is
. . .
begin
   loop
      accept Initiate_Replacement (Id : in Processor_Id) do
         Processor := Id;
      end Initiate_Replacement;
      -- consult task/processor table for Processor
         . . .
      Data_Manager_P.Provide_Data (. . .);
         . . .
   end loop;
end Replacement_Service;
```

Figure 16-3.   Replacement Service for Processor P

16.6   Use of Agent Tasks

Our basic assumption of the preservation of the rendezvous between nodes implies a client/server relation for the calling and called task, respectively. If the client task resides on a processor that fails, the state of the server may become inconsistent without the possibility of a state recovery. Barnes [BAR89] has proposed a solution to this

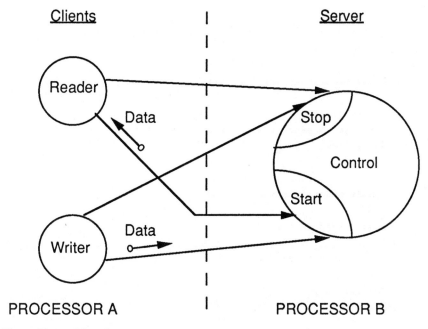

Figure 16-4.   Client/Server Model for Reader/Writer problem

problem (in the context of a client being aborted) by introducing an agent task that operates on behalf of the server, and independent of the scope of the client. The client/server interface is procedural, rather than via a direct rendezvous. The abortion of a task on a uniprocessor system is equivalent to the loss of a task residing on a processor that fails in a distributed system.

The relation between the client and server tasks is illustrated for the classical Reader/Writer problem [BAR89] in Figure 16-4, where the client (calling) tasks (readers and writers) are on one processor, and the server (called) task on another. The basic Ada solution is shown in Figure 16-5 with the package specification and body of Reader_Writer. The details of the task Control are shown in Figure 16-6. A basic assumption here is that the distribution granularity is at the task level, which is different from our previously suggested distribution of packages and virtual nodes.

```
package Reader_Writer is
   procedure Read  (X : out Item);
   procedure Write (X : in  Item);
```

```
end Reader_Writer;

package body Reader_Writer is
   V : Item;
   type Service is (Reader, Writer);

   task Control is
      entry Start (S : in Service);
      entry Stop;
   end Control;

   task body Control is separate;

   procedure Read (X : out Item) is
   begin
      Control.Start (Reader);
      X := V;
      Control.Stop;
   end Read;

   procedure Write (X : in Item) is
   begin
      Control.Start (Writer);
      V := X;
      Control.Stop;
   end Write;

end Reader_Writer;
```

Figure 16-5.   Basic Reader/Writer Solution

```
separate (Reader_Writer)

task body Control is
   Readers : Integer := 0;
begin
   loop
      select
         accept Start (S : in Service) do
            case S is
```

```
        when Reader =>
            Readers := Readers +1;
        when Writer =>
            while Readers > 0 loop
                accept Stop;          -- from readers
                Readers := Readers - 1;
            end loop;
        end case;
    end Start;


    if Readers = 0 then
        accept Stop;                  -- from the writer
    end if;
or
    accept Stop;                      -- from readers
    Readers := Readers - 1;
end select;
end loop;
end Control;
```

Figure 16-6. Control and Synchronization of Readers and Writers

---

If a failure occurs in the the called task, the predefined exception Tasking_Error will be raised by the run-time support and transported to the calling task (that contains the procedures Read and Write). The calling task can then take whatever action is required to effect a recovery of the failed task. If a failure occurs on the processor that is hosting the calling task, the called task will not be notified and may end up in an inconsistent state, i.e., the entry Stop within the task Control may never be called. The Readers variable will then not be updated, the state of the system may become inconsistent, and deadlock may occur. It should be noted that the asymmetry in the caller/called relation is in accordance with Ada's semantics and is not caused by the distributed configuration.

The solution suggested in [BAR89, page 315] includes the declaration of agent tasks in the entrance procedures of the package Reader_Writer. The Ada code for the modified package body is shown in Figure 16-7, and includes task types for reader and writer agents. The code for the agent task bodies is included in Figures 16-8 and 16-9. The agent task objects are declared in the bodies of the entrance procedures with the use of allocators (Figure 16-7). As long as these agent tasks are co-located with the Control task, the latter will always complete its function within a given rendezvous even if the original reader or writer (on another processor) should die. A Stop signal will thus always be sent after a Start, and the system will always be consistent. The protocol including the Start and Stop signals has been moved from the caller's processor to the processor where Control resides.

```
package body Reader_Writer is
   V : Item;
   type Service is (Reader, Writer);

   task type Reader_Agent is
      entry Read (X : out Item);
   end Reader_Agent;

   type Reader_Ref is access Reader_Agent;

   task type Writer_Agent is
      entry Write (X : in Item);
   end Writer_Agent;

   type Writer_Ref is access Writer_Agent;

   task Control is
      entry Start (S : in Service);
      entry Stop;
   end Control;

   task body Control      is separate;
   task body Reader_Agent is separate;
   task body Writer_Agent is separate;

   procedure Read (X : out Item) is
      Agent : Reader_Ref := new Reader_Agent;
   begin
      Agent.Read (X);
   end Read;
```

```
   procedure Write (X : in Item) is
      Agent : Writer_Ref := new Writer_Agent;
   begin
      Agent.Write (X);
   end Write;
end Reader_Writer;
```

Figure 16-7.   Reader/Writer Solution with Agents

```
separate (Reader_Writer)

task body Reader_Agent is
begin
   select
      accept Read (X : out Item) do
         Control.Start (Reader);
         X := V;
         Control.Stop;
      end Read;
   or
      terminate;
   end select;
end Reader_Agent;
```

Figure 16-8.   Implementation of Reader Agent

```
separate (Reader_Writer)

task body Writer_Agent is
begin
   select
      accept Write (X : in Item) do
         Control.Start (Writer);
         V := X;
         Control.Stop;
      end Write;
```

```
or

   terminate;
 end select;
end Writer_Agent;
```

Figure 16-9.   Implementation of Writer Agent

The above example illustrates the importance of the distribution scheme and the granularity of the distributed elements. If the granularity is at the task level, a package specification and its entrance procedures may be on one processor, with tasks declared in the package body on another processor. This may require agent tasks to support fault tolerance as outlined above. If the distribution granularity is at the package and virtual node level, the entrance procedures and the declared tasks will always reside on the same processor, and agent tasks will not be required to solve the caller/called problems discussed above. The bodies of both Read and Write and the task Control, as shown in Figure 16-5, will all be co-located on the same processor. Regardless of what happens to the original reader or writer on another processor, the called task (Control) will always be able to complete each rendezvous. This suggests that our chosen distribution granularity supports fault tolerance for this particular problem.

16.7 Summary

A general definition of a fault tolerant system is one that can continue to operate (at least partially) after a failure has occurred. A failure can be caused by either a hardware fault or a software error.

In general, the implementation of fault tolerant real-time systems will include a combination of exception handling, the death notice mechanism, redundant tasks, dynamically created task agents, and redundant data elements. Fault tolerance must be carefully designed into each unique application from the very beginning of the design phase. An ad hoc approach will most likely require costly redesigns of major portions of the system.

If the additional execution overhead is not acceptable for the software solutions proposed, an alternate solution will be to use a hardware architecture that promotes fault tolerance *and* is efficient enough to satisfy the real-time constraints.

Exception handling alone cannot be relied upon to provide fault tolerance. Even if exceptions are propagated between processors, an exception intended to detect a processor failure may never be raised because it happens to reside on the failing processor.

The creation of application packages as major design objects contain the tasks that represent the natural concurrent elements of the system, and these packages are library units (with task masters independent of the main program). The distribution granularity of virtual nodes supports the notion of collecting the masters and their children on the same processor, and thus simplifies the task contexts for fault tolerance.

17

Design Guidelines

The software-first design methodology presented in this book is divided into two separate phases. The first phase includes the determination of the concurrent elements of the system, the transformation of the process abstraction to Ada tasks, the encapsulation of these tasks in Ada packages, and the creation of virtual nodes. The second phase consists of first choosing a set of processors that will support the software solution, and then determining the mapping of virtual nodes to processors.

The guidelines presented in this chapter represent a summary of the design considerations that have been discussed in the previous chapters.

17.1   General Design Strategy

The design methodology used for distributed real-time systems implemented in Ada is highly dependent on the available software development environment and the support for program distribution. If, for example, the best solution for a particular application is a loosely coupled system, adequate support may not be available for the distribution of a single Ada program. In that case we will have to distribute the virtual nodes as multiple Ada programs, and use remote procedure calls or a message passing mechanism for communication between the programs. We would expect, however, that the presently unavailable services and support for the distribution of a single program will become available in the future. Every effort should be made to design a system that can easily be reimplemented when the services become available, without having to perform a major redesign. We are assuming here that the hardware and associated programming support environment required will be acquired from commercial vendors, and not developed as research projects.

Some of the services that may not be available initially include support for remote communication via the Ada rendezvous and remote exception handling. To circumvent some of these limitations, certain restrictions and conventions may have to be imposed on the design methodology. One such restriction may be that only virtual nodes consisting of Ada application packages and associated support modules may be distributed. The primary emphasis of the overall design approach is to produce efficient, portable software that does not have to be redesigned when the desired support for distributed Ada systems becomes available, and the restrictions can be removed.

The sections that follow provide a set of guidelines for designing the various elements of a distributed system. They also include recommendations for imposing a reasonable set of restrictions and conventions for the design and implementation of distributed real-time systems in immature Ada environments.

17.2 Task Allocation

The allocation of tasks to processors has an effect on the composition of a virtual node. Since the virtual nodes are determined before the processors have been selected, there may be an iterative process between the allocation of tasks to processors and the proper composition of a virtual node. The following general guidelines are offered for the allocation of Ada tasks to processors:

1. Tasks intended to handle interrupts must reside on the processor where the interrupts occur. Interrupts should not be propagated to another processor, since the time spent during interprocessor communication may be significant, and subsequent interrupts may be lost.

2. Nested tasks should run on the same processor as the parent. Task objects declared from task types should run on the pro-

cessor containing the task type declaration. This is especially true for dynamic task creations, and will reduce the complexity for implementing a fault tolerant design.

3. The use of task attributes 'Count, 'Callable, and 'Terminated should only be used within the context of a single processor. The time delay in getting this information from another processor could be significant, and the values received no longer valid.

17.3   Virtual Node Composition

Groups of tightly coupled objects are identified and assigned to the same virtual node. These objects are Ada packages, tasks (task bodies as subunits), and subprograms that encapsulate the application and communication tasks. Tight coupling refers here to objects that share memory, and to tasks that rendezvous with a combination of *in* and *out* mode parameters in the same entry call.

Interrupt handlers, typically, have no need to communicate directly and should be placed in different virtual nodes. These nodes should reside on the physical node that represents the external device being handled, as we are not advocating remote propagation of interrupts.

Every effort should be made to make the virtual nodes as independent as possible in anticipation of a possible reconfiguration of the mapping of virtual nodes to physical nodes in a fault-tolerant architecture. This also promotes the portability of programs that can be rehosted on systems that implement a different inter-processor communication mechanism.

The use of conditional and timed entry calls may be restricted and (by convention) only allowed within a virtual node. This will simplify the interfaces between the virtual nodes that end up on different processors.

Task specifications are made in the encapsulating package body, and inter-package entry calls can only be made via the *entrance procedures* specified in the package specification. This is recommended regardless of whether the package is on a node boundary or internal to a node. This rule may have to be modified if the implementation of fault tolerance requires the use of the abort statement. In this case the task specification must be made visible to the aborting task. An alternative is to add a special entrance procedure that calls a task entry whose single function is to self-abort.

Some of the characteristics and restrictions regarding virtual nodes include the following:

1. Virtual nodes in pure loosely coupled systems may not share data. Sharing is allowed, however, within a virtual node.

2. Virtual nodes in tightly coupled systems will always share some data and may have their own local data. Virtual nodes residing in heterogeneous processors may not share data, unless the distribution is transparent and handled entirely by the run-time support, or unless call by reference is the only parameter passing mechanism allowed.

3. If the distribution topology consists of multiple Ada programs, an artificial "empty" node will be created. This will consist of a main program with a "null" body that is loaded with the rest of the virtual nodes that form the single program on each processor.

4. If a single Ada program is distributed, the associated main procedure should be "empty" without any task declarations. This will promote the construction of fault tolerant systems.

5. A virtual node will constitute a significant part of the overall application requirements. This includes one or more tasks and the packages and subprograms that support the functionality of the tasks.

17.4 Communication Between Virtual Nodes

Some of the possible communication mechanisms between remote Ada virtual nodes include remote entry call (REC), remote procedure call (RPC), and message passing. The specific mechanism employed for a given application depends on the communication services available for the chosen target configuration. The preferred mechanism is the REC since the Ada rendezvous can then be used without any restrictions, and the code will be portable.

If the REC is not available, it can be implemented in Ada with a remote rendezvous layer to implement the lower level protocols. An alternative to the REC is the RPC mechanism as implemented for Unix systems by Sun Microsystems. The RPC layer can replace the remote rendezvous layer of REC, or it can be used to implement the lower level protocols of the REC. The RPC model can be used by multiple programs, i.e., a separate program on each processor, as well as by a single program with distributed virtual nodes. The processors can be either homogeneous or heterogeneous, and load balancing has to be designed as part of the application program.

Synchronous or asynchronous message passing represent other alternatives for providing remote communication between virtual nodes. A set of general message passing primitives written in Ada are not readily available, and such an approach would be closely tailored to a specific application.

Every effort should be made to shield the application nodes from the communication services. This provides a portable design that can be adapted for different targets and communication models. The REC approach provides the loosest coupling between the application code and the communication mechanism. If the application makes direct use of RPC services, the code is less portable than what we can accomplish with the REC. The least portable solution will occur with the use of message passing, since the application code will be making direct calls to the message passing services. These services will be target dependent, and the application code will have to be modified as the system is ported to another architecture.

A distinction may have to be made between a simple rendezvous and timed or conditional rendezvous. The latter two cases require timing services to properly interpret the global meaning of the expiration for the timed entry call, and the "immediate" condition for the conditional call. The simple entry call does not require any global timing services. If global timing services are not available, timed and conditional entry calls may have to be restricted to local virtual nodes. In other words, the Ada rendezvous can be used without restrictions within a virtual node, whereas conditional and timed entry calls may not be used between virtual nodes.

The choice of a remote communication scheme will not be based entirely on the desire for creating portable code. An important design consideration for real-time systems is efficiency, and the available communication options must be evaluated with this in mind.

17.5 Exception Handling

The use of exception handling in distributed systems is highly dependent upon the available run-time support. An early design decision may be, for example, to restrict exception handlers to the exceptions raised within a virtual node, or within virtual nodes residing on the same processor.

There are no semantics specified for propagating exceptions between Ada programs, and all exception handlers must be local to a given program. If remote propagation of exceptions is allowed between multiple, communicating Ada programs, a message passing or RPC mechanism must be implemented, and all exceptions must be tagged as local or remote. If a single program is distributed across processors, the propagation is transparent, and in accordance with the normal propagation semantics.

17.6   Database Design

The design of databases for a distributed environment presents a distinct challenge, with considerably higher complexity than for a uniprocessor system. If most of the queries to the database are via remote accesses, significant time could be spent during inter-processor communication, and this may create a bottleneck for the whole system.

Local communication is much more efficient than remote communication, and every effort should be made to minimize the amount of remote communication required. This could mean, for example, that we would place sensor data received with a data acquisition processor, and a track file with the processor that maintains the tracks. There should be a close correspondence in locality between a virtual node and the data structures it needs to access. The decision of where to place virtual nodes relative to the data they access should be based on a minimization of communication costs and response time.

An analysis must first be made of the data rates required to support the queries made by the various virtual nodes. Processors with sufficient processing power, and communications channels with sufficient bandwidths must then be selected. The bandwidth of a primary system bus represents a design limitation for the data to be passed between processors and memories. Data associated with individual processors may instead be stored in local memories and accessed via special subsystem buses. This will offload the primary bus and improve the overall throughput of the system.

A separate database machine may be selected to support the major data structures and the associated queries. Most commercially available database machines include a query language as the primary (and possibly only) interface for access to the data elements. It is important that this interface be compatible with Ada, and that it will support the construction of portable code. One drawback to the use of SQL as an interface, for example, is that it only supports a very limited set of data types. We can thus not take advantage of the numerous data types available in Ada, since we can only use the subset in the queries that corresponds to SQL.

17.7   Processor Selection

Processors are selected to support the software solution by analyzing the processing power required for the virtual nodes and the bandwidth of the communication medium for their interfaces. This analysis uses the specification of the performance requirements, the level of fault tolerance, and the amount of required spare capacity to determine a specific set of processors. The following criteria can be used as a guide in the selection of suitable processors for a given real-time system:

1. *Device drivers.* The external devices in a real-time system typically operate at widely differing speeds, and processors should be chosen to match these speeds. It is not cost effective to choose all the processors based on the fastest external device. Other considerations include the I/O mode of the device, i.e., whether it is an interrupt driven or a polling device. Interrupts must be handled immediately to prevent loss of data, whereas a polling function is less critical. A separate processor can be used to support each device driver.

2. *Special functions.* Some of the virtual nodes may represent special functions such as digital signal processing or a database application. Processors may be available that are optimized for these functions. That may include special RISC architectures that are tailored to these applications. A separate processor can be used for each function, or functions can be combined on the same processor.

3. *Time-critical functions.* Virtual nodes that contain time-critical functions require a fast processor that can accurately and efficiently handle the starting and ending of timed events. This could be an executive with a low overhead for context switching and message passing in Ada rendezvous. We assume that the designers have minimized the number of Ada tasks that

reside in these virtual nodes to keep the run-time overhead to an absolute minimum. A critical factor in the choice of processors is the timing accuracy of the executive for the expiration of a delay, and the termination and reactivation of tasks.

4. *Performance requirements.* Certain functions may be computation-intensive, and a processor with the required MIPS or MFLOPS rating must be chosen. The required speed rating can usually be calculated from the given requirements.

5. *Processor homogeneity.* A typical distributed real-time system will usually consist of a mixture of heterogeneous processors of different word lengths and processing powers. If a reasonable choice can be made between homogeneous and heterogeneous processors, the former should be chosen to simplify the compilation, linking, and loading phases, and the communication interfaces. Where only different processing speeds are required, a family of processors can usually be chosen, such as the Motorola 680x0 or Intel 80x86. The software development environment will most likely be uniform for all the processor elements within a given family. It is also likely to be easier to interface between the processors in a family than between heterogeneous processors made by different manufacturers. Another consideration that may weigh against heterogeneous systems is the added overhead of the transformations between the various data representations.

6. *Fault tolerance.* If fault tolerance is to be designed into the application, great care must be exercised in choosing the processors. Considerations must be given to redundant processors, redundant buses or LANs, and how difficult it will be to reconfigure the virtual nodes within the context of the run-time support and/or operating system. Tasks must be created and activated dynamically, and virtual node images must be reconfigured either to the redundant processors or to the remaining processors that have not yet failed.

7. *Expandability.* The capability of expanding the functionality of a system may influence the selection of processors and their interfaces. A system using standard buses or LANs such as VMEbus, Multibus II, Futurebus, or Ethernet are easier to expand in a modular fashion than a system using customized buses and LANs. Here is another example of the advantage of

using a processor family. An existing 68030 processor, for example, may later be replaced by a 68040 with only minimal impact on the real-time software architecture. The impact on the code generators and run-time support will depend on how different the next member of the family is, e.g., if it changes from a 16-bit to a 32-bit processor.

8. *Interfacing capabilities.* The interfacing capabilities between the distributed processors are extremely important characteristics in a real-time system. The bandwidth for data transfers between the processors must be sufficient, and there must be adequate control programs to prevent bus contentions from becoming a constraint in bus-based systems. If a LAN is chosen, not only is a sufficient bandwidth required, the overhead associated with the additional communication services must be within reasonable limits. If a bus is chosen, the interfacing processors that are connected to the bus must be selected carefully to be compatible with the characteristics of the bus. This could, for example, be a family of 80x86 processors and controllers. If the bus is, instead, a VMEbus, a family of 680x0 processing elements could be chosen.

9. *Processor / memory compatibility.* The processor/memory combinations must be chosen with care. A fast processor with associated slow memory will most likely result in the processor remaining idle for one or more clock cycles, and will not have the effective throughput of the processor's nominal MIPS or MFLOPS rating. The tradeoff here is that the faster memory may become disproportionately expensive. Some of the faster processors with extremely high clock rates employ a combination of fast (very expensive) cache memory and somewhat slower (less expensive) primary memory for an effective zero wait state operation.

10. *Physical location and size constraints.* It is sometimes desirable to place a processing element physically close to a sensor or actuator, e.g., at an axis where a robot arm is moved, or in a heat seeking missile. The choice of processor and memory may be limited by the restrictions imposed by the physical environment, and the smallest possible configuration with the highest MIPS or MFLOPS to support the performance requirements will be the preferred choice. The physical location of the various processors will also determine how they should be inter-

faced. If all the processors fit within the same chassis, they can be connected via high-speed buses. If they are distributed throughout a building, however, one or more LANs will be required.

These selection rules are not all-inclusive, but form a good basis for making the proper selection of the hardware configuration. This is not an easy task and should be done in cooperation with hardware engineers who fully understand the characteristics of various microprocessor chip designs and how they should be interfaced.

17.8   Selection of Bus Interfaces

Some of the most important factors to consider in choosing a bus for a particular system design are:

1. Whether or not the bus conforms to a standard specification.

2. The expected future compatibility for an expanded system, e.g., a migration from a 16-bit to a 32-bit bus structure.

3. The arbitration method used in minimizing contention for the bus.

4. The total bandwidth of the bus, measured either as data transfers in Mbytes/second, or I/O operations/second.

5. The board size, which determines the number of modules that can be connected to the bus.

6. The connector type(s) that the board is using, e.g., some boards use a combination of two different connectors for full 32-bit data paths and addressing.

17.9   Distribution Specification

The last step in the design methodology is to map the virtual nodes to the processors selected. The performance of this step requires a mechanism to specify the distribution, and tools to interpret the specification and to load the virtual nodes on their respective processors. The basic assumption for considering various means of specifying the distribution is that the Ada language standard is not changed. It may change at a later date in accordance with Ada 9x, but for our purposes we do not anticipate these language extensions and modifications. One of the primary problems facing a designer of distributed real-time systems in Ada is that so little support is currently available from commercial vendors. Several distribution schemes have been proposed and partially developed in research centers, but their implementations are not yet available as off-the-shelf commercial products.

If there are no distribution specifications available, the designers are forced to use multiple Ada programs that will be loaded separately on the chosen processors.

Special Ada pragmas can be used as a distribution specification, provided, of course, that a vendor has implemented the pragmas as a part of the compilation system for the chosen processors. The use of special pragmas has the disadvantage to the user that the code will most likely not be portable, since different vendors will probably implement different pragmas. The vendors will have to modify their existing compilation systems to support these special pragmas.

A special syntax for the distribution specification can be used within an Ada program, but this will require a preprocessor to interpret the non-application statements. A disadvantage to the users is that two different sets of statements are intermingled in the same Ada module. The vendors do not have to modify their compilation system, but they do have to develop the preprocessor and associated support.

The preferred method for distribution specification is to have a separate tool independent of the Ada application code. The distribution and mapping of virtual nodes are described with Ada-like syntax separate from the application code. This means that the application code is free of foreign statements and special pragmas, and maintenance should be less than for the other approaches mentioned. An example of a separate specification is the APPL as suggested in [JHA89]. The vendors do not have to modify their compilation systems, but they do have to develop the necessary tools and support for the specification.

17.10   Fault Tolerance

Distributed systems offer excellent opportunities for implementing fault tolerant mechanisms, where functions can be regenerated and relocated to other processors that have not failed. Redundant processors can also be used to replace the ones that are failing (this approach can also be used with uniprocessor systems). The general scheme for providing fault tolerance includes the following steps:

1. *Failure detection.* The failing processor must be identified as soon as possible before the remaining system is corrupted.

2. *Fault diagnosis.* An immediate assessment must be made of the extent of the damage, and data must be generated that can effect a possible recovery.

3. *Recovery.* Based on the data created during the diagnostic phase, an attempt is made to restore the system to its full or reduced operational state. This may include load balancing, aborting and creating tasks, restoring critical data elements, and creating message data for later analysis. The execution of a recovery scheme is based on the implementation of a specific failure semantic. Since the ARM does not include such a semantic, the recovery rules become a part of the overall design decisions that must be made for the given application.

The recovery of a lost task could be made much simpler if we establish a set of guidelines for task contexts and the distribution of tasks. Such guidelines will include:

1. The main procedure should not include any task declarations or global variables, and should only have a *null* statement in the executable part. This implies that we use the main procedure only to start the elaboration process. If the context of this procedure is lost with a faulty processor, it will not affect the context of the rest of the application modules. We only have to recover the tasks that are co-located with the main procedure on the processor that failed.

2. All application tasks should be embedded in library packages. This separates the task masters and align them with the major application packages. Library packages and their embedded tasks are then independent of the main program. The fact that task termination is not defined for tasks in library packages is not a problem, since the typical real-time application is intended to run "forever" anyway.

3. Child tasks should be distributed with their masters whenever possible. This will reduce the complexity of determining proper task context for task recovery. It will also support the Ada semantics for the abortion of a master task, which assumes that all the master's children are also aborted.

These guidelines are fully supported by the design methodology specified in earlier chapters. The creation of application packages as major design objects contain the tasks that represent the natural concurrent elements of the system, and these packages are library units (with task masters independent of the main program). The distribution granularity of virtual nodes supports the notion of collecting the masters and their children on the same processor, and thus simplifying the task contexts.

17.11 Summary

This chapter represents a compendium of the various design considerations described in earlier chapters. Mostly summary statements are included here to provide an overview of the overall design methodology, and to provide a starting point for the planning of the design of a distributed real-time system in Ada. The details of each section can be found by referring back to the appropriate chapter. The initial planning must carefully analyze the available services, tools, and run-time support for a distributed real-time system in Ada. The lack of some of these may drastically influence the design decisions to be made during the early planning stages.

A

Case Study 1: Robot Controller

In this case study we will apply our design methodology for distributed real-time systems to the solution of a general purpose robot control system. This problem was originally introduced by Gomaa [GOM84] in his presentation of Design Approach for Real-Time Systems (DARTS). The problem was used in [NIE88] to illustrate the design methodology for real-time systems on uniprocessors. We are using the same problem here, and expand the solution given in [NIE88] to include distributed systems.

The robot controller problem is particularly attractive as an inherently concurrent system with several parallel functions. It is sufficiently complex to illustrate the complete methodology, and we can make reasonable problem simplifications to limit the size of our presentation.

The methodology utilizes the software-first two-phase approach: (1) we first design the system without regard for the hardware, and (2) determine the best hardware configuration that will support the software design.

A.1 Problem Specification

The functions of our robot system are to control several axes of motion of the robot, and to interface with a control panel and with I/O sensors. The problem is specified in terms of the control panel functions and the required states of the system. The external interfaces are described for the control panel, the robot, and the sensors. The required processing of inputs, outputs, and stored program commands completes the problem specification. The problem specification suffices as a mini–requirements document and forms the basis for the analysis and design phases.

A.1.1   Control Panel Functions

The system is controlled by an operator who uses a set of push buttons and a program selector dial on a control panel, as shown in Figure A-1. The small circles in this figure illustrate lights that indicate the state of the system. The system state-transition diagram is shown in Figure A-2. The system functions associated with the control panel are the following:

1. *Power on.* The operator pushes the ON button to power up the system.

2. *Power off.* The operator pushes the OFF button to turn the system off.

3. *Manual mode.* When the MANUAL button is pushed, the system is waiting until the operator either hits the RUN button for executing a selected program, or the OFF button to power the system off. (A real robot can also be operated manually without the use of preprogrammed operations. We are ignoring this mode here.)

4. *Program select.* The operator can select a particular program to be executed by turning the PROGRAM SELECT switch to the appropriate program identification number. (We can assume that a number of programs are already stored in memory, and can be executed via a proper program identification number.)

5. *Run (Start).* The system transitions to a running state and starts to execute the program selected by the operator.

6. *Stop.* When the STOP button is pushed, the system is suspended and waiting for another panel input of either RUN to

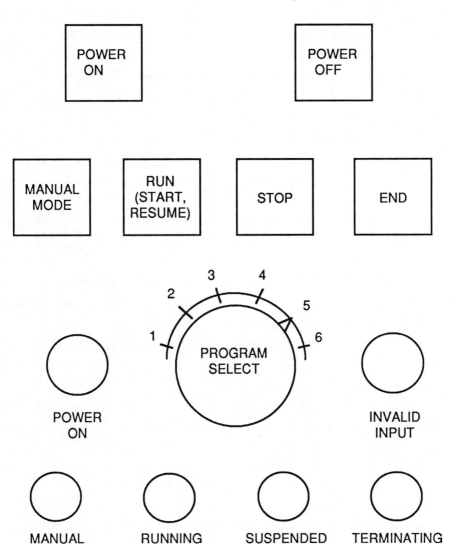

Figure A-1.   Control Panel Layout

resume execution, or END to terminate execution of the current program.

7. *Run (Resume).* Execution will continue with the current program when the RUN button is pushed and the system is in a suspended state.

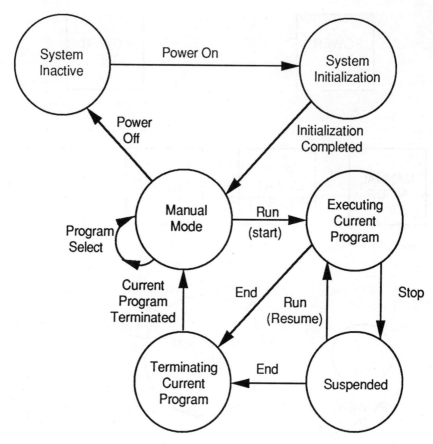

Figure A-2.   State-Transition Diagram

8. *End.* The current program will terminate from either a running state or a suspended state when the END button is pushed.

A summary of the various states and state transitions is illustrated in Figure A-2.

A.1.2 External Interfaces

The system must provide the following interfaces to external devices:

1. *Control Panel*

    a. *Input.* Control panel inputs are accepted as commands. The Run (Start) command also needs a program identification number indicated by the program select switch. The format for the commands is a string of ASCII characters (assume the length of the string is one). The program identification number is a single ASCII character.
    b. *Output.* Control panel outputs are created and sent to the control panel to reflect the current state of the system. The format for the outputs is an ASCII string (assume a length of one).

2. *Robot Axes*

    a. *Input.* Inputs (feedback signals) are read from the robot buffer to determine the current position of an axis. Assume a single digit axis number, and two-digit values for an (x,y,z) triplet.
    b. *Output.* Outputs are created and sent to the robot as axis commands. The format of these commands is ASCII strings. Assume a length of 16 characters for each command.

3. *Sensors*

    a. *Input.* Inputs are received from the sensors as they report critical values. Assume these values are two-digit integer numbers.
    b. *Output.* Outputs are created and sent to the sensors to establish critical values. Assume a single sensor and a critical pressure of x PSI, where x is a two digit integer value. (In a real robot system there can be several sets of sensors controlling the motion.)

A.1.3 Processing

The robot control system will perform the following processing functions:

1. *Control panel inputs.* Control panel inputs will be accepted and validated. Invalid commands will not be further processed, and

an error signal will be returned to the control panel (this will register on the panel as a light indicating an input error, as shown in Figure A-1). Valid panel input will be processed, based on the current system state, to determine if a new program should be executed, or if the current program should continue execution. A request to end execution of the current program can also be processed.

2. *Control panel outputs.* Appropriate outputs will be created and sent to the control panel to indicate the current state of the system, and to report invalid input.

3. *Program interpretation.* When a request for the execution of a new set of program commands is accepted, the system will first fetch the program from memory using the program identifier. The system will then interpret the various commands of the prestored program. The commands include arithmetic statements, logical statements, I/O commands to the sensors, and motion commands to the robot.

4. *Motion commands.* The system performs mathematical transformations on the data, and converts the data to the required format for axis data (axis block). The axis block is sent to an axis controller that interfaces with the robot. The system must be prepared to stop sending axis blocks to the controller when a stop command is received, and to resume the sending when a run command is received (while in the suspended state). The axis controller generates an acknowledgement when it has completed the processing of an axis block. This acknowledgement is a signal to continue the interpretation of the program statements.

5. *Sensor commands.* Processing is performed to send the required output to the sensors and to read sensor input. Assume that we read the input after polling a status register to detect a change that indicates that a new value is available.

This completes the requirements specification, and we are now ready to start the analysis and design phase.

A.2 Context Schema

The context schema of the robot controller is illustrated by the context diagram shown in Figure A-3. The single transformation repre-

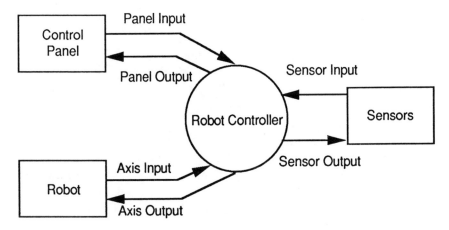

Figure A-3.   Context Diagram

sents the entire system we are going to design and implement. The context diagram also shows the external interfaces between our control system and the environment, and the sources and destinations of data flows that enter and leave the system. Inputs are received from the control panel, and are used to transition the system to the appropriate state. Outputs are returned to the panel as signals that turn on lights to remind the operator of the current status of the system, and to indicate invalid input. Inputs indicating the current position of the various axes are received from the robot, and outputs are sent to the robot as commands for the proper positioning of the axes. The system sends outputs to the sensors in the form of critical measures such as maximum pressure allowed on an element to be manipulated, or extreme position points for any of the axes or the robot hand. Inputs are received from the sensors periodically, or when any of the critical measures have been reached.

A.3   Edges-In Approach

The Edges-In approach is employed by first determining the processes required to interface with the external devices. Figure A-4 represents a concurrent process graph that shows five processes interfacing with the external devices. We have used the first rule of the Process Selection Rules (see Section 12.2) and assigned a process to each external device. The remaining functionality of the robot controller is contained in the "Middle Part" and will be decomposed later. It is possible that during this decomposition some functionality may be shifted from the middle part to the edge processes, and some

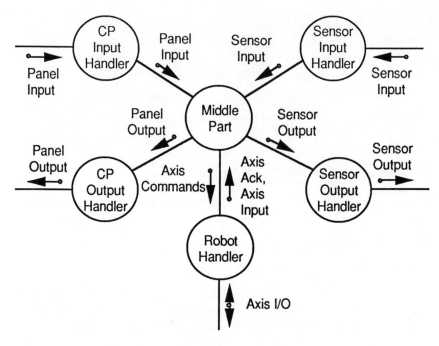

Figure A-4. Preliminary Concurrent Process Graph

of these processes may then not be pure device handlers. The five preliminary edge processes are:

1. *CP Input Handler.* This process will interface with the control panel and accept the inputs received via interrupts. The inputs will consist of commands, or a command and a program identification number.

2. *CP Output Handler.* The control panel output handler will be sending signals that reflect the current state of the system, or invalid input commands, to the panel. These signals will be interpreted by the panel and transformed to the appropriate panel lights.

3. *Sensor Input Handler.* This process will poll the sensors periodically to determine if a critical value has been reached.

4. *Sensor Output Handler.* This process is scheduled on demand whenever new sensor output is required.

5. *Robot Handler.* This process interacts with the robot to control the axes. Our preliminary choice is to assign a single process to this function rather than a separate process to axis input and output. The input and output to the axes are closely related and should be handled by a single process. The input from the robot represent feedback resulting from a motion command sent as output to the robot.

A.4   Decomposing the Middle Part

To decompose the middle part, we use data flow diagrams (DFDs) and a set of heuristics (see the process selection rules in Section 12.2) to determine a suitable set of processes. The DFD for the robot controller is shown in Figure A-5, and represents a functional restatement of the problem specification (including the edge functions).

We use our heuristics to combine the transforms of the middle part into processes, as shown in Figure A-6. This figure depicts all the robot controller processes, including the three for the external devices.

The transforms Validate Panel Input and Interpret Panel Input have been combined into the process CP Processor based on temporal cohesion. We want to make sure that the panel input is interpreted immediately after it has been validated. This may not be the case if the transform Interpret Panel Input was located in another process.

The transforms Interpret Program Statement, Process Motion Command, and Process I/O Command have been combined into the process Program Interpreter based on functional cohesion.

The transforms Output Axis Data and Receive Axis Ack have been combined into the process Axis Manager based on temporal cohesion. A new axis block will not be sent to the transform Control Axis until an acknowledgement for the current axis block has been received. Our system would not gain any efficiency by having Receive Axis Ack as a separate process, because Output Axis Data would have to wait for the acknowledgement in either case before it could send the next axis block.

A.5   Process Interfaces

The processes identified in Figure A-6 are pictured in the process structure chart shown in Figure A-7, and it includes all the logical interfaces between the processes. A loose coupling is normally re-

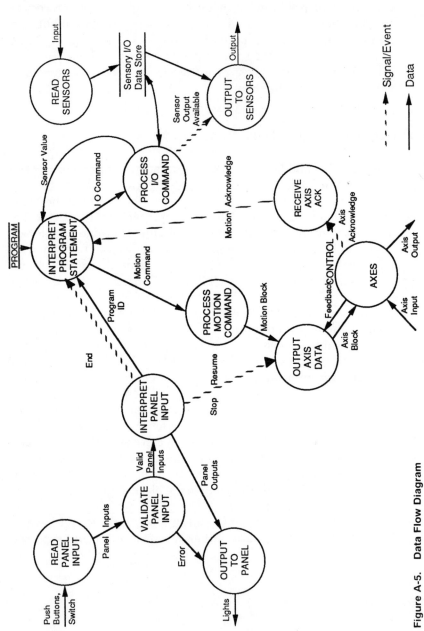

Figure A-5.   Data Flow Diagram

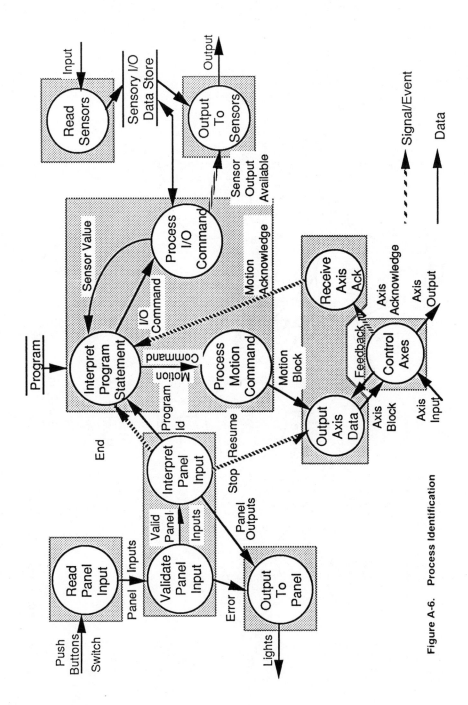

Figure A-6.   Process Identification

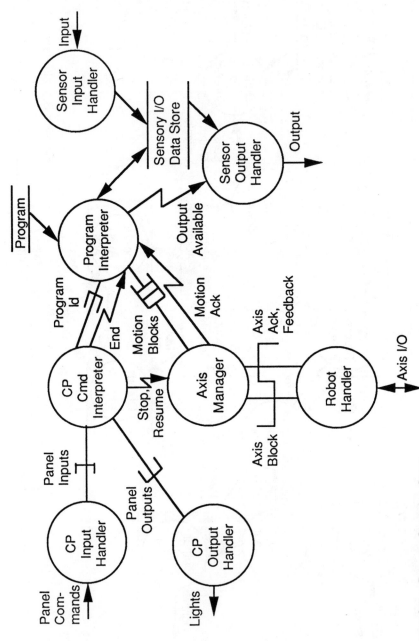

Figure A-7.   Process Structure Chart

quired when data is passed between a device driver and an internal process. This eliminates the need for the device driver to be kept waiting while data is being processed. Loose coupling in Ada is implemented by introducing a buffer task between the producer/consumer pair of Ada tasks, and adds to the run-time overhead. It is thus prudent to scrutinize the need for loose coupling, and only implement it when it is absolutely required. Inputs and outputs between the control panel and the internal tasks occur infrequently, and the data does not need to be buffered. We can thus tolerate a tight coupling between CP Input Handler and CP Processor, and between CP Processor and CP Output Handler without the risk of losing any data.

For a Run (Start) command, CP Processor will pass the program identification number to Program Interpreter. This will occur infrequently, and there is no need to place a buffer between these two processes. When CP Processor encounters an End command, it will send an End signal to Program Interpreter, indicating that the current program should be terminated.

Motion blocks are generated by Program Interpreter and consumed by Axis Manager. Some of these blocks will imply short axis moves, whereas others will imply long moves. A loose coupling is required here, and a buffer between these two processes will smooth out the differences in the processing time of the various blocks.

When Program Interpreter encounters an I/O sensor command, it is required to wait until the current axis motion is completed before it can execute the I/O command. It will wait for an acknowledgement from Axis Manager indicating that all axis blocks associated with a motion have been completed. This will be implemented with a signal from Axis Manager to Program Interpreter.

When CP Processor receives a Stop or Run (Resume) command from the input panel, it sends these commands as signals to Axis Manager.

When Axis Manager receives a motion block from Program Interpreter, it checks to see if a Stop signal has been received. If so, it waits for a Resume signal from CP Processor. If it has not received a Stop signal, or if it receives a Resume signal, Axis Manager sends an axis block to Robot Handler and waits for an acknowledgement that the block has been processed. This creates a very tight coupling between Axis Manager and Robot Handler.

The Sensory I/O Data Store pool contains the current values of the sensor data. When Program Interpreter executes an I/O sensor command, it updates the sensory data in the pool and signals Sensor

Output Handler that new output is available. Sensor Input Handler periodically scans the sensors and updates the database when changes are detected.

A.6   Introducing Intermediary Processes

The next step in our methodology is to translate the processes shown in Figure A-7 into Ada application tasks, and to introduce intermediary Ada tasks to implement the required coupling between some of the producer/consumer pairs. Tight coupling in Ada is represented by the rendezvous between two tasks, with the tightest occurring when a combination of *in* and *out* parameters are used in the entry call [NIE86]. Loose coupling is implemented with buffer tasks and/or other intermediary tasks. A signal is implemented with a parameterless entry call.

The panel input data passed between CP Input Handler and CP Processor and the panel output data passed between CP Processor and CP Output Handler will be accomplished with Ada rendezvous.The passing of the program identification number between CP Processor and Program Interpreter (as a result of a Run (Start) command), will be implemented using the Ada rendezvous with the identification number as a parameter. The End command will be sent as a signal via a parameterless entry call. The latter will also be the mechanism for sending the signals Stop and Resume from CP Processor to Axis Manager. The Resume signal occurs as a result of a Run (Resume) command received from the control panel.

The motion blocks passed between Program Interpreter and Axis Manager will be stored in the intermediary buffer task Buffer_Motion_Blocks as shown in Figure A-8.

A signal will be sent via a parameterless entry call by Program Interpreter to inform Sensor Output Handler that new sensor data is ready for output.

The tight coupling between Axis Manager and Robot Handler will be implemented with an entry call from Axis Manager to Robot Handler. The completion of the rendezvous will constitute an implicit acknowledgement, provided that all the processing of the axis block is performed inside the rendezvous.

The process structure illustrated in Figure A-7 shows three processes accessing the pool Sensory I/O Data Store. This pool must be

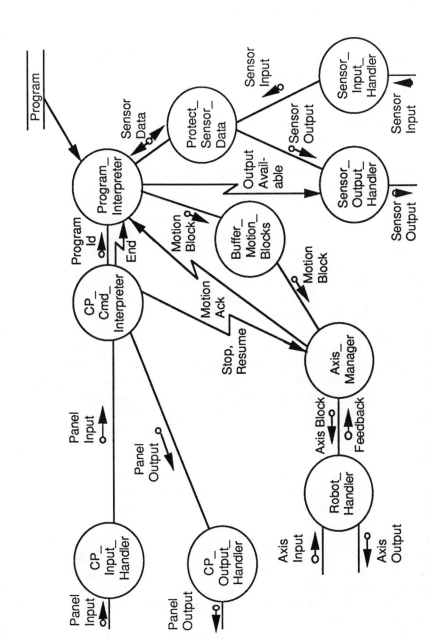

Figure A-8.   Ada Task Graph (before caller/called decisions)

protected to prevent an erroneous program. This protection is provided with the task Protect Sensor Data. The pool will be declared inside the task body, and can only be accessed via entry calls.

The complete set of Ada tasks that represents the concurrency model of our solution is shown in Figure A-8. We can now make the necessary caller/called decisions to complete the Ada task interfaces.

A.7   Caller/Called Decisions

To aid us in making the proper caller/called decisions, we utilize the heuristics given in Section 12.5 Any task that interfaces with interrupt driven devices needs to have a task entry associated with the interrupt, and is thus called with respect to the device. This is the case for CP_Input_Handler, CP_Output_Handler, and Robot_Handler. Sensor_Input_Handler will be polling the sensor for input and will not be called. Sensor_Output_Handler will be placing output in the sensor hardware buffer and will have an interrupt entry.

Buffer tasks are always pure servers by convention, and Buffer_Motion_Blocks is thus called. Similarly, the monitor task (Protect_Sensor_Data) protecting the sensor database is also a pure server.

The task CP_Cmd_Interpreter is idle until it receives an input from CP_Input_Handler, and it is logical to make the former the caller. This also retains CP_Input_Handler as a pure server and CP_Cmd_Interpreter as a pure caller, provided the latter calls CP_Output_Handler. The output to the control panel is a simple operation and will not prevent CP_Cmd_Interpreter from receiving new input.

The task CP_Cmd_Interpreter determines the type of command received from the operator and where the command should be sent. Since CP_Cmd_Interpreter knows *why* the command is received and where it is to be sent, it is logical to have it be a caller with respect to Program_Interpreter.

A signal is always sent from the producer to the consumer. This determines the direction of Stop and Resume from CP_Cmd_Interpreter to Axis_Manager; End from CP_Cmd_Interpreter to Program_Interpreter; Motion_Ack from Axis_Manager to Program_Manager; and Output_Available from Program_Interpreter to Sensor_Output_Handler.

Axis_Manager fetches motion blocks from Buffer_Motion_Blocks and creates axis blocks. It is an algorithmically complex task, and we make it a caller with respect to Robot_Handler.

This completes the caller/called decisions for this set of tasks, and the resulting task interfaces are shown in Figure A-9. Since Ada tasks cannot exist by themselves as library units, our next design step is to encapsulate them in packages.

A.8 Ada Packaging

The tasks shown in Figure A-9 have been encapsulated in Ada packages as shown in Figure A-10. Packaging decisions have been made based on functionality and minimization of coupling (see [NIE88, Chapters 13 and 22]).

The package Control_Panel contains the two tasks that interface with the control panel, CP_Input_Handler and CP_Output_Handler. The package CP_Processing contains the task CP_Cmd_Interpreter. The package Motion includes the task Program_Interpreter and the buffer task for motion blocks. The package Sensors includes the two tasks that interface with the sensors, and the monitor task that protects the sensor database. If there is a possibility that the two sensor interface tasks will end up on two different processors, they should be placed in separate packages. Here we are assuming that they will both be on the same processor.

The package Axis contains the task Axis Manager that creates the axis blocks. Even though this task is functionally and temporally associated with the Robot_Handler, the latter is placed in a separate package to facilitate the distribution of virtual nodes. These two tasks will quite likely end up on different processors, and the task Robot_Handler is placed by itself in the package Robot.

We have now determined the structure of our real-time system, and can start to implement this design using an Ada PDL.

A.9 Program Design Language (PDL)

The PDL phase consists of transforming the design described in Figure A-10 into a programming structure using Ada constructs. The top-level design illustrates the overall structure using Ada package specifications and bodies. The details of the algorithms are deferred to the detailed design using the *separate* construct. A description of the top-level design phase is given below, followed by an outline of the detailed design.

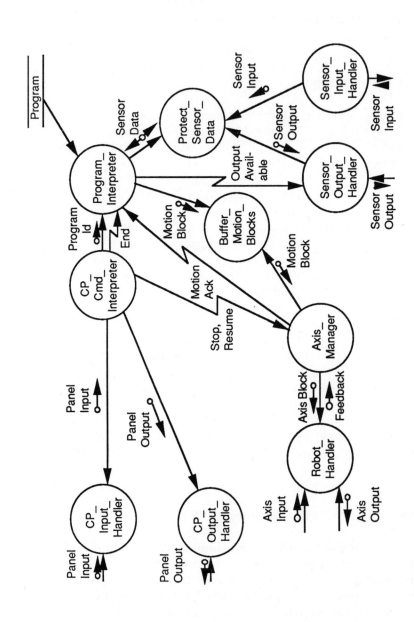

Figure A-9.   Ada Task Graph (after caller/called decisions)

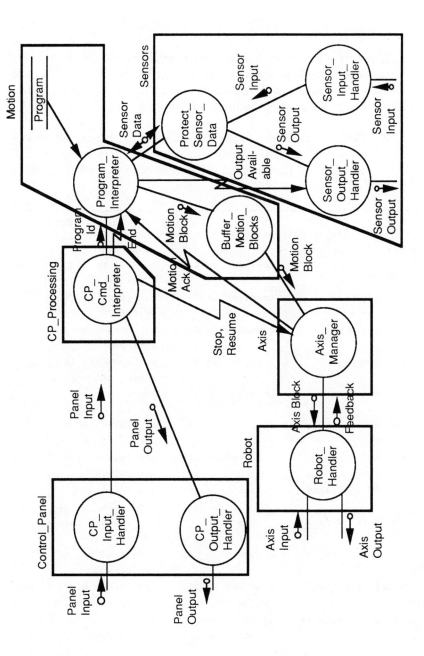

Figure A-10.   Ada Package Graph

A.9.1   Top-Level Design

The robot controller top-level design is as follows:

1. *Helper Packages.* Helper packages must be prepared in a bot-tom-up fashion before we start the top-level design of the application packages in a top-down fashion. The following components are used by the application packages:

    a. Definitions. This package contains constants, adaptation parameters, types, and subtypes that are used globally throughout the program. The Ada code is shown in Figure A-11.

```
----------- Global Definitions -----------
package Definitions is
    Max_CP_Chars       : constant := 2;   -- max length of CP
                                           -- command
    Max_CP_Input       : constant := 10;  -- max input to be
                                           -- buffered
    Max_CP_Output      : constant := 10;  -- max output to be
                                           -- buffered
    Max_Commands       : constant := 36;  -- max commands in
                                           -- a program
    Command_Length     : constant := 16;  -- length of
                                           -- program command
    Max_Motion_Chars   : constant := 24;  -- max length of
                                           -- Motion block
    Max_Axis_Chars     : constant := 12;  -- max length of
                                           -- Axis block
    Max_Motion_Blocks  : constant := 10;  -- max motion
                                           -- blocks to buffer
    Max_Sensory_Data   : constant := 8;   -- max sensory data
                                           -- to buffer
    Feedback_Data      : constant := 20;  -- length of robot
                                           -- feedback
    Sensor_Data_Length : constant := 26;  -- max length of
                                           -- sensory data
    Sensor_Scan_Period : constant Duration := 3.0;
                                           -- scan sensors every 3 seconds
```

```
subtype CP_Index         is Positive range 1 .. Max_CP_Chars;
subtype Motion_Index     is Positive range 1 .. Max_Motion_Chars;
subtype Axis_Index       is Positive range 1 .. Max_Axis_Chars;
subtype CP_Input         is String (CP_Index);
subtype CP_Output        is Integer range 1 .. 9;
subtype Motion_Command   is String (1 .. Command_Length);
subtype Axis_Command     is String (1 .. Command_Length);
subtype Motion_Block     is String (Motion_Index);
subtype Axis_Block       is String (Axis_Index);
subtype Feedback         is String (1 .. Feedback_Data);
subtype Sensory_Data     is String (1 .. Sensor_Data_Length);
subtype Program_Command  is String (1 .. Command_Length);
subtype Program_Id       is Character;
subtype Command_Index    is Positive range 1 .. Max_Commands;
type Command_Type is
   record
      Index   : Positive;
      Command : Program_Command;
   end record;


type CP_Command     is (Run_Start, Stop, End_Program,
                                            Run_Resume);
type State_Type     is (Manual, Running, Suspended);
type CP_Input_Code is ('S', 'H', 'E', 'R');
              -- S: Start;  H: Stop; E: End; R: Run;


type CP_Output_Code is (R_On_M_Off, T_On_M_On, S_Off_R_On,
R_Off_S_On, Invalid_On);

   -- R_On_M_Off : Running off, Manual on
   -- T_On_M_On  : Terminating on, Manual on
   -- S_Off_R_On : Suspended off, Running on
   -- R_Off_S_On : Running off, Suspended on
   -- Invalid_On : Invalid on
for CP_Output_Code use (1, 2, 3, 4, 9);


end Definitions;
```

Figure A-11. Global Definitions

b. Robot_HW_Dependencies. This package contains hardware dependencies for the devices that our tasks need to interface with. Absolute addresses (fictitious) are listed for interrupts and buffers for the control panel input and output, the robot axes, and the sensors. The skeleton Ada code is shown in Figure A-12.

```
--------- Hardware Dependent Constants ---------
--------- Sample only; furnish values for each device ---

package Robot_HW_Dependencies is

    CP_In_Int_Address       : constant := 16#00A0#;
                                    -- Control panel input
    CP_In_Buff_Address      : constant := 16#00A4#;
                                    -- input buffer

    CP_Out_Int_Address      : constant := 16#00B0#;
                                    -- Control panel output
    CP_Out_Buff_Address     : constant := 16#00B4#;
                                    -- output buffer

    Axis_In_Int_Address     : constant := 16#00C0#;
                                    -- Robot input
    Axis_In_Buff_Address    : constant := 16#00C4#;
                                    -- input buffer

    Axis_Out_Int_Address    : constant := 16#00D0#;
                                    -- Robot output
    Axis_Out_Buff_Address   : constant := 16#00D4#;
                                    -- output buffer

    Sensor_In_Buff_Address  : constant := 16#00E4#;
                                    -- input buffer

    Sensor_Out_Int_Address  : constant := 16#00E8#;
                                    -- Sensor output
    Sensor_Out_Buff_Address : constant := 16#00F0#;
                                    -- output buffer
end Robot_HW_Dependencies;
```

Figure A-12. Hardware Dependencies

It should be noted that the two helper packages shown in Figures A-11 and A-12 contain global entities and a collection of hardware dependencies, respectively. This is appropriate for a uniprocessor solution and for tightly coupled systems that share memory. For loosely coupled systems, however, it may be prudent to distribute this information to the virtual nodes that need the information. Another approach is to include these two packages in every local memory of the loosely coupled processors, with an obvious overhead of memory space.

2. *Communication packages.* Only a single communication package was used in this solution:

a. Buffer_Overwrite. The generic package specification shown in Figure A-13 contains generic parameters for the size of the buffer, and the type of elements to be stored. This particular buffer will be implemented to overwrite the oldest elements, rather than to lose input when the buffer is full.

```
generic
   Size : in Natural := 20;
   type Item is private;

package Buffer_Overwrite is
   procedure Enqueue (I : in Item);
   procedure Dequeue (I : out Item);
   pragma Inline (Enqueue, Dequeue);
end Buffer_Overwrite;

package body Buffer_Overwrite is
   task Buffer is
      entry Enqueue (I : in Item);
      entry Dequeue (I : out Item);
   end Buffer;

   task body Buffer is separate;

   procedure Enqueue (I : in Item) is
   begin
      Buffer.Enqueue (I);
   end Enqueue;
   procedure Dequeue (I : out Item) is
```

```
begin
   Buffer.Dequeue (I);
end Dequeue;
```

```
end Buffer_Overwrite;
```

Figure A-13.   Buffer_Overwrite (spec and body)

---

3. *Application Packages.* The following application packages were
   prepared for the robot controller top-level design:

   a. Control_Panel. The package specification and body are
      shown in Figure A-14. The specification part only contains
      comments for calls made to program units in another pack-
      age. Entrance procedures are not required here, since no
      calls are made from other packages. The body part contains
      the specification of the two tasks that interface with the
      control panel. The interrupt entries are associated with
      hardware addresses via the importation of Robot_HW_De-
      pendencies. The details of the task implementations are de-
      ferred with the *separate* statement.

```
with Definitions;  use Definitions;
package Control_Panel is
   procedure Provide_Panel_Input (CP_In :  out CP_Input);
   procedure Take_Panel_Output   (CP_Out : in CP_Output_Code);
end Control_Panel;
```

```
with Robot_HW_Dependencies;  use Robot_HW_Dependencies;
package body Control_Panel is
   task CP_Input_Handler is
      entry Provide_Panel_Input (CP_In : out CP_Input);
      entry CP_In_Interrupt;
      for CP_In_Interrupt use at CP_In_Int_Address;
   end CP_Input_Handler;

   task CP_Output_Handler is
      entry Take_Panel_Output (CP_Out : in CP_Output_Code);
      entry CP_Out_Interrupt;
      for CP_Out_Interrupt use at CP_Out_Int_Address;
   end CP_Output_Handler;
```

```
task body CP_Input_Handler  is separate;
task body CP_Output_Handler is separate;
procedure Provide_Panel_Input (CP_In  :  out CP_Input)
                                                 is separate;
procedure Take_Panel_Output   (CP_Out : in CP_Output_Code)
                                                 is separate;

end Control_Panel;
```

Figure A-14.   Control_Panel (spec and body)

---

b. Robot. The package specification and body are shown in
    Figure A-15. The specification contains an entrance proce-
    dure for input of an axis block, and the body contains the
    declaration for the task Robot_Handler.

```
with Definitions;  use Definitions;
package Robot is
   procedure Take_Block (A_Block : in Axis_Block;
                         F_Data :  out Feedback);
end Robot;

with Robot_HW_Dependencies;
package body Robot is
   task Robot_Handler is
      entry Take_Block (A_Block : in Axis_Block;
                        F_Data :  out Feedback);
      entry Axis_In_Interrupt;
      for Axis_In_Interrupt use at Axis_In_Int_Address;

      entry Axis_Out_Interrupt;
      for Axis_Out_Interrupt use at Axis_Out_Int_Address;
   end Robot_Handler;

   task body Robot_Handler is separate;
   procedure Take_Block (A_Block : in Axis_Block;
                         F_Data :  out Feedback) is separate;
end Robot;
```

Figure A-15.   Robot (package spec and body)

---

c. CP_Processing. The package specification and body are shown in Figure A-16. The specification part contains the declaration of entrance procedures for access to the panel input and output buffers. The body part contains the task declaration for CP_Cmd_Interpreter which validates and transfers panel input and prepares panel output. A generic package is instantiated for buffer tasks of panel input and output. The nested package CP_Manager is an object that will be used by the task CP_Cmd_Interpreter. The implementations of CP_Cmd_Interpreter and CP_Manager have been deferred.

```
with Definitions;  use Definitions;
package CP_Processing is
   -- Calls
      -- Control_Panel.Provide_Panel_Input
      -- Control_Panel.Take_Panel_Output
      -- Motion.Start_Program
      -- Motion.End_Event
      -- Axis.Stop
      -- Axis.Resume
end CP_Processing;


with Buffer_Overwrite;
package body CP_Processing is
   task CP_Cmd_Interpreter is
   -- Calls
      -- Control_Panel.Provide_Panel_Input
      -- Validate_Panel_Input
      -- Send_Input_Command
      -- Send_Panel_Output
   end CP_Cmd_Interpreter;


   package CP_Manager is
      procedure Validate_Panel_Input
                        (Panel_Input : in CP_Input;
                         Valid :        out Boolean;
                         Command :     in out CP_Command;
                         Program_No : out Program_Id);
      procedure Send_Input_Command (Command : in out CP_Command;
                                    Id :       in Program_Id);
```

```
      procedure Send_Panel_Output (Command : in out CP_Command;
                                    Valid :   in Boolean);
   end CP_Manager;


   package body CP_Manager      is separate;
   task body CP_Cmd_Interpreter is separate;


end CP_Processing;
```

Figure A-16.   CP_Processing (spec and body)

---

d. Axis. The package specification shown in Figure A-17 contains parameterless entrance procedures for the signals Stop and Resume. The package body contains the declarations for the procedure Prepare_Axis_Block, and the task Axis_Manager. The implementations of these two program units are deferred by using the *separate* construct.

```
package Axis is
   -- Calls
      -- Motion.Motion_Ack
      -- Motion.Dequeue_Motion_Block
      -- Robot.Robot_Handler
   procedure Stop;
   procedure Resume;
end Axis;


with Definitions;  use Definitions;
package body Axis is
   procedure Prepare_Axis_Block (M_Block : in  Motion_Block;
                                 A_Block : out Axis_Block) is
                                                         separate;
   task Axis_Manager is
      entry Stop;
      entry Resume;
      -- Calls
         -- Motion.Motion_Ack
         -- Motion.Dequeue_Motion_Block
         -- Robot.Robot_Handler
   end Axis_Manager;
```

```
    task body Axis_Manager is separate;
    procedure Stop          is separate;
    procedure Resume        is separate;
end Axis;
```

Figure A-17.   Axis (spec and body)

---

e. Motion. The package specification and body are shown in Figure A-18. Entrance procedures in the specification part include Start_Program and Dequeue_Motion_Block, and End_Event and Motion_Ack for the signals to end the current program and motion block acknowledgement. The package body includes an instantiation of the generic buffer package for buffering of motion blocks, a declaration of the virtual machine Program_Commands, and a declaration of the task Program_Interpreter. The implementations of the application machine and the task are deferred.

```
with Definitions;  use Definitions;
package Motion is
   -- Calls
      -- Sensors.Update_Data
      -- Sensors.Output_Available
      -- Sensors.Provide_Sensor_Data
   procedure Start_Program (Id : in Program_Id);
   procedure End_Event;
   procedure Motion_Ack;
   procedure Dequeue_Motion_Block (M_Block : out Motion_Block);
end Motion;


with Buffer_Overwrite;
package body Motion is
-- Instantiate buffer task for motion blocks
   package Buffer_Motion_Blocks is new Buffer_Overwrite
           (Size => Max_Motion_Blocks,
             Item => Motion_Block);
   package Program_Commands is
      function End_Of_Program return Boolean;
      function Motion_Command (Cmd_Index : Command_Index)
                                          return Boolean;
      function Sensor_Input_Command (Cmd_Index : Command_Index)
                                          return Boolean;
```

```
      procedure Process_Motion_Command
                          (Cmd_Index : in  Command_Index;
                           M_Block :   out Motion_Block);
      procedure Process_Sensor_Output
                          (Cmd_Index : in  Command_Index;
                           Sen_Data :  out Sensory_Data);
      procedure Process_Sensor_Input
                          (Cmd_Index : in  Command_Index;
                           Sen_Data :  out Sensory_Data);
  end Program_Commands;


  package body Program_Commands is separate;


  task Program_Interpreter is
     entry Start_Program (Id : in Program_Id);
     entry End_Event;
     entry Motion_Ack;

     -- Calls
        -- Buffer_Motion_Blocks.Enqueue
        -- Sensors.Update_Data
        -- Motion_Command (function)
        -- Process_Motion_Command
        -- Process_Sensor_Output
        -- Process_Sensor_Input
  end Program_Interpreter;


  task body Program_Interpreter is separate;


  procedure Start_Program (Id : in Program_Id) is separate;
  procedure End_Event                          is separate;
  procedure Motion_Ack                         is separate;
  procedure Dequeue_Motion_Block (M_Block : out Motion_Block) is
                                                       separate;
end Motion;
```

Figure A-18.   Motion (spec and body)

---

f.   Sensors. The package specification and body for Sensors
     are shown in Figure A-19. The specification includes en-
     trance procedures for access to the sensor pool. The pack-
     age body contains declarations for the task that protects

the sensor database and the tasks that interface with the sensors. The task implementations are deferred.

```ada
with Definitions;  use Definitions;
package Sensors is
   procedure Update_Data (Sen_Data : in out Sensory_Data);
   procedure Output_Available;
   procedure Provide_Sensor_Data (Sen_Data : out Sensory_Data);
end Sensors;


with Robot_HW_Dependencies;  use Robot_HW_Dependencies;
package body Sensors is
   task Protect_Sensor_Data is
      entry Update_Data    (Sen_Data : in out Sensory_Data);
      entry Take_Input     (Sen_Data : in Sensory_Data);
      entry Provide_Output (Sen_Data : out Sensory_Data);
   end Protect_Sensor_Data;

   task Sensor_Output_Handler is
      entry Output_Available;
      entry Sensor_Output;
      for Sensor_Output use at Sensor_Out_Int_Address;

      -- Calls
         -- Protect_Sensor_Data.Provide_Output
      -- H/W interface
         -- Places output in the sensor H/W buffer
   end Sensor_Output_Handler;

   task Sensor_Input_Handler is
   -- Calls
      -- Protect_Sensor_Data.Take_Input
   -- H/W interface
      -- Polls sensors for new input data
   end Sensor_Input_Handler;

   task body Protect_Sensor_Data   is separate;
   task body Sensor_Output_Handler is separate;
   task body Sensor_Input_Handler  is separate;

   procedure Update_Data (Sen_Data : in out Sensory_Data)
                                              is separate;
```

```
   procedure Output_Available is separate;
   procedure Provide_Sensor_Data (Sen_Data : out Sensory_Data)
                                                is separate;
end Sensors;
```

Figure A-19.   Sensors (spec and body)

---

4. *Main Procedure.* Ada requires a main program to start the elaboration process of packages and their objects, subprograms, and tasks. This main procedure is called Robot_Controller and is shown in Figure A-20. This procedure simply imports the package Control_Panel and has a null body. This is sufficient to start the elaboration of the other packages (which contain their own *with* clauses) and the activation of tasks encapsulated within these packages. Code to be used during the testing phase could be placed in this driver: declarations of simulation tasks and subprograms, test data, and so on.

```
with Control_Panel;
procedure Robot_Controller is
begin
   null;
end Robot_Controller;
```

Figure A-20.   Robot Controller Main procedure

This completes the top-level design phase. The next step of the design process is to supply the Ada subunits that contain the details of the robot controller implementation.

A.9.2   Detailed Design

The detailed design consists of supplying all the subunits that were deferred during the top-level design, and having the Ada compiler check interfaces and proper importation of required entities. These entities should be imported by having the subunits, rather than the package specification or body that creates the stub, *with* the necessary packages and subprograms, if possible. This will reduce the amount of recompilation required if the imported library units are changed.

The paragraphs that follow only provide a list of the subunits for the communication package and application packages specified during the top-level design phase. The details of the implementation of the subunits are not important here, since we are illustrating the design methodology for a distributed system. The emphasis is how we distribute the software modules, not algorithmic detail. In general, all of the subunits should be loaded on the same processor as the unit that created the corresponding stub. This will reduce the complexity of the distribution scheme and minimize remote communication.

The following paragraphs list the subunits identified during top-level design. The remaining sections in this appendix deal with the selection of processors, the creation of virtual nodes, and how to map the virtual nodes to the distributed architecture.

1. Communication Packages

    a. Buffer_Overwrite Subunits

        1. task body Buffer

2. Application Packages

    a. Control_Panel Subunits

        1. task body Cp_Input_Handler
        2. task body CP_Output_Handler
        3. procedure Provide_Panel_Input
                           (CP_In : out CP_Input)
        4. procedure Take_Panel_Output
                           (CP_Out : in CP_Output_Code)

    b. Robot Subunits

        1. task body Robot_Handler
        2. procedure Take_Block (A_Block : in Axis_Block;
                             F_Data : out Feedback)

c.   CP_Processing Subunits

```
1. task body CP_Cmd_Interpreter
2. package body CP_Manager
3. procedure Determine_Command
                    (Panel_Input : in CP_Input;
                     Command :     in out CP_Command;
                     Program_No :  out Program_Id)
4. procedure Validate_Command
                    (Command : in out CP_Command;
                     Valid :    out Boolean)
5. procedure Validate_Panel_Input
                    (Panel_Input : in CP_Input;
                     Valid :        out Boolean;
                     Command :      in out CP_Command;
                     Program_No :   out Program_Id)
6. procedure Send_Input_Command
                    (Command : in out CP_Command;
                     Id :       in Program_Id)
7. procedure Send_Panel_Output
                    (Command : in out CP_Command;
                     Valid :    in Boolean)
```

d.   Axis Subunits

```
1. task body Axis_Manager
2. procedure Prepare_Axis_Block
                    (M_Block : in Motion_Block;
                     A_Block : out Axis_Block)
3. procedure Stop
4. procedure Resume
```

e.   Motion Subunits

```
1. package body Program_Commands
2. task body Program_Interpreter
3. procedure Start_Program (Id : in Program_Id)
4. procedure End_Event
5. procedure Motion_Ack
6. procedure Dequeue_Motion_Block
                    (M_Block : out Motion_Block)
```

```
  7. function End_Of_Program return Boolean
  8. function Motion_Command
                        (Cmd_Index : Command_Index)
                                    return Boolean
  9. function Sensor_Input_Command
                        (Cmd_Index : Command_Index)
                                    return Boolean
 10. procedure Process_Motion_Command
                        (Cmd_Index : in Command_Index;
                         M_Block :    out Motion_Block)
 11. procedure Process_Sensor_Output
                        (Cmd_Index : in Command_Index;
                         Sen_Data :   out Sensory_Data)
 12. procedure Process_Sensor_Input
                        (Cmd_Index : in Command_Index;
                         Sen_Data :   out Sensory_Data)
```

f.   Sensors Subunits

```
  1. task body Sensor_Input_Handler
  2. task body Sensor_Output_Handler
  3. task body Protect_Sensor_Data
  4. procedure Update_Data (Sen_Data : in out Sensory_Data)
  5. procedure Output_Available
  6. procedure Provide_Sensor_Data
                        (Sen_Data : out Sensory_Data)
```

The detailed design phase is now completed, and any remaining code (for example, for the procedure Prepare_Axis_Block) and test drivers and simulators are supplied during the code and unit test phase on the host machine.

The first phase of our software-first approach is now completed, and for the second phase we select processors and virtual nodes, and map the virtual nodes to the distributed architecture.

A.10   Selecting Processors

A set of processors is selected using the guidelines suggested in Chapter 14. Using the first rule, we pick one processor to handle the inputs to and outputs from the control panel, another processor to interface with the robot, and a third to handle sensor input and output. The remaining functionality to determine the motion commands and the axis movements is assigned to a fourth processor.

It may at first appear that the control panel consists of two "devices," but the operator makes infrequent input operations and waits for a reply. There is thus a temporal relation between the input and output portions of the panel, and a single processor is sufficient to handle both the panel input and output.

The processor that handles the robot interfaces is co-located with the robot for optimum response. After the axis motion data is sent, fast response is required for the feedback data. This processor should not be burdened with any other processing.

A single processor can handle both the sensor input and output. After the critical values are set, the output handler task is idle until the next set of output is requested. The input handler task polls the sensor for changed values and needs the processor most of the time without interference from the output handler task. This is easily accomplished by giving the input handler task a higher priority. The processor is co-located with the sensor for optimum response time when a critical value is exceeded.

The processor assigned to handle the motion commands and axis movements is computationally intensive. It will perform coordinate conversions in multiple coordinate systems, and will utilize matrix algebra in the solution of the motion equations. This will require a powerful processor with a floating point coprocessor. The processor pair will reside in the same chassis as the control panel processor.

The four processors selected to handle the robot controller functions are the following:

1. Control_Panel_Processor

2. Robot_Processor

3. Sensor_Processor

4. Motion_Processor

The next step is to determine the appropriate interfaces between the processors. The Control_Panel_Processor and the Motion_Processor are located in the same chassis and be connected via a backplane such as a VMEbus or Multibus. Shared memory can also be utilized for these two processors (i.e., they are tightly coupled). The other two processors are remote from the main chassis and remote from each other. They represent loosely coupled nodes and will have their own memory. They will be connected to the other two processors via a LAN, such as Ethernet, as shown in Figure A-21. This figure represents the distributed architecture for the robot controller system.

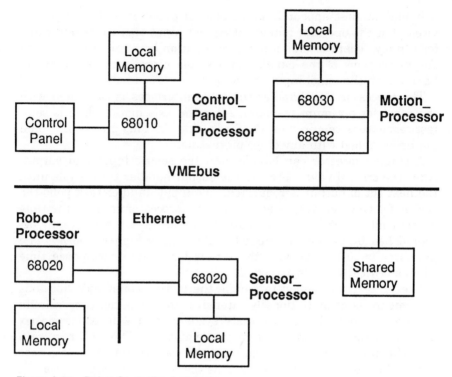

Figure A-21   Robot Controller Architecture

The next step in the selection of the hardware architecture is to analyze the processing power required for each of the three processors, and the bandwidth of the communication medium for their interfaces. This analysis uses the specification of the performance requirements, the level of fault tolerance, and the amount of spare capacity to determine a specific set of processors. The performance analysis should be conducted as a joint effort between the software designers and at least one hardware engineer.

If we assume that an adequate performance analysis has been conducted, a sample (fictitious) solution for the hardware architecture is shown in Figure A-21. A family of Motorola 68000 processors connected via a VMEbus and Ethernet represent the chosen solution for the robot controller system. A 68010 is sufficient for the interface with the control panel, whereas a 68030 and the floating point processor 68882 is required for the processing of the motion equations. These three processors are all in the same chassis and can communicate via a VMEbus. The interfaces to the robot and to the sensors are implemented with separate 68020 processors. These processors are remotely located from the main chassis, and are interfaced to the other processors via Ethernet. We thus have a mixture of tightly and loosely coupled nodes. The virtual nodes residing in the processors in the main chassis have shared memory, and are considered tightly coupled. The virtual nodes in the processors connected to the LAN only have local memory, with all communication across the LAN, and are considered loosely coupled.

In a real situation, a considerable amount of modelling and prototyping would be done with the selected architecture before the system is implemented in its final configuration. For our purposes, however, we assume that the architecture presented in Figure A-21 is a suitable configuration for the robot controller.

The final step in the design methodology is to map the software to the distributed architecture. This is done by first determining the composition of the virtual nodes, and then mapping the virtual nodes to the processors.

A.11   Virtual Nodes

The virtual node composition is based on the application packages shown in Figure A-10. The major criteria for the creation of virtual nodes are that the nodes can easily be migrated between processors for a given architecture and that the whole system can be transported to another architecture with only minimal design and coding changes. The Ada packages, tasks, and subprograms developed during top level and detailed design are combined into the following virtual nodes:

1. VN_Control_Panel

    a. Control_Panel (package spec and body)
    b. CP_Input_Handler (task body)
    c. CP_Output_Handler (task body)
    d. Provide_Panel_Input (procedure body)
    e. Take_Panel_Output (procedure body)
    f. Definitions (package spec)
    g. Robot_HW_Dependencies (package spec)

2. VN_Robot

    a. Robot (package spec and body)
    b. Robot_Handler (task body)

    c.   Take_Block (procedure body)
    d.   Definitions (package spec)
    e.   Robot_HW_Dependencies

3. VN_Axis

    a.   Axis (package spec and body)
    b.   Axis_Manager (task body)
    c.   Prepare_Axis_Block (procedure body)
    d.   Stop (procedure body)
    e.   Resume (procedure body)
    f.   Definitions (package spec)

4. VN_Sensors

    a.   Sensors (package spec and body)
    b.   Sensor_Input_Handler (task body)
    c.   Sensor_Output_Handler (task body)
    d.   Protect_Sensor_Data (task body)
    e.   Update_Data (procedure body)
    f.   Output_Available (procedure body)
    g.   Provide_Sensor_Data (procedure body)
    h.   Definitions (package spec)
    i.   Robot_HW_Dependencies (package spec)

5. VN_CP_Processing

    a.   CP_Processing (package spec and body)
    b.   CP_Cmd_Interpreter (task body)
    c.   CP_Manager (package spec and body)
    d.   Determine_Command (procedure body)
    e.   Validate_Command (procedure body)
    f.   Validate_Panel_Input (procedure body)
    g.   Send_Input_Command (procedure body)
    h.   Send_Panel_Output (procedure body)
    i.   Definitions (package spec)

6. VN_Motion

    a.   Motion (package spec and body)
    b.   Program_Interpreter (task body)
    c.   Buffer_Overwrite (generic package spec and body)
    d.   Buffer (task body)

e. Program_Commands (package spec and body)
f. End_Of_Program (function body)
g. Motion_Command (function body)
h. Sensor_Input_Command (function body)
i. Process_Motion_Command (procedure body)
j. Process_Sensor_Output (procedure body)
k. Process_Sensor_Input (procedure body)
l. Start_Program (procedure body)
m. End_Event (procedure body)
n. Motion_Ack (procedure body)
o. Dequeue_Motion_Block (procedure body)
p. Definitions (package spec)

These virtual nodes include the Ada modules that comprise the concurrent solution to the robot controller system. The final step is to distribute the nodes over the chosen set of processors.

A.12   Mapping Virtual Nodes to Processors

The mapping of the virtual nodes to processors is as follows:

1. Control_Panel_Processor

   a. VN_Control_Panel
   b. VN_CP_Processing

2. Robot_Processor

   a. VN_Robot

3. Motion_Processor

   a. VN_Axis
   b. VN_Motion

4. Sensor_Processor

   a. VN_Sensor

To get the virtual nodes linked, loaded, and executed on their respective processors requires an adequate compilation system and run-time support. This is not readily available for a loosely coupled

Ada system, and may have to be developed using the equivalent of Unix primitives and, perhaps, APPL as described in an earlier chapter.

A.13 Exercises

The following exercises are suggested for this case study:

1. Assume that your analysis indicates that the VN containing Axis_Manager should reside on the Robot_Processor, rather than the Motion_Processor. What are the tradeoffs? How does this change in the mapping affect your design? How extensive are the changes to be made in the source code?

2. Change the hardware architecture from being based on a VME-bus to using a Multibus II. What are the tradeoffs between the two approaches? Are the VNs affected by this change?

3. For the architecture shown in Figure A-21, would you make any restrictions in the use of the Ada rendezvous? What about exception handling.

4. Implement a skeleton message passing mechanism from the Axis_Manager task on the Motion_Processor to the Robot_Handler task on the Robot_Processor.

5. Implement the following change in the problem specification: If the program interpreter detects a sensor value that exceeds a critical value, it immediately sends a signal to the axis manager to halt the current motion command. How does this change affect the design of the virtual nodes, and the mapping of virtual nodes to processors?

6. Conduct a detailed performance analysis that will determine the required MIPS and MFLOPS (or other measures) for the number (but not necessarily type) of processors suggested in the text. Make up a set of requirements for the frequency and type of operator input, sensor response, robot interfaces, and processing power for the motion equations. Modify the architecture suggested in the text to reflect your analysis.

B

Case Study 2: Air Traffic Control System

This case study is designed to provide a model of a distributed real-time system that illustrates the design methodology described in Part 4. The process abstraction of concurrent elements is first determined without concern for the distributed architecture. The distribution of virtual nodes to processors is considered as a second development phase.

The following sections present a problem specification, the environment for the Air Traffic Control System (ATCS) software development, the edges-in approach followed by decomposition of the middle part into concurrent elements, and the use of PDL to illustrate the top-level and detailed design for the Ada modules that will be combined into virtual nodes. Distribution approaches for the virtual nodes are given for the suggested distributed architecture.

B.1 Problem Specification

The ATCS displays aircraft tracks obtained from radar sites on a user console. The system accepts radar data inputs about track location, and operator inputs to establish new tracks or change the location of a specified track. The term "track" is used to describe attri-

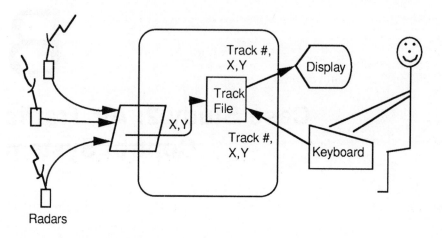

Radars

Figure B-1.   ATCS Overview

butes associated with a specific aircraft, ship, missile, point, etc. Examples of track attributes include track type, speed, heading, hostile, or friendly. A track (limited to aircraft in this case study) is displayed on the console with icons that identify some of the track attributes. As the attributes are updated, the same icons are displayed at different locations on the screen and illustrate the movements of non-stationary objects.

Figure B-1 illustrates a system picking up an aircraft on radar and shows the ATCS interaction with the radar, operator and display.

One of the ATCS functions is to periodically extrapolate all aircraft locations of the tracks kept in the database. It also periodically updates the display, independently of the radar input. The ATCS level of resolution is the meter, and the system provides for tracking on a two-dimensional grid of 100,000 meters in each direction.

There are three methods of updating an aircraft location in ATCS:

1.   Operator initiation or change of a track.

2.   Radar inputs that correlate with an established track.

3.   ATCS extrapolation at periodic intervals.

The remainder of the specification uses Ada-style names for certain system parameters, such as the frequency of periodic update or number of aircraft tracks. Such parameters are called *adaptation data*. They are to be prominently located and easy to find in the coded solution, and changes to such parameters are to require nothing more than a single change to a literal value and a recompilation. The literal values for the adaptation data will be given at the end of the software requirements.

The operator initiates tracks by providing a location as a set of (x, y) coordinates and a track number of zero. The ATCS assigns track numbers from a pre-assigned block of integer values. It may have as many as Maximum_Number_Of_Tracks tracks. After assignment of a track number, the track is recorded in the track file and is said to be established. For simplicity in this case study the ATCS does not immediately inform the operator of the track number. The number is displayed when the ATCS periodically displays the aircraft locations. The operator may change the location of an aircraft by providing the track number (other than zero) and a new set of coordinates for that track. For simplicity in this example, tracks are never dropped.

The radar provides input as a set of (x, y) coordinates. The data is provided from a number of different radars with varying acquisition rates, and the data is thus presented to ATCS asynchronously.

The ATCS is only concerned with the tracks that have been initiated (i.e., established) by the operator. It attempts to correlate each radar input (x, y) with an established track. If the input coordinates are within Proximity meters of an established track, the input is then said to be successfully correlated with the track. This new input is considered to be the new valid location of the established track, and the track file is updated with the new location. If the radar input does not successfully correlate with any of the established tracks, it is ignored. For simplicity, we are not concerned with "best" correlation. Assume that the first correlation found is correct.

The (x, y) pair and the time of last update are kept in the track file (database). The (x, y) pairs are updated (extrapolated) by the system on a periodic basis, i.e., at Update_Periodic intervals. For simplicity, assume all aircraft are moving at the same Velocity_Of_Aircraft (i.e., at the same speed and in the same direction (northeast)).

All tracks in the track file are displayed at Display_Periodic intervals. The display consists of the track number and some symbol or icon (our design of the ATCS is not concerned with the details of the display) placed at the coordinates provided by ATCS.

The following items are considered adaptation data:

1. Update_Periodic = 1 second. All the tracks in the track file should be updated every second.

2. Display_Periodic = 5 seconds. All the tracks in the track file should be displayed every 5 seconds.

3. Maximum_Number_Of_Tracks = 200. The software should be sized to handle a maximum of 200 tracks.

4. Proximity = 1000 meters. If the correlation calculation shows a point obtained from the radar data to be within 1000 meters of a data point in the track file, that track is updated with the new data.

5. Velocity_Of_Aircraft = 1000 kilometers per hour to the northeast. All aircraft are assumed to have this same velocity.

6. Speed = 200 meters per second in each of x and y directions. All aircraft are assumed to have this same speed.

We have simplified the aircraft extrapolation calculation by assuming that a velocity of 1000 kilometers per hour to the northeast is about 280 meters per second to the northeast, or 200 meters per second in each of the x and y directions. Therefore, the extrapolation consists of adding 200 to each of the x and y coordinates for each second (or fraction of a second) since the last update. The resulting adaptation data is the Speed in the x and y directions

B.2   Context Schema

The context diagram for ACTS is shown in Figure B-2. Radar inputs are received in the form of (x,y) coordinate pairs. These inputs occur asynchronously and must be accepted at any time, and only as little as possible of the incoming data should get lost.

Inputs are received from the operator any time a new track is to be added to the system, or whenever the operator wants to update an established track. The operator furnishes a track number of zero for a new track to be established, and the coordinates for the new track. For an established track, the operator provides the track number and the corresponding coordinates for the update.

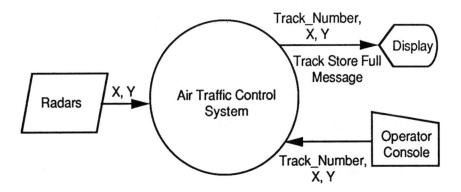

Figure B-2.   Context Diagram

All the tracks in the track file are displayed periodically on the operator's display device. The output data appears with a track number at the corresponding (x,y) coordinates. If the operator requests a track to be added when the track file is full, a message is displayed to inform the operator that the request was denied.

Our task is to design the real-time control program that will interface with the external devices and perform the functionality given in the problem specification. We will use the software-first design methodology described in Chapter 12.

B.3   Edges-In Approach

The first step we will take to develop a solution to the problem stated by the ATCS requirements, is to identify the processes required to interface with the external devices shown in the context diagram in Figure B-2. Since ATCS interfaces with three external devices, there should be a process in the ATCS for each of these devices. Figure B-3 shows the processes for the ATCS edge functions. The large "Middle Part" represents the primary functionality of the system and will be decomposed later. The three edge processes are virtual machines that operate concurrently. They are described as follows:

1. *Operator Handler.* The Operator Handler obtains a track number and set of coordinates from the operator. If the track number is zero, the coordinates are sent to the Middle Part to initi-

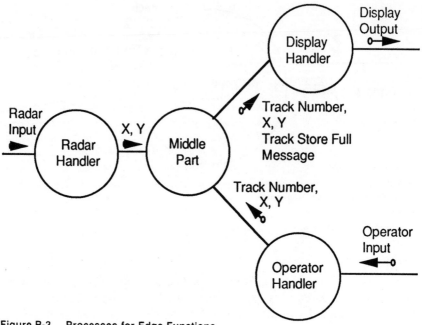

Figure B-3.   Processes for Edge Functions

ate a track. Otherwise, the track number and coordinates are sent to the Middle Part to change the location of an aircraft established as an existing track. If the track file is full, the Middle Part prepares a signal to notify the operator that the attempt to initiate a track was not successful. (For simplicity in this problem, the only response to the signal is the output of a message, prepared in the Middle Part.) If the operator has not input any information, this process is blocked and waiting for input.

2. *Display Handler.* The Display Handler periodically obtains the complete set of tracks from the Middle Part and displays the track number and corresponding coordinates of each track.

3. *Radar Handler.* The Radar Handler takes sets of coordinates from the radar and passes them to the Middle Part. The specifications of these handlers are shown in the PDL description presented in a later section in this appendix.

B.4   Decomposing the Middle Part

The Middle Part is also a virtual machine, just like the device handlers. It is not a primitive process, however, and has to be decomposed into its inherent concurrent elements. The system represented by the Middle Part takes sets of coordinates from the Radar Handler and attempts to correlate them with established tracks. If the coordinates correlate successfully, they are used as the new location of the track.

New tracks are established and track coordinates are changed, based on input from the Operator Handler. Periodically, track coordinates are extrapolated. When requested, the track file is provided to the Display Handler and prepared for display on the console.

The Middle Part is quite complicated, and its functionality is illustrated in the DFD shown in Figure B-4. It contains more than a single concurrent function, and must simultaneously perform three tasks:

1. Be prepared to take a track from the Radar Handler.

2. Be prepared to accept a call, asynchronously, from either the operator or display interfaces.

3. Keep track of time until the next extrapolation of tracks.

The decomposition of the Middle Part into a set of cooperating sequential processes is shown in Figure B-5.

A separate process is established for each of the radar, display, and operator interactions. Each process includes the transforms Get Radar Data, Get Track Data, and Get Operator Input, respectively. We have included the transform Determine Time for Next Display in the process that interacts with the display handler since they represent two highly cohesive functions with a temporal relationship.

The four transforms that set values in the track file have been combined into a single process that will protect the track file. This process will be implemented as a monitor and will provide the required mutual exclusion for access to the track file.

Even though the transform Determine Extrapolate Time is cohesive with Extrapolate Track Information, the latter must be part of the monitor, which is independent of time. The former transform is chosen as a separate process since it deals with the periodicity

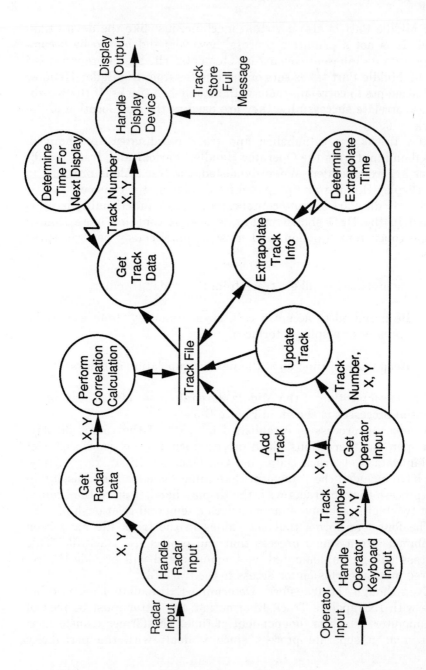

Figure B-4.   Data Flow Diagram

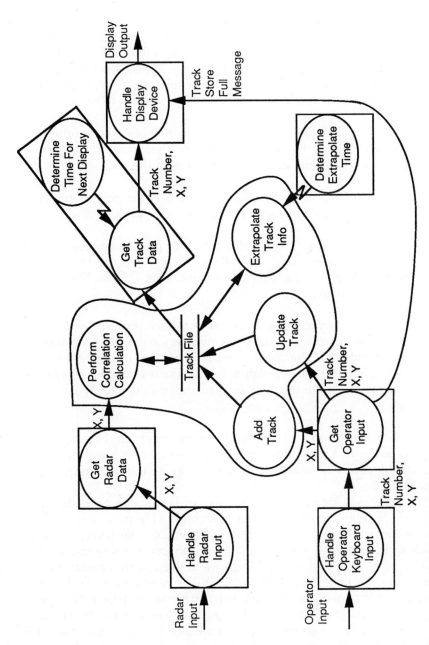

Figure B-5.   Process Identification

(a temporal condition) for determining when the track file should be extrapolated.

We have now completed the decomposition of the Middle Part, and we have a model of the concurrent elements of our solution. These elements are concurrent virtual machines, and illustrate the decomposition of the middle part by the use of *process abstraction*. All the processes are shown in the process structure chart in Figure B-6, and the processes of the Middle Part are described as follows:

1. *Monitor Track File.* The Monitor accomplishes all the functions connected with the manipulation of the track file (pool). It guarantees mutual exclusion for access to the pool.

2. *Extrapolation Timer.* The Extrapolation Timer process tells the Monitor when it is time to extrapolate all tracks.

3. *Display Interface.* The Display Interface process determines the time for the next display of all the tracks, gets the track information from the Monitor, and sends this information to the Display Handler.

4. *Operator Interface.* The Operator Interface process gets coordinates and corresponding track numbers from the operator device handler. If the track number is zero, coordinates are sent to the Monitor to establish a new track. If the track number is not zero, coordinates are sent to the monitor to update that track.

The notation shown for the Extrapolation Timer and Display Interface processes in Figure B-6 indicates processes that have a periodic aspect; the period is indicated near the loop, as in the example, Update_Periodic.

The processes shown in Figure B-6 can be considered nodes in a network of interconnected virtual machines. This structure is "flat" and not hierarchical, as is the case when we use the layered virtual machine concept (see Chapter 15) to decompose the sequential part of a single-thread process. Although we arrived at this design by decomposing the middle part, these machines represent a single layer of concurrent elements; they are not further decomposed into lower layers of concurrent machines. Large processes can be decomposed into a hierarchy of layered virtual machines for the sequential processing within each separate process.

We next consider the interfaces between the processes.

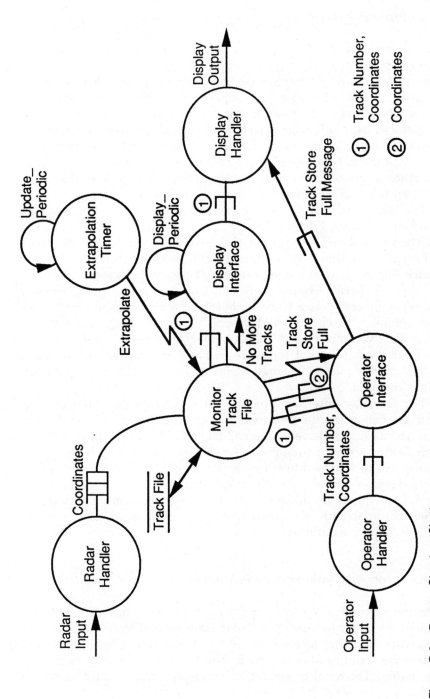

Figure B-6.   Process Structure Chart

B.5   Process Interfaces

The decomposition of the Middle Part and the device handlers are shown in the process structure chart in Figure B-6. This group of concurrent top-level virtual machines represents the design of our solution as a set of cooperating sequential processes and their interfaces. The interface between Radar Handler and Monitor Track File is pictured as a buffer for the channel data Coordinates obtained by Radar Handler. This allows the handler to operate in synchronization with the natural speed of the radar device, and is not dependent on other processing elements in the system. This will provide for a minimum loss of incoming radar data.

The track file must be protected, and will reside entirely within the Monitor Track File process.

When the period expires for the next extrapolation of the track information, a signal is sent from Extrapolation Timer to Monitor Track File. No data is passed between these two processes.

When the period expires for the next display of tracks, the Display Interface process gets a track number and corresponding coordinates from Monitor Track File, and passes it to the Display Handler process. This continues until Display Interface receives a signal from Monitor Track File that there are no more tracks to send. The track information is passed as single-element channel data, and no buffering is required.

The Operator Interface process waits to receive a track number and associated coordinates from the operator handler. The data is received as single-element channel data. If a track is to be added, the coordinates are sent to Monitor Track File without any buffering. A signal will be returned to Operator Interface if the track store is full. This signal is passed on to the display handler as a message. If the operator requests an update of a track, the track number and associated coordinates are sent from Operator Interface to Monitor Track File without any buffering.

B.6   Introducing Intermediary Processes

The only intermediary tasks required is for the proper implementation of the buffer between the Radar Handler and Monitor Track File processes. Our first attempt would be to introduce a buffer task, but this would require Monitor Track File to be a caller with respect to the buffer. The monitor should be a pure server, and we thus add a

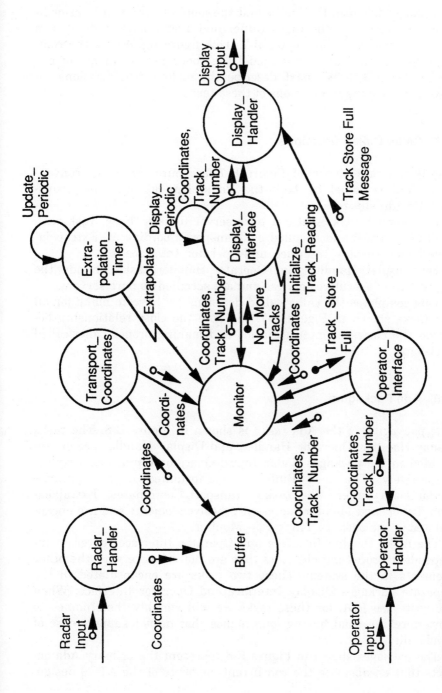

Figure B-7.   Ada Task Graph

transporter between the buffer and the monitor. The two intermediaries are shown as the tasks Buffer and Transport_Coordinates in the Ada task graph in Figure B-7. This figure represents the complete set of Ada tasks that model the concurrent elements of our design for ATCS. We next describe the caller/called decisions we have made for the interactions of these tasks.

B.7 Caller/Called Decisions

The Buffer task shown in Figure B-7 is a pure server (by convention), and is called by both the Radar_Handler and the Transport_Coordinates tasks.

The Monitor task is also a pure server (it is a "busy" task with multiple entries) and is called by Transport_Coordinates, Extrapolation_Timer, Display_Interface, and Operator_Interface.

The Display_Handler and Operator_Handler tasks provide the equivalent of executive services and are specified as pure servers.

This completes the caller/called decisions we have to make for all the tasks shown in Figure B-7. We note the close relationship between the choice of intermediaries and making proper caller/called decisions.

B.8 Ada Packaging

The packaging of the Ada tasks is shown in Figure B-8. The tasks Radar_Handler, Operator_Handler, and Display_Handler are encapsulated in the packages Radar_Input, Operator_Input, and Display, respectively. The task Buffer is encapsulated in the package Radar_Data_Buffer. The tasks Transport_Coordinates, Extrapolation_Timer, and Monitor represent cohesive elements and are encapsulated in the package Track_File_Monitor.

The tasks Display_Interface and Operator_Interface represent independent processing elements that are not cohesive with the other elements in the system. These two tasks are encapsulated in the separate packages Display_Interface and Operator_Interface. When we write the PDL for these tasks we will simplify their names to "Interface" to avoid having long names that do not support ease of readability.

The packages shown in Figure B-8 represent the primary Ada objects that encapsulate the concurrent elements of the ATCS design.

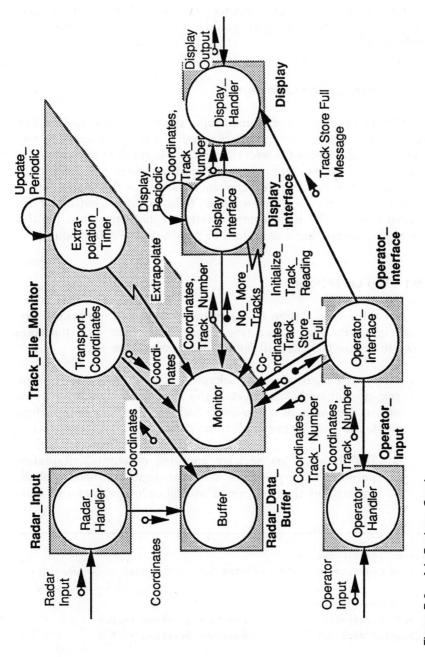

Figure B-8.   Ada Package Graph

These packages will be combined into virtual nodes and mapped to the processors we select for a distributed solution. If we only needed a uniprocessor solution, the packages shown in Figure B-8 encapsulate concurrent elements that would compete for the services of a single processor.

B.9   Program Design Language

The PDL phase consists of transforming the design described in Figure B-8 into a programming structure using Ada constructs. The top-level design illustrates the overall structure using Ada package specifications and bodies. The details of the algorithms are deferred to the detailed design using the *separate* construct. A description of the top-level design phase is given below, followed by an outline of the detailed design. The algorithmic details are not important for this case study; the emphasis is on how to distribute the Ada modules.

B.9.1   Top-Level Design

The ATCS top-level design is described in terms of the package taxonomy given in Chapter 12 (see Figure 12-7). The Ada packages shown in Figure B-8 fall into the following categories:

1. *Helper packages.* Helper packages must be prepared in a bottom-up fashion before we start the top-level design of the application packages in a top-down fashion. The following components are used by the application packages:

   a. Definitions. This package contains constants, adaptation parameters, types, and subtypes that are used globally throughout the program. The Ada code is shown in Figure B-9.

```
package Definitions is
    type Coordinates  is range -100_000 .. 100_000;   -- needed for
                                                       -- proximity
        -- Adaptation data
        Update_Periodic          : constant Duration := 1.0;
        Display_Periodic         : constant Duration := 5.0;
```

```
Maximum_Number_Of_Tracks : constant := 200;
Proximity                : constant := 1000;   -- correlation
                                               -- parameter
Speed                    : constant := 200;

-- Type definitions

type Track_Count is range 0 .. Maximum_Number_Of_Tracks;
subtype Track_Number is Track_Count range 1 .. Track_Count'Last;
end Definitions;
```

Figure B-9.   Global Definitions

---

2. *Communication packages.* The following communication packages are included:

a. Radar_Data_Buffer. The package specification shown in figure B-10 contains the entrance procedures Enqueue and Dequeue for storing and retrieving radar data, respectively. The task Radar_Handler (in the package Radar_Input) puts the radar data into the buffer by calling Enqueue. ATCS retrieves the data by calling Dequeue. The task Buffer is declared in the package body, and the details are deferred by the *separate* statement. The entrance procedures call their respective task entries.

```
with Definitions;   use Definitions;
package Radar_Data_Buffer is
   procedure Enqueue (X, Y :  in Coordinates);
   procedure Dequeue (X, Y : out Coordinates);
end Radar_Data_Buffer;

package body Radar_Data_Buffer is
   task Buffer is
      entry Enqueue (X, Y : in Coordinates);
      entry Dequeue (X, Y : out Coordinates);
   end Buffer;

   task body Buffer is separate;
```

```
procedure Enqueue (X, Y : in Coordinates) is
begin
   Buffer.Enqueue (X, Y);
end Enqueue;

procedure Dequeue (X, Y : out Coordinates) is
begin
   Buffer.Dequeue (X, Y);
end Dequeue;

end Radar_Data_Buffer;
```

Figure B-10.   Radar_Data_Buffer (spec and body)

3. *Application Packages.* The following application packages constitute the ATCS top-level design:

   a. Radar_Input. This package only encapsulates the task Radar_Handler, which interfaces with the radar input device. There are no entrance procedures since there are no interfaces to any of the other application packages. The package specification and body are shown in Figure B-11.

```
package Radar_Input is
   -- Calls
      -- Radar_Data_Buffer.Enqueue
end Radar_Input;

with ATCS_HW_Dependencies;   use ATCS_HW_Dependencies;
package body Radar_Input is
   task Radar_Handler is
      entry Radar_Interrupt;
      for Radar_Interrupt use at Radar_Interrupt_Address;
   end Radar_Handler;

   task body Radar_Handler is separate;

end Radar_Input;
```

Figure B-11.   Radar_Input (spec and body)

b. Display. This package contains the task Display_Handler and entrance procedures for displaying a track, and a message if the track store is full. The task includes an entry for handling interrupts from the display device. The package specification and body are shown in Figure B-12.

```
with Definitions;  use Definitions;
package Display is
    procedure Display_A_Track (X, Y :      in Coordinates;
                                Track_ID : in Track_Number);
    procedure Display_Message (Message  : in String);
end Display;


with ATCS_HW_Dependencies;  use ATCS_HW_Dependencies;
package body Display is
    task Display_Handler is
        entry Display_A_Track (X, Y :      in Coordinates;
                                Track_ID : in Track_Number);
        entry Display_Message (Message  : in String);
        entry Display_Interrupt;
        for Display_Interrupt use at Display_Interrupt_Address;
    end Display_Handler;

    task body Display_Handler is separate;

    procedure Display_A_Track (X, Y :      in Coordinates;
                                Track_ID : in Track_Number)
                                                      is separate;
    procedure Display_Message (Message : in String) is separate;
end Display;
```

Figure B-12. Display (spec and body)

c. Operator_Input. This package encapsulates the task Operator_Handler and provides an entrance procedure for getting data from the operator. The package specification and body are illustrated in Figure B-13.

```
with Definitions;  use Definitions;
package Operator_Input is
```

```
    procedure Get_Data_From_Operator (X, Y :      out Coordinates;
                                      Track_ID : out Track_Number);
end Operator_Input;


with ATCS_HW_Dependencies;  use ATCS_HW_Dependencies;
package body Operator_Input is
    task Operator_Handler is
        entry Get_Data_From_Operator
                            (X, Y :      out Coordinates;
                             Track_ID : out Track_Number);
        entry Operator_Interrupt;
        for Operator_Interrupt use at Operator_Interrupt_Address;
    end Operator_Handler;


    task body Operator_Handler is separate;


    procedure Get_Data_From_Operator
                           (X, Y :      out Coordinates;
                            Track_ID : out Track_Number)
                                                     is separate;
end Operator_Input;
```

Figure B-13.   Operator_Input (spec and body)

---

d. Track_File_Monitor. This package encapsulates the track
    store and the operations allowed on individual tracks. The
    package specification shown in Figure B-14 includes en-
    trance procedures to add a track, initialize the reading of
    tracks, obtain the next track for output to the display de-
    vice, and update a track. Exceptions are specified for at-
    tempting to add a track when the track store is full, and
    when the last track has been read for display output. The
    body part contains task declarations for the task Monitor
    which will guarantee mutual access to the track file; Ex-
    trapolation_Timer which monitors the expiration of time
    intervals between extrapolations; and Transport_Coordi-
    nates which gets radar data from Buffer and sends this
    data to Monitor for correlation.

```
with Definitions;  use Definitions;
package Track_File_Monitor is
    procedure Add_Track (X, Y : in Coordinates);
```

```
   Track_Store_Full : exception; -- raised by Add_Track

   procedure Initialize_Track_Reading;

   procedure Next_Track  (X, Y :      out Coordinates;
                          Track_ID : out Track_Number);
   No_More_Tracks : exception; -- raised by Next_Track

   procedure Update_Track (X, Y :      in Coordinates;
                           Track_ID : in Track_Number);


   -- Calls
      -- Radar_Data_Buffer.Dequeue
      -- Track_File_Manager.Add_Track
      -- Track_File_Manager.Initialize_Track_Reading
      -- Track_File_Manager.Next_Track
      -- Track_File_Manager.Update
      -- Track_File_Manager.Correlate
      -- Track_File_Manager.Extrapolate
end Track_File_Monitor;



package body Track_File_Monitor is
   task Monitor is
      entry Initialize_Track;
      entry Add       (X, Y :      in  Coordinates);
      entry Next       (X, Y :      out Coordinates;
                        Track_ID : out Track_Number);
      entry Update     (X, Y :      in  Coordinates;
                        Track_ID : in  Track_Number);
      entry Correlate (X, Y :      in  Coordinates);
      entry Extrapolate;


   -- Calls
      -- Track_File_Manager.Initialize_Track_Reading
      -- Track_File_Manager.Next_Track
      -- Track_File_Manager.Add_Track
      -- Track_File_Manager.Update
      -- Track_File_Manager.Correlate
      -- Track_File_Manager.Extrapolate
   end Monitor;



   task Extrapolation_Timer is
```

```
-- Calls
    -- Monitor.Extrapolate

    -- Delays for appropriate extrapolation interval and tells
    -- Monitor that it is time to extrapolate
end Extrapolation_Timer;


task Transport_Coordinates is
-- Calls
    -- Radar_Data_Buffer.Dequeue
    -- Monitor.Correlate

    -- Transports a set of coordinates from the buffer to
    --   the track file Monitor
end Transport_Coordinates;


task body Monitor               is separate;
task body Extrapolation_Timer   is separate;
task body Transport_Coordinates is separate;


procedure Add_Track (X, Y : in Coordinates) is separate;
procedure Initialize_Track_Reading is separate;
procedure Next_Track   (X, Y :      out Coordinates;
                        Track_ID : out Track_Number)
                                      is separate;
procedure Update_Track (X, Y :      in Coordinates;
                        Track_ID : in Track_Number)
                                      is separate;
end Track_File_Monitor;
```

Figure B-14.   Track_File_Monitor (spec and body)

---

e. Operator_Interface. The package specification given in Figure B-15 only lists the calls made to entrance procedures in other packages; no entrance procedures are required for this package. The package body contains the declaration for the task Interface which gets data from the operator and sends it to the Monitor task.

```
package Operator_Interface is
   -- Calls
      -- Operator_Input.Get_Data_From_Operator
      -- Display.Display_Message
      -- Track_File_Monitor.Add_Track
      -- Track_File_Monitor.Update_Track
end Operator_Interface;

package body Operator_Interface is
   task Interface is
      -- Calls
         -- Operator_Input.Get_Data_From_Operator
         -- Display.Display_Message
         -- Track_File_Monitor.Add_Track
         -- Track_File_Monitor.Update_Track
   end Interface;

   task body Interface is separate;

end Operator_Interface;
```

Figure B-15.   Operator_Interface (spec and body)

f. Display_Interface. The package specification given in Figure B-16 lists the calls made to entrance procedures in other packages; no entrance procedures are required for this package. The package body includes the declaration of the Interface task which gets track data from the Monitor task and passes the data to the display handler.

```
package Display_Interface is
   -- Calls
      -- Track_File_Monitor.Initialize_Track_Reading
      -- Track_File_Monitor.Next_Track
      -- Display.Display_A_Track
end Display_Interface;

package body Display_Interface is
   task Interface is
```

```
    -- Calls
       -- Track_File_Monitor.Initialize_Track_Reading
       -- Track_File_Monitor.Next_Track
       -- Display.Display_A_Track
    end Interface;


    task body Interface is separate;


end Display_Interface;
```

Figure B-16.   Display_Interface (spec and body)

---

g. Track_File_Manager. The generic package specification shown in Figure B-17 includes the generic type parameters Track_Count and Coordinates, and all the procedures that operate on the track file. The track file is declared in the package body and is hidden from the other tasks and subprograms in the system. This is a generic *helper* package of the type data manager to be used by the Monitor task, and is implemented as a resource, or object manager [NIE88].

```
generic
   type Track_Count is range <>;
   type Coordinates is range <>;

package Track_File_Manager is
   subtype Track_Number is Track_Count range 1 .. Track_Count'Last;

   procedure Add_Track (X, Y : in Coordinates);
   Track_Store_Full : exception; -- raised by Add_Track

   procedure Initialize_Track_Reading;

   procedure Next_Track   (X, Y :      out Coordinates;
                           Track_ID : out Track_Number);
   No_More_Tracks : exception; -- raised by Next_Track

   procedure Update_Track (X, Y :      in Coordinates;
                           Track_ID : in Track_Number);
   procedure Correlate (X, Y : in Coordinates);
```

```
    procedure Extrapolate;
end Track_File_Manager;


with Calendar;
package body Track_File_Manager is
    type Track_Record is
        record
            X, Y    : Coordinates;
            Update  : Calendar.Time;
        end record;

    type Track_File is array (Track_Number) of Track_Record;

    Tracks : Track_File; -- This is the object (resource)

    Last_Track  : Track_Count := Track_Count'First;
    Track_Index : Track_Count := Track_Count'First;

    procedure Add_Track (X, Y : in Coordinates) is separate;
    procedure Initialize_Track_Reading          is separate;
    procedure Next_Track  (X, Y :      out Coordinates;
                           Track_ID : out Track_Number) is separate;
    procedure Update_Track (X, Y :      in Coordinates;
                            Track_ID : in Track_Number) is separate;
    procedure Correlate (X, Y : in Coordinates) is separate;
    procedure Extrapolate is separate;
end Track_File_Manager;
```

Figure B-17.   Track_File_Manager (spec and body)

The package Track_File_Manager shown in Figure B-17 was not identified as a result of the decomposition into concurrent processes. Rather, it resulted from a realization that a number of functions that were required by the Monitor task could be appropriately grouped together as a package of services. This is an important point which illustrates that not all top-level design components are identifiable as a result of the analysis of concurrency and the mapping of concurrency from the problem space into the solution space. As the design progresses, similar helper packages may be discovered and will have to be developed before the top-down process can continue. (Remember that any importation of a library unit requires that at least a skeleton structure of that unit must exist in the library.)

B.9.2   Detailed Design

The detailed design phase consists of supplying the details of the subunits that were deferred by the *separate* statement during the top-level design phase.

In this case study we will only provide a list of the subunits, rather than the PDL with all the details. The emphasis here is on how we distribute the software modules on the chosen architecture, and subunits should be distributed with the module that created the stub. Detailed PDL of the implementation of the subunits can be found in [NIE88, Appendix D]. The paragraphs that follow describe the subunits identified during top-level design, and any additional packages or subprograms determined during detailed design.

1. Application Packages

    a. Radar_Input Subunits

            1. task body Radar_Handler

    b. Display Subunits

            1. task body Display_Handler
            2. procedure Display_A_Track (X, Y :   in Coordinates;
                                          Track_ID : in Track_Number)
            3. procedure Display_Message (Message : in String)

    c. Operator_Input Subunits

            1. task body Operator_Handler
            2. procedure Get_Data_From_Operator

                                     (X, Y :   out Coordinates;
                                      Track_ID : out Track_Number)

    d. Track_File_Monitor Subunits

            1. task body Monitor
            2. task body Extrapolation_Timer
            3. task body Transport_Coordinates
            4. procedure Add_Track (X, Y : in Coordinates)
            5. procedure Initialize_Track_Reading
            6. procedure Next_Track   (X, Y :   out Coordinates;
                                       Track_ID : out Track_Number)

```
7. procedure Update_Track (X, Y :    in  Coordinates;
                           Track_ID : in  Track_Number)
```

e. Operator_Interface Subunits

```
1. task body Interface
```

f. Display_Interface Subunits

```
1. task body Interface
```

g. Track_File_Manager Subunits

```
1. procedure Add_Track (X, Y : in  Coordinates)
2. procedure Initialize_Track_Reading
3. procedure Next_Track (X, Y :     out Coordinates;
                         Track_ID : out Track_Number)
4. procedure Update_Track (X, Y :     in Coordinates;
                           Track_ID : in Track_Number)
5. procedure Correlate (X, Y : in Coordinates)
6. procedure Extrapolate
```

2. Main Procedure. Execution of an Ada program starts with the main procedure. Prior to execution, packages *with*ed by the main procedure must be elaborated. The chain of elaboration causes the execution of all parts of the program. The main procedure for ATCS is shown in Figure B-18. The packages Operator_Interface and Display_Interface are imported to start the chain of elaboration. The executable part of the main procedure is simply a null statement.

```
with Operator_Interface;
with Display_Interface;

procedure ATCS is
begin
   null;
end ATCS;
```

Figure B-18. ATCS Main Procedure

We have now reached a point in the design where both the interfaces and the internal logic of the tasks are well defined. All that remains is the filling in of final data structures, and the completion of coding details to implement the algorithms defined if any pseudocode was included in the PDL in the subunits. This completes the first phase of our software-first approach, and we now turn our attention to how the software modules should be distributed.

B.10   Selecting Processors

A suitable processor architecture for this problem is chosen with the aid of the selection rules suggested in Chapter 14. Using the first rule, we pick one processor for handling the radar input and another for the console interface. The console interface includes both a keyboard and a display, but we consider this a single device that can be handled by one processor. Most of the operations for this processor will be associated with displaying track information. Operator inputs will occur infrequently, and represent only a small portion of the overall processing for the console.

The remaining functionality includes the operations on the track file, the interface with the operator handler, and the interface with the display handler. For a large number of tracks, e.g., on the order of 1000, the operations on the track file can be quite extensive and will require a separate processor (2nd rule). The interface tasks for the operator handler and display handler do not represent a significant amount of processing and can be included with the console processor.

We have thus selected three processors to handle the required computation for ATCS:

1. Radar_Input_Processor

2. Console_Processor

3. Track_Mgt_Processor

The next step is to determine the appropriate interfaces between the three processors. If we assume that the radar sensors are co-located with the operator console (e.g., for a mobile military unit), a LAN is not required and the processors can all reside in the same chassis. This means that they can be connected via a common back-

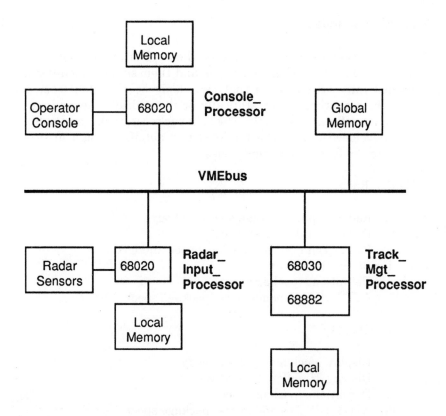

Figure B-19.   ATCS Hardware Architecture

plane such as a VMEbus or Multibus environment. If the sensors were located remotely from the console, a different communication medium such as a LAN (e.g., Ethernet) would have to be used.

Assuming that we have performed an adequate performance analysis, we have arrived at the architecture shown in Figure B-19. We have chosen a family of Motorola 68000 processors connected via a VMEbus. A 68020 handles the radar input, a 68030 with a 68882 floating point coprocessor manages the track file operations, and another 68020 is used for the interface with the operator console. We have chosen a tightly coupled architecture where the data is shared in a global memory. Each processor also has its own local memory.

The final step in the design methodology is to map the software to the distributed architecture.

B.11   Virtual Nodes

The virtual node selection is based on the application packages illustrated in Figure B-8. These packages and their support modules are combined into virtual nodes that can easily be migrated from one processor to another either statically or dynamically, depending on the support software available. The Ada packages, tasks, and subprograms developed during the top-level and detailed design are combined into the following virtual nodes:

1. VN_Radar

    a. Radar_Input (package spec and body)
    b. Radar_Handler (task body)
    c. Radar_Data_Buffer (package spec and body)
    d. Buffer (task body)
    e. Definitions (package spec)
    f. ATCS_HW_Dependencies (package spec)

2. VN_Display

    a. Display (package spec and body)
    b. Display_Handler (task body)
    c. Definitions (package spec)
    d. ATCS_HW_Dependencies (package spec)

3. VN_Operator_Input

    a. Operator_Input (package spec and body)
    b. Operator_Handler (task body)
    c. Get_Data_From_Operator (procedure body)
    d. Definitions (package spec)
    e. ATCS_HW_Dependencies (package spec)

4. VN_TK_File_Monitor

    a. Track_File_Monitor (package spec and body)
    b. Monitor (task body)
    c. Extrapolation_Timer (task body)
    d. Transport_Coordinates (task body)
    e. Add_Track (procedure body)
    f. Initialize_Track_Reading (procedure body)
    g. Next_Track (procedure body)

    h. Update_Track (procedure body)

    i. Definitions (package spec)

5. VN_Operator_IF

    a. Operator_Interface (package spec and body)

    b. Interface (task body)

6. VN_Display_IF

    a. Display_Interface (package spec and body)

    b. Interface (task body)

7. VN_TK_File_Mgr

    a. Track_File_Manager (package spec and body)

    b. Add_Track (procedure body)

    c. Initialize_Track_Reading (procedure body)

    d. Next_Track (procedure body)

    e. Update_Track (procedure body)

    f. Correlate (procedure body)

    g. Extrapolate (procedure body)

These virtual nodes include all of the Ada modules that represent the concurrent solution to ATCS. The remaining step is to disperse the nodes over the distributed architecture.

B.12 Mapping Virtual Nodes to Processors

The mapping of the virtual nodes to processors is as follows:

1. Radar_Input_Processor

    a. VN_Radar

2. Console_Processor

    a. VN_Operator_Input

    b. VN_Operator_IF

    c. VN_Display

    d. VN_Display_IF

3. Track_Mgt_Processor

   a. VN_TK_File_Monitor
   b. VN_TK_File_Mgr

To get the virtual nodes linked and loaded on the proper processors and executed in the distributed environment, we need an Ada compilation system and run-time support that has the required services. One such system is MTOS executive (Industrial Programming, Inc.) and TeleGen 2 Ada compiler (TeleSoft). Even though MTOS does not recognize virtual nodes directly, Ada tasks can be specified as "local," and earmarked for a given processor with the following MTOS function:

```
function Execute_On_Given_Processor (Processor : MTOS_Int)
                            return MTOS_Result;
```

The function call is placed in the task body for each local MTOS task. The local tasks are only executed on their respective processors, rather than with symmetric multiprocessing which is the default for global MTOS tasks. Ada rendezvous and exception handling can be used just as for a uniprocessor design, and remote entry calls and remote exception propagation are transparent to the application.

B.13 Exercises

The following exercises are suggested for this case study:

1. Assume that you cannot use MTOS, and that the only other support systems available do not allow remote entry calls or remote propagation of exceptions. You are forced to have multiple Ada programs executing in each processor. How will this affect your design? Make a detailed list of all the changes required in your software.

2. How can the paradigm of *entrance procedures* be extended to facilitate the RPC mechanism?

3. What are the changes that must be made to the ATCS virtual nodes if we use an RPC mechanism?

4. Implement a skeleton RPC mechanism for inter-processor communication of two ATCS tasks.

5. Implement an echo server (see Chapter 13) between the Console_Processor and the Track_Mgt_Processor for track data (can be simulated on a uniprocessor).

6. Discuss the positioning of instructions and data with regard to local vs. global memory and bus contention for the ATCS architecture shown in Figure B-19.

References

ABR87   Abraham, J.A. et al., Fault Tolerance Techniques for Systolic Arrays, *Computer*, July 1987.

ADA89   Approved Ada Language Commentaries, *Ada Letters*, Volume IX, Number 3, Spring 1989.

ALL81   Allworth, S.T., *Introduction to Real-Time Software Design*, Springer-Verlag, New York, 1981.

ALM89   Almasi, G.S. and Gottlieb, A., *Highly Parallel Computing*, Benjamin/Cummings, Redwood City, CA, 1989.

AND89   Anderson, C., Ada 9X Project Report to the Public, *Ada Letters*, May/June 1989.

AND88   Anderson, D.P., A Software Architecture for Network Communication, *Proceedings IEEE 8th International Conference on Distributed Computing Systems*, 1988, pp. 376–383.

ANS87   ANSI/IEEE Standard 1014-1987, An American National Standard IEEE Standard for A Versatile Backplane Bus: VMEbus, Approved March 12, 1987 (IEEE), and September 11, 1987 (ANSI).

ARE89   Arevalo, S. and Alvarez, A., Fault Tolerant Distributed Ada, *Ada Letters*, July/August 1989.

ARV78   Arvind, K.P. et al., An Asynchronous Programming Language and Computing Machine, Technical Report TR 114a,

Dept. of Information and Computer Science, University of California, Irvine, December 1978.

ATK88 Atkinson, C. et al., *Ada for Distributed Systems*, Cambridge University Press, Cambridge, England, 1988.

BAB88 Babb II, R.G., *Programming Parallel Processors*, Addison-Wesley, Inc., Reading, MA, 1988.

BAR88 Barnes, J. and Whitby-Strevens, C., High-Performance Ada Using Transputers, *Defense Computing*, September-October 1988.

BAR89 Barnes, J., *Programming in Ada*, 3rd ed., Addison-Wesley, Reading, MA, 1989.

BEN82 Ben-Ari, M., *Principles of Concurrent Programming*, Prentice-Hall International, Englewood Cliffs, NJ, 1982.

BER87 Bershad, B.N. et al., A Remote Procedure Call Facility for Interconnecting Heterogeneous Computer Systems, *IEEE Transactions on Software Engineering*, Volume SE-13, Number 8, August 1987.

BER88 Bergsten, B. et al., An Advanced Database Accelerator, *IEEE Micro*, October 1988.

BOO83 Booch, G., *Software Engineering with Ada*, Benjamin/Cummings, Menlo Park, CA, 1983.

BOO86 Booch, G., Object-Oriented Development, *IEEE Transactions on Software Engineering*, Volume 12, Number 2, February 1986.

BOO87 Booch, G., *Software Components with Ada*, Benjamin/Cummings, Menlo Park, CA, 1987.

BOR85 Borrill, P.L., Micro Standards Special Feature: A Comparison of 32-Bit Buses, *IEEE Micro*, December 1985.

BRI73 Brinch Hansen, P., Concurrent Programming Concepts, *Computing Surveys*, Volume 5, Number 4, December 1973.

BRI77   Brinch Hansen, P., *The Architecture of Concurrent Programs*, Prentice-Hall, Inc., Englewood Cliffs, NJ, 1977.

BRI78   Brinch Hansen, P., Distributed Processes: A Concurrent Programming Concept, *Comm. ACM*, Volume 21, Number 11, November 1978.

BUR85   Burns, A., *Concurrent Programming in Ada*, Cambridge University Press, Cambridge, England, 1985.

BUR87   Burger, T. and Nielsen, K.W., An Assessment of the Overhead Associated with Using the Ada Tasking Model, *Ada Letters*, January/February 1987.

CAR87   Carroll, J.L. et al., Block-Level Consistency of Replicated Files, *Proceedings of the 7th International Conference on Distributed Computing Systems*, Berlin, 1987, pp. 146–153.

CHE78   Chen, L. and Avizienis, A., N-Version Programming: A Fault Tolerance Approach to Reliability of Software Operation. *Eighth Annual International Conference on Fault-Tolerant Computing*, Toulouse, France, 1978.

CLA89   Clapp, R.M. and Mudge, T., Ada on a Hypercube, *Ada Letters*, March/April 1989.

CME89   Cmelik, R.F et al., Experience with Multiple Processor Versions of Concurrent C, *IEEE Transactions on Software Engineering*, Volume 15, Number 3, March 1989.

COR87   Cornhill, D. and Sha, L., Priority Inversion in Ada, or What Should be the Priority of an Ada Server Task?, *Ada Letters*, November/December 1987.

CUR89   Curran, L., Choose the Right Parallel Architecture, *Electronic Design*, May 25, 1989.

DAL84   Dalrymple, R., Multiprocessor Architectures Spark Interest in 32-Bit Buses, *Mini-Micro Systems*, December 1984.

DEL88   DelCasale, C., Taking the Mystery out of MIL-STD-1553, *Electronic Design*, October 13, 1988.

DEN79   Dennis, J.B. and Weng, K., An Abstract Implementation for Concurrent Computation with Streams, *Proceedings of the International Conference on Parallel Processing*, August 1979, pp. 201–211.

DES87   Desrochers, G.R., *Principles of Parallel and Multiprocessing*, McGraw-Hill Book Company, New York, 1987.

DIE88   Diede, T. et al., The Titan Graphics Supercomputer Architecture, *Computer*, September 1988.

DIJ68   Dijkstra, E.W., Co-operating Sequential Processes, in *Programming Languages*, F. Genuys (ed.), Academic Press, New York, 1968.

DIJ68a   Dijkstra, E.W., The Structure of the "THE" - Multiprogramming System, *Communications of the ACM*, Volume 11, Number 5, May 1968.

DIJ71   Dijkstra, E.W., Hierarchical Ordering of Sequential Processes, *Acta Informatica*, Volume 1, 1971, pp. 115–138.

DIX88   Dixon, K.B., The Ferranti DVME 785 Relational Processor, Report No. 6902, Issue 5, September 1988.

DOD78   DoD Requirements for High Order Computer Programming Languages, "Steelman," U.S. Department of Defense, June 1987.

DOD83   Reference Manual for the Ada Programming Language, *ANSI-MIL-STD-1815A*, U.S. Department of Defense, 17 February 1983.

DOD88   Military Standard for Defense System Software Development, *DOD-STD-2167A*, 29 February 1988.

DOL84   Dolev, D. et al., Fault Tolerant Clock Synchronization, *PODC Symposium*, August 1984.

DOW88   Dowsing, R.D., *Introduction to Concurrency Using occam*, Van Nostrand Reinhold, London, 1988.

DRA87   Drake, B.L. et al., SLAPP: A Systolic Linear Algebra Parallel Processor, *Computer*, July 1987.

FAL88   Falk, H., Developers Target Unix and Ada with Real-Time Kernels, *Computer Design*, April 1988.

FEN81   Feng, T., A Survey of Interconnection Networks, *Computer*, December 1981.

FLY72   Flynn, M.J., Some Computer Organizations and Their Effectiveness, *IEEE Transactions on Computers*, C-21, No. 9, September, 1972.

FOR85   Ford, G. and Wiener, R., *Modula-2: A Software Development Approach*, John Wiley & Sons, New York, 1985.

FOU87   Foulser, D.E. and Schreiber, R., The Saxpy Matrix-1: A General-Purpose Systolic Computer, *Computer*, July 1987.

GEH84   Gehani, N., *Ada Concurrent Programming*, Prentice-Hall, Inc., Englewood Cliffs, NJ 1984.

GEH86   Gehani, N. and Roome, W.D., Concurrent C, *Software — Practice and Experience*, Volume 16, Number 9, September 1986.

GEH88   Gehani, N. and Roome, W.D., Rendezvous Facilities: Concurrent C and the Ada Language, *IEEE Transactions on Software Engineering*, Volume 14, Number 11, November 1988.

GIL87   Gillenson, M.L., The Duality of Database Structures and Design Techniques, *Communications of the ACM*, Volume 30, Number 12, December 1987.

GOL72   Goldstine, Herman H., *The Computer, Princeton University Press*, Princeton, NJ, 1972.

GOM84   Gomaa, H., A Software Design Method for Real-Time Systems, *Communications of the ACM*, Volume 27, Number 9, September 1984.

GUR85 Gurd, J.R. et al., The Manchester Prototype Dataflow Computer, *Communications of the ACM*, Volume 28, Number 1, January 1985.

GUS84 Gustavson, D.B., Computer Buses — A Tutorial, *IEEE Micro*, August 1984.

HAT88 Hatley, D.J. and Pirbhai, I.A., *Strategies for Real-Time System Specification*, Dorset House Publishing, New York, 1988.

HAY86 Hayes, J.P. et al., A Microprocessor-based Hypercube Supercomputer, *IEEE Micro*, October 1986.

HEL85 Helmbold, D and Luckham, D., Debugging Ada Tasking Program, *IEEE Software*, March 1985.

HOA74 Hoare, C.A.R., Monitors: An Operating System Structuring Concept, *Communications of the ACM*, Volume 17, Number 10, October 1974.

HOA78 Hoare, C.A.R., Communicating Sequential Processes, *Communications of the ACM*, Volume 21, Number 8, August 1978.

HWA84 Hwang, K. and Briggs, F.A., *Computer Architecture and Parallel Processing*, McGraw-Hill, New York, 1984.

IEE88 IEEE Standard 1196-1988, Standard NuBus: A Simple 32-Bit Backplane Bus, Approved 1988.

IEE88a IEEE Standard 1296-1988, Standard for High-Performance 32-Bit Bus, Approved 1988.

IEE88b IEEE Standard 896.1-1988, Standard Backplane Bus Specification of Multiprocessor Architectures (Futurebus), Approved 1988.

INM84 Inmos Ltd., *Occam Programming Manual*, Prentice-Hall, Hemel Hempstead, England, 1984.

INM87 Inmos Ltd., The Transputer Family 1987, Product Information, Inmos, Colorado Springs, CO, 1987.

JHA89   Jha, R. et al., Ada Program Partitioning Language: A Notation for Distributing Ada Programs, *IEEE Transactions on Software Engineering*, Volume 15, Number 3, March 1989.

KAR88   Karp, A.H. and Babb II, R.G., A Comparison of 12 Parallel Fortran Dialects, *IEEE Software*, September 1988.

KER78   Kernigan, B.W. and Ritchie, D.M., *The C Programming Language, Prentice-Hall*, Englewood Cliffs, NJ, 1978.

KER88   Kernigan, B.W. and Ritchie, D.M., *The C Programming Language*, 2d ed., Prentice-Hall, Englewood Cliffs, NJ, 1988. (ANSI C version of KER78.)

KNA87   Knapp, E., Deadlock Detection in Distributed Databases, *ACM Computing Surveys*, Volume 19, Number 4, December 1987.

KNI87   Knight, J.C. and Urquhart, J.I.A., On the Implementation and Use of Ada on Fault-Tolerant Distributed Systems, *IEEE Transactions on Software Engineering*, Volume SE-13, Number 5, May 1987.

KNU69   Knuth, D.E., *The Art of Computer Programming, Volume 1: Fundamental Algorithms*, Addison-Wesley Publishing Company, Reading, MA, 1969.

KUN82   Kung, H.T., Why Systolic Architectures? *Computer*, Volume 15, Number 1, January 1982.

LEB85   LeBlanc, R.J., Debugging Distributed Programs, *IEEE Proceedings COMPSAC 85*, October, 1985, p. 424.

LEV88   Levine, G., The Control of Priority Inversion in Ada, *Ada Letters*, November/December 1988.

LIE85   Liebowitz, B.H. and Carson, J.H., *Multiple Processor Systems for Real-Time Applications*, Prentice-Hall, Englewood Cliffs, NJ, 1985.

LUN84   Lundelius, J. and Lynch, N., A New Fault Tolerant Algorithm for Clock Synchronization, PODC Symposium, August 1984.

MCC87   McCanny, J.V. and McWhirter, J.G., Some Systolic Array Developments in the United Kingdom, *Computer*, July 1987.

MEL86   Mellor, S.J. and Ward, P.T., *Structured Development for Real-Time Systems, Volume 3: Implementation Modeling Techniques*, Yourdon, New York, 1986.

NIE86   Nielsen, K.W., Task Coupling and Cohesion in Ada, *Ada Letters*, July/August 1986.

NIE88   Nielsen, K.W. and Shumate, K.C., *Designing Large Real-Time Systems with Ada*, McGraw-Hill, New York, 1988.

NOE87   Noe, J.D. and Andreassian, A., Effectiveness of Replication in Distributed Computer Networks, *Proceedings of the 7th International Conference on Distributed Computing Systems*, Berlin, 1987, pp. 508–513.

NOV88   Novellino, J., The VXIbus Comes of Age with Specs and Products, *Electronic Design*, October 27, 1988.

OZA88   Ozaki, B.M. et al., Software Fault Tolerance in Architectures with Hierarchical Protection Levels, *IEEE Micro*, August 1988.

PER84   Persch, G. and Dausmann, M., The Intermediate Language DIANA, in *Ada Software Tools Interfaces*, Springer Verlag, Berlin, 1984.

PER87   Perrott, R.H., *Parallel Programming*, Addison-Wesley Publishing Company, Reading, Mass., 1987.

PIT87   Pitteli, F. and Garcia-Molina, H., Recovery in a Triple Modular Redundant Database System, *Proceedings of the 7th International Conference on Distributed Computing Systems*, Berlin, 1987, pp. 514–520.

POU87   Pountain, D. and May, D., *A Tutorial Introduction to occam Programming*, Inmos Ltd, March 1987.

PYL85   Pyle, I.C., *The Ada Programming Language*, 2d ed., Prentice-Hall International, London, England, 1985.

RAM77   Ramamoorthy, C.V., and Li, H.F., Pipelined Architecture, *ACM Computing Surveys*, March 1977.

RAY88   Raynal, M., *Networks and Distributed Computation*, MIT Press, Cambridge, MA, 1988.

ROS87   Rosenblum, D.S., An Efficient Communication Kernel for Distributed Ada Runtime Tasking Supervisors, *Ada Letters*, March/April 1987.

SHU88   Shumate, K.C., *Understanding Concurrency in Ada*, McGraw-Hill, New York, 1988.

SHU88a   Shumate, K.C. and Nielsen, K.W., A Taxonomy of Ada Packages, *Ada Letters*, March/April 1988.

SIM89   Simpson, D., Rocky Road for Real-Time Unix, *Mini-Micro Systems*, March 1989.

SKI88   Skillicorn, D.B., A Taxonomy for Computer Architectures, *Computer, November*, 1988.

STA84   Stallings, W., Local Networks, *Computing Surveys*, Volume 16, Number 1, March 1984.

STA88   Stallings, W., *Handbook of Computer-Communications Standards*, Volume 3, Department of Defense (DoD) Protocol Standards, Macmillan, New York 1988.

SUN86   Remote Procedure Call Protocol Specification, Remote Procedure Call Programming Guide, and External Data Representation Protocol Specification, Sun Micro Systems, Mountain View, CA, 1986.

TAU84   Taub, D.M., Arbitration and Control Acquisition in the Proposed IEEE 896 Futurebus, *IEEE Micro*, August 1984.

TED84   Tedd, M. et al., *Ada for Multi-Microprocessors*, Cambridge University Press, Cambridge, England, 1984.

TEL88   TeleAda-LAN User Manual, TeleLogic AB, Sweden, 1988.

TUC88   Tucker, L.W. and Robertson, G.G., Architecture and Applications of the Connection Machine, Computer, August 1988.

VIS88   Vishnubhotla, P., Issues in Implementing Ada on Multiprocessors, *Proceedings IEEE 8th International Conference on Distributed Computing Systems*, 1988, pp. 45–48.

VOL89   Volz, R.A. et al., Translation and Execution of Distributed Ada Programs: Is It Still Ada? *IEEE Transactions on Software Engineering*, Volume 15, Number 3, March 1989.

YOU79   Yourdon, E. and Constantine, L.L., *Structured Design*, Prentice-Hall, Englewood Cliffs, NJ, 1979.

YOU82   Young, S.J., *Real Time Languages, Design and Development*, Ellis Horwood, Chichester, England, 1982.

Index